CRITICAL PEDAGOGIES IN PHYSICAL EDUCATION, PHYSICAL ACTIVITY AND HEALTH

Critical Pedagogies in Physical Education, Physical Activity and Health explores critical pedagogy – and critical work around the body, health and physical activity – within physical education. By examining the complex relationships between policies and practice, and how these are experienced by young people, it elucidates the need for critical pedagogy in contemporary times.

With contributions from leading international experts in health and physical education, and underpinned by a critical, socio-cultural approach, the book examines how health and physical education are situated across various international contexts and the influence of policy and curriculum. It explores how health is constructed by students and teachers within these contexts as well as how wider spaces and places beyond formal schooling influence learning around the body, health and physical activity. Finally, it considers what progressive pedagogies might 'look like' within health and physical education. Chapters utilise empirical work within the field to explore various topics of relevance to critical pedagogy, drawing on theoretical insights while providing practical applications and concluding with reflection points to encourage readers to consider the relevance for their own contexts.

Designed to support pedagogical study in a range of contexts, this book will be of particular interest to undergraduate and postgraduate students, teachers and researchers with an interest in physical education, physical activity and health and the role they play in young people's lives.

Julie Stirrup is a Lecturer in Sport Pedagogy and Physical Education at Loughborough University, UK. Julie is a former physical education teacher and currently works across undergraduate and teacher education programmes. Julie's research explores physical education and its role within the curriculum and young people's lives, with a specific focus on issues of equity and inclusion, social class and health discourse.

Oliver Hooper is a Research and Teaching Associate at Loughborough University, UK. Oliver's research explores young people's experiences within physical education, health and youth sport contexts, with a specific focus on the experiences of marginalised youth. He is particularly interested in youth voice and the use of participatory methods to facilitate young people's meaningful involvement in research.

CRITICAL PEDAGOGIES IN PHYSICAL EDUCATION, PHYSICAL ACTIVITY AND HEALTH

Edited by Julie Stirrup and Oliver Hooper

Routledge
Taylor & Francis Group

LONDON AND NEW YORK

First published 2022
by Routledge
2 Park Square, Milton Park, Abingdon, Oxon OX14 4RN

and by Routledge
605 Third Avenue, New York, NY 10158

Routledge is an imprint of the Taylor & Francis Group, an informa business

British Library Cataloguing-in-Publication Data
A catalogue record for this book is available from the British Library

Library of Congress Cataloging-in-Publication Data
Names: Stirrup, Julie, editor. | Hooper, Oliver, editor.
Title: Critical pedagogies in physical education, physical activity, and
health / edited by Julie Stirrup and Oliver Hooper.
Description: Abingdon, Oxon ; New York, NY : Routledge, 2021. |
Includes bibliographical references and index.
Identifiers: LCCN 2021006036 (print) | LCCN 2021006037 (ebook) |
ISBN 9780367423667 (paperback) | ISBN 9780367435844 (hardback) |
ISBN 9781003003991 (ebook)
Subjects: LCSH: Physical education and training–Social aspects. |
Health–Social aspects. | Critical pedagogy.
Classification: LCC GV342.27. C73 2021 (print) | LCC GV342.27 (ebook) |
DDC 613.7–dc23 LC record available at
https://lccn.loc.gov/2021006036 LC ebook record available at
https://lccn.loc.gov/2021006037

ISBN: 978-0-367-43584-4 (hbk)
ISBN: 978-0-367-42366-7 (pbk)
ISBN: 978-1-003-00399-1 (ebk)

Typeset in Bembo
by KnowledgeWorks Global Ltd.

We dedicate this book to our families who have supported us unconditionally and to the many colleagues who have influenced our careers to date.

CONTENTS

LIST OF FIGURES

CONTRIBUTORS

Laura Alfrey is currently Course Leader for the Bachelor of Education (Health and Physical Education) within the Faculty of Education at Monash University (Australia). Laura's research focuses on Health and Physical education (HPE), sport and physical activity contexts and the ways which policy, professional learning and practice contribute to inclusive and educative experiences for all young people. Laura is on the Editorial Board for 'Curriculum Studies in Health and Physical Education', the International Advisory Board for 'European Physical Education Review' and the College of Reviewers for 'Sport, Education and Society'. She works closely with ACHPER (Australian Council for Health, Physical Education and Recreation), is on the ACHPER Tertiary Engagement and Research subcommittee and is a co-convenor of the AARE (Australian Association for Research in Education) HPE Special Interest Group. Above all, she loves supporting teachers and coaches in creating inclusive HPE, sport and physical activity experiences.

Lorraine Cale is a Professor of Physical Education and Sport Pedagogy in the School of Sport, Exercise and Health Sciences at Loughborough University, and an Adjunct Professor at the University of Limerick in Ireland. She is a former physical educator and current physical education teacher educator, and her research interests centre broadly on the promotion of physical activity and healthy lifestyles within schools, both within and beyond the curriculum. Lorraine publishes her research in both academic and professional journals and has presented at numerous national and international conferences. Over the years, she has also produced practical resources and designed and delivered professional development for physical education teachers. In addition, Lorraine has formerly served as an elected member of the Executive Committee for the UK's Association for

Physical Education and is an honoured member in recognition of her significant contribution to the Association's aims and objectives.

Estelle Damant is a University Teacher in Physical Education and Sport Pedagogy in the School of Sport, Exercise and Health Sciences at Loughborough University. She is a former physical education teacher and currently teaches across undergraduate- and postgraduate-physical-education-related courses at the university, including the PE PGCE. Her PhD examined the enactment of health-related aspects of the NCPE in a state secondary school.

Robyne Garrett is a Senior Lecturer in physical education, dance and teaching methodologies in the School of Education at the University of South Australia. Her research interests include gender, social justice, embodied and creative pedagogies, whiteness and sport. Current projects include creative and body-based approaches to maths, socially just pedagogies for disadvantaged students and whiteness investigations of curriculum. Her PhD thesis entitled *How Young Women Move* investigated the construction of gender in physical activity contexts for young women. The post-structural research employed a storytelling approach, which resulted in a series of 'physical stories', now utilised as a strategy for the development of critical reflection in teacher training courses. Her research methodologies include narrative storytelling, case studies and action research approaches. Her teaching roles focus on developing critical and embodied pedagogies in student teachers.

Göran Gerdin is an Associate Professor in the Department of Sport Science at Linnaeus University, Sweden. His research focuses on how issues of gender, bodies, spaces and (dis)pleasures shape students' participation, enjoyment and identities in school Health and Physical Education. Lately, he has also been researching the practices and enactment of socially critical perspectives in Physical Education Teacher Education (PETE) and HPE with a focus on inclusion, democracy, equity and social justice. In his work, Göran draws on qualitative and participatory visual methodologies as informed by poststructural, Foucauldian and Butlerian thinking. He is currently responsible for the PETE programme at Linnaeus University, Sweden, and has over 10 years of university teaching experience in New Zealand and Sweden. He is on the editorial board for the journal *Curriculum Studies in Health and Physical Education* and a convenor in the Research in Sport Pedagogy network for the European Educational Research Association (EERA).

Kass Gibson trained as a Physical Education teacher in New Zealand in the early 2000s. Since then he has taught in schools, colleges and universities in New Zealand, Japan, Canada and the UK where he is an Associate Professor at Plymouth Marjon University. Kass' research uses a range sociological theories and research methodologies to understand the relationships and effects between different ways of knowing, meanings, experiences and practices in physical education, physical activity, sport and public health.

Shirley Gray is a Senior Lecturer in Physical Education at the University of Edinburgh. She was a former physical education teacher and teaching fellow. She now teaches primarily on the MA Physical Education Programme within the School of Education and Sport. Shirley's research explores how teachers understand and enact curriculum policy, and how they might be supported in their learning to provide all students with positive and socially just learning experiences in physical education. More specifically, her research focuses on issues relating to gender and equality, social and emotional learning, pupil motivation and the professional learning of teachers. Shirley has published and edited in peer-reviewed journals and books in the areas of physical education curriculum, pedagogy, health and gender.

Jo Harris is an Emeritus Professor of Physical Education and Sport Pedagogy in the School of Sport, Exercise and Health Sciences at Loughborough University. Jo taught in secondary schools for 12 years and has been a teacher educator for 32 years. Jo's research focuses on health-related learning in physical education and the promotion of active lifestyles, and she regularly publishes in professional and academic journals and presents at national and international conferences. Jo has attained the status of Principal Fellow of the Higher Education Academy, received awards for research-informed teaching and co-published a book with Human Kinetics on 'promoting active lifestyles in schools'. Jo has held prominent roles within and been the recipient of a number of awards from national physical education subject associations for her significant and sustained contribution to the profession.

Oliver Hooper is a Research and Teaching Associate in the School of Sport, Exercise and Health Sciences at Loughborough University, UK. Oliver's research explores young people's experiences within physical education, health and youth sport contexts with a specific focus on the experiences of marginalised youth. He is particularly interested in youth voice and the use of participatory methods to facilitate young people's meaningful involvement in research. Oliver has published various articles, papers and book chapters in these areas and routinely attends international conferences to present on this work. He is a convenor for the Early Career Researcher Network of the British Educational Research Association and the Sport Pedagogy Network of the European Educational Research Association. He also sits on the Editorial Boards of *Sport, Education and Society* and the *British Educational Research Journal*.

Dillon Landi is a Lecturer in the School of Education at the University of Strathclyde (Glasgow, UK). He conducts research at the intersection of health and education, with expertise in qualitative methods, critical theory, and gender/sexuality. Previously, he served as a faculty member at Towson University (Maryland, USA) and the University of Auckland (New Zealand). Prior to academia, Dillon served as a teacher and district supervisor for Health, Physical Education and Sport in New Jersey (USA). Dillon has a PhD in Education from the University of Auckland and two postgraduate degrees (EdM and MA) from Columbia University (New York, USA).

Carla Luguetti is a Lecturer in Physical Education and Health in the College of Sport and Exercise Science, and research fellow in the Institute for Health and Sport at Victoria University, Australia. Her line of research focuses on topics of sport pedagogy and social justice, and it is underpinned by critical pedagogy and feminist studies. As an Early Career Researcher and member of the Sport, Diversity and Social Change Research Group, Carla is working with diverse young people to co-create empowering possibilities through sport. She has a significant publication track record in collaboration with researchers from all over the globe (US, UK, Ireland, Australia and South America) in peer-reviewed journals and papers for international conferences.

Sarah MacIsaac is a Lecturer in Physical Education at the Moray House School of Education and Sport at the University of Edinburgh. Sarah's research lies within the sociology of health, the body and Physical Education. Her recent research has investigated young people's use of social media and its impact on social power relations, embodied identities and experiences of, and engagement with, the physical education environment. She is also currently exploring how teachers can facilitate young people to engage critically with contemporary bodily culture using an experiential, embodied approach to critical inquiry.

Louise McCuaig is an Associate Professor in the School of Human Movement and Nutrition Sciences at the University of Queensland. Her research and teaching focus on the health work conducted by schools and teachers. Currently, Louise has taken an opportunity to return to school settings to serve as Head of Pastoral Programs and establish a new research centre at Matthew Flinders Anglican College on the Sunshine Coast, Australia.

Brent McDonald is a Senior Lecturer and research fellow in the Institute for Health and Sport and a member of the Sport, Diversity and Social Change Research Group at Victoria University, Australia. His research focuses on two clearly identified areas: the sociology of sport and Japanese studies. Brent's research in the sociology of sport has concentrated on race, migration and identity, specifically contextualised within post-colonial Australian society. Driven by a social justice agenda, his work seeks to deconstruct dominant and common-sense notions of diversity, inclusion and race, and in doing so understand persistent inequities and exclusionary practices that occur in sport, exercise and physical education spaces.

Amanda Mooney is the Associate Head of School (Teaching and Learning) in the School of Education at Deakin University, and an Associate Professor in Health and Physical Education (HPE) Teacher Education. Following a decade of teaching HPE in secondary schools, Amanda teaches units related to Curriculum, Pedagogy and Assessment in HPE. Amanda's research draws on qualitative methodologies to examine cultural and societal factors, particularly gender, that shape identities, professional practice and pedagogies in Physical Education, Health Education and Sport. Her more recent work examines the role that space, place, rurality and social class have on learners and their wellbeing in school, university and sporting (community and elite sport) contexts. Collectively this work seeks to promote more equitable, enjoyable and meaningful experiences for youth through the lens of critical pedagogy, and she has published a number of peer-reviewed journal articles and book chapters in HPE.

Bonnie Pang is a Lecturer at the University of Bath, an Adjunct Fellow at the Institute for Culture and Society, Western Sydney University and a recipient of the prestigious Marie Sklodowska-Curie Individual Fellowship (2019–2020). She directs an innovative research program on Rethinking Health Experiences and Active Lifestyles with Chinese communities (REHEAL-C) which focuses on Chinese diasporas in physical activity and health-related experiences. The research is underpinned by socio-cultural perspectives, Chinese philosophies and a range of ethnographic methods and arts-based methods. She has published in key journals and is an author of two books: Interpreting the Chinese Diaspora: Socialisation, Identity and Resilience According to Pierre Bourdieu (2019), and Understanding Diversity, Differences and Social Justice in Physical Education: Enduring Challenges and Possible Direction in a Translocated World (forthcoming), both with Routledge Publisher. She is an editorial member of Sport, Education and Society.

Dawn Penney is a professorial research fellow in the School of Education at Edith Cowan University and an Adjunct Professor in the Faculty of Education at Monash University. Dawn's research centres on developments in policy, curriculum and assessment in Health and Physical Education (HPE) and seeks to bring to the fore issues of equity amidst 'reforms'. She has worked with government agencies, curriculum authorities, schools and sport organisations in collaborative research and evaluation projects in Australia, New Zealand, the UK and South Korea to inform and support advances in provision of quality HPE and sport for all young people. Dawn has published extensively in international journals and continues to explore critical lines of inquiry in her own research and in her work with research students.

Kirsten Petrie is an Associate Professor in Te Wānanga Toi Tangata Division of Education at The University of Waikato, Aotearoa New Zealand. She is formerly teacher of health and physical education (HPE) in secondary schools, and lecturers in the areas of primary school HPE, coach education and public health. She has published and presented widely on health and physical education in primary schools on matters relating to teacher development, curriculum and policy and the impact of external providers. She is co-editor of The Routledge Handbook of Primary Physical Education (Griggs and Petrie, 2017). Her research demonstrates a commitment to collaborative participatory action research with colleagues in university and school settings, with a view to actively creating policy and practice to enhance learning for all.

Darren Powell is a Senior Lecturer in the Faculty of Education and Social Work, University of Auckland, New Zealand. He uses critical ethnography and critical social theory to interrogate the connections between public health and public education. Darren's research focuses on the impact of corporations and philanthropy on children's lived experiences and understandings of health and fatness, both in schools and beyond. He is currently the Principal Investigator on a Royal Society Te Apārangi Marsden Fund Fast-Start Grant to study the impact of marketing 'health' to children.

Joe Piggin is a Senior Lecturer in Sport Management and Policy at Loughborough University's School of Sport, Exercise and Health Sciences in the UK. Joe's research covers three main areas including the translation of sport policy into practice, the politics of physical activity and articulations of risk in policy. He has recently published a book called The Politics of Physical Activity and is a co-editor of the Routledge Handbook of Physical Activity Policy and Practice.

Rachel Sandford is a Senior Lecturer in Young People and Sport in the School of Sport, Exercise and Health Sciences at Loughborough University, UK. She is Programme Director for the undergraduate Sport Science, Coaching and Physical Education degree and teaches modules related to critical pedagogy and the sociology of physical education. Rachel's research centres on young people's attitudes towards, experiences of and development in/through sport and physical activity. Her work is underpinned by a youth voice perspective and a desire to facilitate meaningful involvement in research for children and young people. She has a particular interest in issues around popular culture, embodied identity and positive youth development, with recent work focused on care experienced youth. Rachel has published widely in refereed journals and books in the areas of sociology, physical education and health.

Katarina Schenker is an Associate Professor in the Department of Sport Science at Linnaeus University, Sweden. Her research concern school Health and Physical Education (HPE), HPE teacher education and also the Swedish Sports Movement. Her interests are especially mechanisms of inclusion and exclusion in relation to democracy, equity and social justice. Inspired by the German didactics, she studies ontological and epistemological-related decisions in the schooling context. She has been engaged in research on higher education practices for 20 years. Currently, she chairs the advisory board of the secondary school subject teacher diploma at Linnaeus University, and she is one of the directors of the board of the Swedish Research Council for Sport Science.

Leigh Sperka is an Associate Lecturer in the School of Human Movement and Nutrition Sciences at the University of Queensland. She has a Bachelor of Health, Sport and Physical Education (Honours) and Doctor of Philosophy, both from the University of Queensland. Leigh teaches courses on Health and Physical Education (HPE) curriculum, pedagogy and assessment as well as leadership and research in HPE. Her research focuses on the outsourcing of education. This includes investigating decision-making around the practice, how outsourcing impacts curriculum, pedagogy and assessment, and student perspectives of outsourced lessons.

Julie Stirrup is a Lecturer in Physical Education and Sport Pedagogy in the School of Sport, Exercise and Health Sciences at Loughborough University. She is a former physical education teacher and currently teaches on the undergraduate Sport Science, Coaching and Physical Education programme as well as the PE PGCE. Julie's research centres on PE and its role within the curriculum and young people lives from the early years through to secondary education. She has a particular interest in issues of social class and health discourse, with recent work focusing on primary school children's experiences of PE delivered through outsourcing. Julie has published in peer-reviewed journals and books in the areas of physical education and health.

Sue Sutherland is a Professor of Physical Education Teacher Education in the Department of Human Sciences at Ohio State University. She teaches undergraduate and graduate courses in adventure-based learning, social justice, disability sport, elementary physical education methods, qualitative research and teaching in higher education. Sue's research focuses on the use of social justice education in physical education and physical education teacher education, adventure-based learning in K-12/higher education and social and emotional learning. Sue has written books, book chapters and peer-reviewed journal articles in the areas of physical education/teacher education, social justice, adventure-based learning and social and emotional learning.

Kylie Thompson teaches health and physical education (HPE) at Auckland University of Technology, Aotearoa New Zealand. She has previously been a HPE teacher in secondary schools and held various advisory and moderation roles in the physical education sector. Kylie has recently enrolled in a PhD and aims to explore how teachers make sense of and teach social and moral capabilities in physical education.

Jennifer L. Walton-Fisette is Director of Teacher Education and Professor of Physical Education Teacher Education at Kent State University. Prior to joining

KSU in 2008, she previously taught physical education and health in Rhode Island. She obtained her BS in physical education from Rhode Island College, MS in sport pedagogy from Ithaca College and EdD in Physical Education Teacher Education from the University of Massachusetts-Amherst. Her teaching responsibilities include Secondary Physical Education Content, Inquiry into Professional Practice, Development and Analysis of Game Performance, Introduction to Physical Education, Fitness and Sport, Analysis of Motor Skills, Curriculum Development and Forms of Inquiry. She has more than 40 refereed journal publications, 4 books and over 80 states, national and international conference presentations, in the areas of curriculum, teaching and learning; pedagogical practices, and social justice issues related to physical education. Her current scholarship centres on social justice, equity and policy issues within physical education at the K-12 and higher education levels.

Rosie Welch is a Lecturer in curriculum and pedagogy in the Faculty of Education, Monash University, Australia. Her teaching and research engages with the socio-cultural complexities of health education across school, teacher education, institutional, government and community settings.

Oli Williams holds a postdoctoral research fellowship awarded by The Healthcare Improvement Studies Institute and is based at King's College London. He received undergraduate and postgraduate degrees from the School of Sport, Exercise and Health Sciences at Loughborough University and completed his PhD in the Department of Sociology at the University of Leicester. He subsequently became a Lecturer in Physical Activity and Public Health at the University of Abertay Dundee before being awarded the NIHR CLAHRC West Dan Hill Fellowship in Health Equity, which he took up at the University of Bath. He researches health inequalities, the promotion of healthy lifestyles, stigma related to body weight and size, participatory research methods and equitable intervention. He is an active promoter of health equity and social change and co-founder of the art collective Act With Love: www.actwithlove.co.uk.

Gareth Wiltshire is a Lecturer in the School of Sport, Exercise and Health Sciences at Loughborough University with teaching responsibilities mapping across sport management, sport policy and physical education. His research is largely informed by concepts and theories derived from sociology, but he engages with researchers, practitioners and literature across a range of disciplines. Beyond the physical education context, his other research interests include the social determinants of physical activity and health inequalities, exercise and health for organ transplant recipients and research methodology.

Alison Wrench is a Senior Lecturer in Health and Physical Education studies at the University of South Australia. She is also the Program Director for the Professional Doctorate program. Alison's research program centres on socially critical and culturally responsive pedagogies in HPE, inclusion and just schooling outcomes. This program includes the investigation of processes of becoming a socially critical HPE teachers and linkages between teacher subjectivities and pedagogical practices. Her research interests extend to in-service and pre-service teacher practitioner inquiry and student led inquiry into localised health and physical activity issues 'that matter'. Alison is an active member of the Pedagogies for Justice group within the Research in Education Inclusion Concentration at the University of South Australia. She is also a member of a network of Australian and UK researchers investigating schooling in complex and vulnerable communities.

INTRODUCTION

Critical pedagogy – and, more widely, critical work around the body, health and physical activity – has a long history within the subject of physical education (PE). Such work has been evident since at least the 1980s (e.g. Tinning, 1985; Kirk, 1986; Kirk & Tinning, 1990) and has (arguably) had a consistent presence since. While critical pedagogy has been variously defined over the years, we argue that, principally, critical pedagogy is concerned with interrogating, exposing and challenging the inequities and injustices evident within educational systems and societies. It highlights the social, cultural and political processes involved in knowledge construction and the power differentials inherent within these – serving to elucidate both how and why certain individuals might be marginalised or excluded within a given context. While we do not contest that many young people have positive experiences within PE, we cannot ignore the considerable evidence that many do not – typically on account of particular facets of their intersectional identities. Indeed, scholarship within PE has continued to demonstrate that – despite the efforts of many committed academics and practitioners, over a considerable period of time – the PE context can be one which is marginalising and exclusionary for many young people (Fitzpatrick, 2019). Understandably, concerns have, therefore, been expressed with regard to the progress (or lack thereof) that the critical movement has made within (health and) PE[1] in recent years (e.g. Leahy, Burrows, McCuaig, Wright & Penney, 2016; Fernández-Balboa, 2017; Fitzpatrick, 2019).

Whilst there are many interrelated factors that have arguably impeded the progress of the critical movement within PE, we find ourselves returning to early work by Tinning (1991) in relation to what we consider to be a principal factor in this regard. Tinning (1991) argues that questions of pedagogy relate fundamentally to what practitioners view as the central issue of concern. Building on this work, in the context of critical pedagogy, Fitzpatrick (2019, p. 1131) argues that those practitioners who are concerned with issues of inequity and injustice are more likely to 'enact a much more nuanced and student-centred approach, one which attends directly to relations of power, social hierarchies and exclusion'. Such assertions lead us to believe, therefore, that in progressing the critical movement within (health and) PE, there is a need to focus on supporting practitioners to engage with this agenda. Pringle, Larsson and Gerdin (2019) have recently emphasised the need to focus more closely on how the critical movement is translated from research into practice and we, similarly, feel that more work is needed in this space. Indeed, it was such sentiments that led us to conceive this edited book, with the ambition that it might make a (small) contribution to such efforts – particularly given renewed calls for critical pedagogy within (health and) PE (e.g. Fitzpatrick, 2019; Kirk, 2019a; Tinning, 2020).

Against this backdrop, we have begun to witness reinvigorated efforts to engage with practitioners in the 'doing' of critical pedagogy. Hickey, Mooney and Alfrey (2019) have argued that in seeking to do so – and to support the translation of research into practice – we must focus on critical pedagogy as a *verb*. They contend that 'with a focus on "doing", critical activations largely emanate from a desire to make changes to the status-quo to precipitate purposeful learning encounters for students and to challenge inequities' (Hickey et al., 2019, p. 2). We similarly believe that a focus on the 'doing' of the critical movement within (health and) PE has the potential to move this agenda forward, though we recognise that there is not a singular way to 'do' critical pedagogy. It is for such reasons that, in compiling this edited book, we purposefully chose to refer to critical pedagogies in the plural in an effort to recognise the diverse ways in which this movement might be enacted within practice in (health and) PE.

Hickey and Mooney (2019) provide support in this regard by suggesting that there is much value in conceptualising critical pedagogy along a continuum when seeking to explore how this might be enacted within practice. They describe the various ways in which critical pedagogy might be approached 'in action', from more subtle efforts which serve to foster reflection in practitioners (e.g. Garrett & Wrench, 2011) through to those which are overtly disruptive in seeking to bring about pedagogical change (e.g. Shelley & McCuaig, 2018). Certainly, scholars have provided us with detailed accounts of how critical pedagogy might be enacted within practice in recent years (e.g. Fitzpatrick & Russell, 2015; Alfrey, O'Connor & Jeanes, 2017; Wrench & Garrett, 2020), though each evidences that in working towards this agenda there will be challenges encountered and constraints faced along the way. Reflecting on such efforts, Alfrey and O'Connor (2020, p. 300) assert that 'through engaging with and enacting practices driven by a critical agenda we can begin to transform some [health and physical education] teachers' philosophies and practice'. However, they emphasise that this 'is on the proviso that teachers have a range of resources … available to them when they need them' (Alfrey & O'Connor, 2020, p. 300). Evidently, the translation of the critical movement from research into practice is far from straightforward. But, as Alfrey and O'Connor (2020) note, it is possible given the necessary support and resources. While we are not so naïve as to suggest that this edited book will miraculously hasten the advancement of the critical movement, we do hope that it might be one resource that students within the field can draw upon as they seek to engage with this critical agenda. We recognise that whilst there exists much high-quality scholarship around critical pedagogy within the field, it can be a difficult and daunting area of study for students within (health and) PE – particularly given its complex and contested nature.

Critical Pedagogies in Physical Education, Physical Activity and Health was borne out of our desire to support students to engage with this critical agenda. The book comprises four sections: Situating Health and Physical Education within an International Context (Section I); Exploring Constructions of Health within (Physical) Education (Section II); Locating Places of and Spaces for Health (Section III); and Engaging with Progressive Pedagogies in Health and Physical Education (Section IV). Over the course of these four sections, and by drawing on contributions from leading scholars within the field, we seek to make evident how curriculum – and policy more broadly – shape what is (and can be) done in the name of (health and) PE and how this might facilitate (or not) engagement with this critical agenda. We endeavour to elucidate how the experiences shaped by such curricula influence knowledge construction around the body, health and physical activity within (health and) PE and, further, to demonstrate how learning about these is no longer confined to formalised boundaries of education with public pedagogies arguably more evident than ever before. Finally, we seek to outline how practitioners might engage with more progressive pedagogies in pursuit of this critical agenda, providing examples of critical pedagogy 'in action'. Each section within the book commences with a prelude written by an eminent scholar within our field, serving to support the reader to engage with the 'bigger picture' ideas that span the various chapters within each section as well as across the book as a whole. Whilst chapters and sections can be read in isolation, we hope that readers are inspired to engage beyond just one or two chapters or sections in order to delve deeper into this important area of study. Each chapter within these different sections shares common features in that they utilise empirical work within the field to explore their particular topic of focus, drawing on theoretical insights while providing practical applications. Chapters are generally located within a specific context – recognising the contextual nature of much critical work – though each concludes with a series of reflection points that encourage the reader to consider how the discussion might relate to their own context. We hope that these act as a stimulus for further thought about what is presented within each chapter, as well as perhaps being a precursor to action in line with our ambition to support engagement with the critical movement.

We have found that the editing of this book has prompted much thought and discussion for us as to where we are at with the critical movement and how (health and) PE might move forward. Whilst there have been renewed calls for critical pedagogy within the subject, we take heed of the warning by

Tinning (2020, p. 980) that 'while critical pedagogy might be needed more than ever, the contemporary conditions for critical pedagogy in [PE] are even more problematic' than they were in the early 2000s. However, whilst many of these conditions might be 'against us', we feel that there is one condition that provides much hope for the critical movement – young people and their desire to play a role in bringing about positive change. We have increasingly witnessed young people engaging in critical agendas around issues such as race rights in line with the #BlackLivesMatter movement, as well as sustainability and climate action. Young people have also helped to advance the #MeToo movement concerned with sexual violence and made progress in promoting and protecting the rights of women and girls. Young people have advocated for and stood as allies to those that may be marginalised within society such as LGBTQ+ communities and Indigenous peoples. Evidently, young people are willing, able and keen to engage in critical agendas. The (health and) PE context offers many opportunities to engage young people in critical thought, debate and action and can be a powerful means through which to interrogate, expose and challenge the inequities and injustices evident within educational systems and societies. Following the assertion by Kirk (2019b) that young people's lives are increasingly shaped by precarity, we feel that the subject of (health and) PE has all the more reason to embrace its responsibility and to work towards fulfilling its potential in progressing the critical movement. While we acknowledge that this will be a challenging endeavour, it is certainly a worthwhile one and one which we hope this edited book makes a contribution to.

Julie Stirrup and Oliver Hooper, November 2021

Note

1 We use the term (health and) PE within this introduction to denote the varying conceptualisations of the subject internationally, recognising that within our own context this is principally PE.

References

Alfrey, L. & O'Connor, J. (2020). Critical pedagogy and curriculum transformation in secondary health and physical education. *Physical Education and Sport Pedagogy*, 25 (3), 288–302.

Alfrey, L., O'Connor, J. & Jeanes, R. (2017). Teachers as policy actors: Co-creating and enacting critical inquiry in secondary health and physical education. *Physical Education and Sport Pedagogy*, 22 (2), 107–120.

Fernández-Balboa, J. M. (2017). A contrasting analysis of the neo-liberal and socio-critical structural strategies in health and physical education: Reflections on the emancipatory agenda within and beyond the limits of HPE. *Sport, Education and Society*, 22 (5), 658–668.

Fitzpatrick, K. (2019). What happened to critical pedagogy in physical education? An analysis of key critical work in the field. *European Physical Education Review*, 25 (4), 1128–1145.

Fitzpatrick, K. & Russell, D. (2015). On being critical in health and physical education. *Physical Education and Sport Pedagogy*, 20 (2), 159–173.

Garrett, R. & Wrench, A. (2011). Negotiating a critical agenda in middle years physical education. *The Australian Educational Researcher*, 38 (3), 239–255.

Hickey, C. & Mooney, A. (2019). Critical scholarship in physical education teacher education: A journey, not a destination, in R. Pringle, H. Larsson & G. Gerdin (Eds.) *Critical Research in Sport, Health and Physical Education*. London: Routledge.

Hickey, C., Mooney, A. & Alfrey, L. (2019). Locating criticality in policy: The ongoing struggle for a social justice agenda in school physical education. *Movimento*, 25 (1), e25063.

Kirk, D. (1986). A critical pedagogy for teacher education: Toward an inquiry-oriented approach. *Journal of Teaching in Physical Education*, 5 (4), 230–246.

Kirk, D. (2019a). A new critical pedagogy for physical education in 'turbulent times': What are the possibilities?, in R. Pringle, H. Larsson & G. Gerdin (Eds.) *Critical Research in Sport, Health and Physical Education*. London: Routledge.

Kirk, D. (2019b). *Precarity, Critical Pedagogy and Physical Education*. London: Routledge.

Kirk, D. & Tinning, R. (1990). *Physical Education, Curriculum and Culture: Critical Issues in the Contemporary Crisis*. London: Falmer Press.

Leahy, D., Burrows, L., McCuaig, L., Wright, J. & Penney, D. (2016). *School Health Education in Changing Times: Curriculum, Pedagogies and Partnerships*. London: Routledge.

Pringle, R., Larsson, H. & Gerdin, G. (2019). *Critical Research in Sport, Health and Physical Education*. London: Routledge.

Shelley, K. & McCuaig, L. (2018). Close encounters with critical pedagogy in socio-critically informed health education teacher education. *Physical Education and Sport Pedagogy*, 23 (5), 510–523.

Tinning, R. (1985). Physical education and the cult of slenderness: A critique. *ACHPER National Journal*, 108 (1), 10–14.

Tinning, R. (1991). Teacher education pedagogy: Dominant discourses and the process of problem setting. *Journal of Teaching in Physical Education*, 11 (1), 1–20.

Tinning, R. (2020). Troubled thoughts on critical pedagogy for PETE. *Sport, Education and Society*, 25 (9), 978–989.

Wrench, A. & Garrett, R. (2020). Navigating culturally responsive pedagogy through an Indigenous games unit. *Sport, Education and Society*. DOI: 10.1080/13573322.2020.1764520.

SECTION I

Situating health and physical education within an international context

INTRODUCTION

Dawn Penney

The four chapters in this section centre on different international contexts and developments while all directing attention to the importance of 'policy matters' in health and physical education (HPE). Collectively, the chapters explore different policy contexts, texts and the influence of policy actors in HPE, including teachers and teacher educators. They also bring to the fore notable similarities in HPE internationally. With official texts identified as often more flexible than prescriptive, an important issue to explore across these chapters is why there is little evidence of policy enactment that challenges the authority of established dominant discourses in HPE.

In Chapter 1, Stirrup and Damant follow previous policy research in the HPE field that has advocated for more engagement with the complex and political nature of policy. Policy is understood not merely as official texts, but as a process in which all HPE professionals play a part. Stirrup and Damant reaffirm that education policy – and particularly policy relating to health and wellbeing – is far from neutral, in the English context, at least. It reflects dominant political and social agendas, including the advancement of neoliberal ideals, and is designed to promote those agendas through formal primary and secondary schooling and via informal education in the pre-school years.

Focusing on curriculum policy in England, Stirrup and Damant explore the positioning and nature of 'health' in the National Curriculum for Physical Education (NCPE) and how this relates to the wider sphere of public policy. The marginality of health in the NCPE stands in sharp contrast to the public and political positioning of physical education (PE) in England as a critical site within which children will learn to be active, fit and healthy for life. Stirrup and Damant point to neoliberal values and a performative culture in education as powerfully shaping and inherently narrowing thinking about health in PE in England, but also pupils' experiences of health in PE in schools. They argue that the outsourcing of PE in primary schools limits the health discourses that teachers (or sports coaches) draw on, meaning that health interests remain marginal to an overriding focus on sport, performance and competition in PE. While some opportunities for teaching and learning about health may arise outside of PE time in primary schools, we see that targeted 'health' initiatives and programmes are no guarantee that broader understandings of health will be explored within this context.

Turning to health in secondary school PE in England, a strong performance and product orientation of the curriculum is again highlighted. Stirrup and Damant explain that while discourses of 'fitness for life' may be espoused in PE policy in schools, discourses of 'fitness for performance' dominate pedagogical practice. As such, health in secondary PE is typically taught from a narrow, bio-medical perspective aligning with a deficit approach. In this respect, a long line of research and advocacy in PE, that has called for broader conceptualisations of health to be embedded and enacted within the subject, appears to have had little impact. With the NCPE far from precluding the exploration of broader health discourses within and through PE, it is important to reflect on why, to date, there appears to be systemic resistance to such developments in PE curriculum, pedagogy and assessment in England.

Stirrup and Damant's exploration of health in the context of the early years – and more specifically, the Early Years Foundation Stage (EYFS) framework – further highlights that policies, and seemingly practitioners, are focused on what is absent with regard to a child's health, defined in relation to expected behaviours and choices and particular social values. Through the chapter, readers are therefore prompted to look more closely at how the policies and pedagogies of both formal and informal schooling shape the understandings of health that children and young people develop. At the same time, we are challenged to think about where interest and opportunity to think differently about health in PE in England may come from. The following three chapters, which address PE in other international settings, provide useful stimulus in this regard.

In Chapter 2, Gerdin and Schenker examine how health is expressed through formal curriculum in Sweden, as well as how it is enacted in practice. Like Stirrup and Damant (in Chapter 1), they direct attention to the policies and policy relations that have shaped – and continue to shape – these matters over time. However, the social values that Gerdin and Schenker identify as influential in the Swedish context, which centre on social justice, mean that schooling and health appear to have a very different orientation in Sweden. Yet, while physical education and health (PEH) in Sweden is recognised as built on values of democracy, equity and social justice, it is argued that health is marginalised and reduced to a focus on having fun and developing physical fitness within PEH. In examining why and how this situation has arisen, Gerdin and Schenker draw attention to the historical dimension of policy development and enactment. Introducing the concept of 'idrott', they explain the important origins of the discourses of health that have come to gain prominence in the context of PEH. The historical perspective offered, along with the contemporary public health policy context outlined, proves useful for understanding how the PEH curriculum in Sweden is orientated and how this relates to broader public health agendas.

Although PEH in Sweden is identified as a major player in public health policy, Gerdin and Schenker explain that critical research on PEH in Sweden points towards sport and games dominating teaching and learning, with teachers prioritising engagement in physical activity over teaching about health. However, the authors explain that research within PEH also reveals, somewhat ironically, that the approaches adopted – which prioritise the *doing* of sport and games – may actually be counterproductive to the overarching aim of enhancing pupils' engagement in physical activity. Furthermore, the capacity of PEH pedagogy to support meaningful learning about health appears constrained by the noted tendency for health to be thought of, and taught as, 'theory'. PEH teachers in Sweden are reported to be struggling to develop pedagogies that reflect integration of theoretical and practical knowledge, while also now working in a curriculum policy context that has seen neoliberal discourses increasingly re-framing health in PEH in terms of individualism. With pupils positioned as responsible for their own health, Gerdin and Schenker emphasise the need to question the role of PEH in public health promotion.

Exploring possibilities for enhancing practices in PEH in Sweden, and internationally, Gerdin and Schenker introduce an international research project 'Education for Equitable Health Outcomes' (EDUHEALTH), involving researchers from Sweden, Norway and New Zealand. The discussion around the project provides an important reminder of the value of international collaboration to reveal, better understand and seek to counter inequities and injustices in health, schooling and society. As Gerdin and Schenker describe, cultural and pedagogical differences are, in this project, a resource for exploring the different forms that socially just pedagogies in PEH may take.

Chapter 3, by Landi, Walton-Fisette and Sutherland, highlights the complexities of PE in and across the US. In the absence of previous policy scholarship focusing on PE in the US, their analysis of how PE in two states (Maryland and Ohio) is shaped in and by a complex web of governmental and policy relations is particularly insightful. As Landi and colleagues evidence, an appreciation of federal and state structures and responsibilities is key for understanding developments in PE in any state, local education authority (LEA) or indeed school. Further, they highlight how the Society of Health and Physical Educators of America (SHAPE) is a critical player in the policy network of PE, working across different levels of government, having over 200,000 members and most notably, from a policy perspective, developing National Standards documents for outcomes in PE in schools and for initial teacher education. These SHAPE National Standards documents are identified as a key point of reference for federal-, state- and LEA-level policy developments pertaining to PE. Landi and colleagues' overriding emphasis, however, is that despite these, there is notable variation in the expectations of PE and PE teachers, meaning that considerable inequities in PE provision emerge at state, LEA and school levels.

Deeper analysis of PE policy-curriculum-pedagogy dynamics evidenced in Maryland and Ohio reveals further complexities around the policy relations at play across federal, state and local jurisdictions. These relations are shown to, in turn, impact the prime purpose identified for PE, how it is taught and how it is resourced. The examples provided illustrate federal influences amidst decentralised policy structures, with local provision leveraging and consequently reflecting federal health agendas and funding. Similarly, we see ways in which the interests and investment of private institutions are an important part of the decentralised PE policy network. Even in situations of apparent alignment between standards across state and local jurisdictions, Landi and colleagues highlight that critical facets of quality PE remain matters that PE teachers have responsibility for, but for which they are not held accountable.

PE in the US is thus characterised by Landi and colleagues as a 'mixed bag', with varied quality and various inequities in relation to pupils' opportunities and experiences. In considering what it will take to change this situation, they contend that a shift in purpose is a necessary prerequisite to shifting pedagogy; that PE in the US will not change until it is no longer seen and positioned as an intervention. Their call is, therefore, for PE to be refocused on 'education *about* the physical', breaking the history of years of 'training *for* the physical'. For the authors, such a shift is needed to put young people at the centre of pedagogy in PE and for PE across the US to connect meaningfully with issues of diversity.

In the final chapter in this section, Chapter 4, McCuaig turns attention specifically to assessment policy. While assessment policy remains arguably both under-explored and underdeveloped in HPE research and practice, this chapter focuses on the role that assessment policy can play in advancing an educative orientation in HPE. McCuaig provides an overview of assessment in HPE in the state of Queensland, echoing aspects of the previous chapter by Landi and colleagues, and drawing attention to federal-state policy relations and the relative freedoms associated with state-level policy developments in HPE in Australia. The chapter also serves to reiterate the importance of locating policy developments in HPE in their historical context. McCuaig then presents two contrasting stories of curriculum reform as a means via which to examine the critical role of assessment in securing an overall educative, rather than interventionist, focus in HPE. In this respect, the chapter neatly picks up on the conceptual and pedagogical shift that Landi and colleagues highlighted a need for in PE in the US.

In looking firstly at the Australian Curriculum for HPE (AC:HPE), McCuaig draws attention to the risks that the curriculum writers took, particularly in making explicit that salutogenic theory was underpinning a strengths-based approach. She outlines the significance of this and the four other propositions or 'big ideas' that shaped the AC:HPE as an official policy text but also as a vision for HPE pedagogy in schools across Australia. Next, McCuaig focuses on the development of Senior Health as a subject in Queensland, which contrasts to the development of the AC:HPE in that in the senior school curriculum context, far more prescriptive assessment specifications were the prime driver of curriculum reform. Additionally, however, as McCuaig illustrates, in the context of Senior Health, the curriculum reform process was able to extend to provide detail on the pedagogical approaches to be used in teaching. In many respects, therefore, the Senior Health curriculum reform directly addressed matters of alignment of curriculum, pedagogy and assessment.

Assessment is presented by McCuaig as a lens through which HPE professionals can critically evaluate the realisation (or not) of the educative intent of HPE curricula. She also recognises, however, that some features of the broader policy context, and practices arising from it, continue to privilege behavioural rather than educative discourses. Similar to the situation in England, described by Stirrup and Damant (Chapter 1), this includes the practice of outsourcing HPE in primary schools. In closing, McCuaig points to the 'double-edged sword' of assessment specifications and associated accountability mechanisms. As with other chapters in this section, more prescriptive policy is not necessarily being advocated, but there is recognition that more flexible policy frameworks can sustain inequities while simultaneously providing openings for innovation.

Individually, and collectively, the chapters in this section bring to the fore the complexity and importance of looking more closely and critically at policy development and policy enactment in HPE. All offer valuable prompts for reflection and for 'healthy' debates!

1

HEALTH, PHYSICAL EDUCATION AND THE CURRICULUM

Julie Stirrup and Estelle Damant

Introduction

Ball, Maguire and Braun (2012, p. 19) remind us that 'policy creates context, but context also precedes policy'. Policies, be they related to education or otherwise, reflect dominant ideas and are shaped by, as well themselves shaping, the cultural, social and political norms of any context. As such, polices – including school curricula – are always political and value laden, emerging from the context in which they are written (Ball, 2006). Policy agendas for physical education (PE) in England, as in many countries (e.g. Australia, New Zealand, Scotland), are driven by expectations that the subject will impact positively on children's health and well-being, acting as a vehicle through which to address wider societal concerns such as sedentary lifestyles and obesity. As Ayo (2012, p. 100) suggests, 'health consciousness has become deeply engrained within our social fabric' and, certainly, within many Western (and Westernised) countries, public discourses and media headlines point to a 'crisis of obesity' portending danger and general doom and gloom around children and youth (see Evans, Evans & Rich, 2003; Gard & Wright, 2005).

Specifically, neoliberal ideals such as corporatisation and privatisation have created a consumer culture among children and adults alike, a culture which has permeated the contexts of education, health and well-being (see Chapter 8, this volume). Likewise, notions of risk are increasingly prevalent and are becoming embedded in the fabric of curriculum and practice within schools (see Leahy & Harrison, 2004). In recent years, we have seen, for example, growing pressures on parents to equip their children with the skills and habits required for future success and the subsequent amelioration of risk, be it enrichment activities (Stirrup, Duncombe & Sandford, 2015), the provision of 'healthy' snacks and lunches (Rich & Evans, 2013) or engagement with homework and the provision of a 'home environment conducive to learning' (Vincent, 2017, p. 543).

Against this backdrop, a growing body of literature (Burrows, Wright & Jungersen-Smith, 2002; Evans, Davies, Rich & De Pian, 2013; Powell & Fitzpatrick, 2015) has been concerned with addressing young people's experiences, interpretations and negotiations of health imperatives in schools, with schools increasingly held up as sites which should respond to health concerns by 'educating' young people to be healthy (Gard & Wright, 2005). Within England, health education has been placed under the broader educational remit of PE and Personal, Social and Health Education (PSHE). However, recent curriculum developments have seen the addition of relationships education (at primary level) and relationships and sex education (at secondary level) as well as the repositioning of health education as statutory within England from September 2020. This, alongside the increasing focus on health and well-being in the most recent Ofsted[1] education inspection framework (2019), illustrates that health within the curriculum is increasingly associated with notions of ameliorating risk and developing pupils as healthy citizens.

Within this chapter, we explore what curriculum policy looks like in England and how it is enacted across formal and informal schooling contexts. In so doing, we seek to provide an overview of health policy and practice within the subject of PE. Prior to exploring curriculum policy in detail, we want to make it clear how the labels of formal and informal schooling have been applied in this chapter. Within England, there are five stages of education: early years, primary, secondary, further and higher; with education compulsory for all children between the ages of 5 and 16. Formal schooling refers to the compulsory education of children between the ages of 5 and 16 in the primary and secondary sectors, and this phase is split into four key stages[2] (or blocks of years) at the end of which pupils' performances are assessed. Informal schooling refers to pre-primary school care/education whether it be nursery, pre-school or childcare. Within England, informal schooling is referred to as the early years and focuses on children aged 0–5. As such, it covers the first year of primary school which is the last year of the Early Years Foundation Stage (EYFS) curriculum.

Policy background

PE in England is situated within a crowded and complex policy landscape (Harris, Cale, Duncombe & Musson, 2018; Kirk, 2020; Lindsey, Metcalfe, Gemar, Alderman & Armstrong, 2021). Within this arena, numerous competing agendas focus variously on: enhancing sports performance and participation, developing socially engaged citizens and fostering pupils' engagement with healthy active lifestyles. Examples of recent policies include: Physical Education and School Sport for Young People (PESSYP) strategy (Department for Culture, Media and Sport, 2008); A Sporting Future: A New Strategy for an Active Nation (Department for Culture, Media and Sport, 2015); Childhood Obesity: A Plan for Action (Department of Health, 2016); and the School Sport and Activity Action Plan (Department for Education, Department for Digital, Culture, Media & Sport, and Department of Health and Social Care, 2019). Health, specifically, has held a position in some guise within each revision of the National Curriculum since its inception in 1992 where it was positioned as a compulsory component of the National Curriculum for Physical Education (NCPE) and as one of a number of cross-curricular elements (Department for Education and Science and the Welsh Office, 1992; Cale, 2020). However, health has arguably been positioned more prominently and overtly since 'Curriculum 2000' (Department for Education and Employment and Qualifications and Curriculum Authority, 1999), where it appeared more explicitly as one of four key strands of learning.

This overt focus on health is currently evidenced in the aims of the NCPE (Department for Education, 2013, p. 1) where pupils are expected to learn how to:

- Develop a competence to excel in abroad range of activities
- [Be] physically active for sustained periods of time
- Engage in competitive sports and activities
- Lead healthy, active lives

Evidently, the positioning of schools, and PE, as valuable sites for health education and the promotion of active lifestyles is not new (Harris et al., 2018). Yet, to date, there is little evidence that PE has been able to make significant inroads into either the health-related knowledge of young people or their physical activity behaviours (Harris et al., 2018; Cale, 2019; Cale, Harris & Hooper, 2020). This is because, despite much rhetoric to the contrary, PE's role in educating young people about health and physical activity is '*far* from straightforward' (Harris et al., 2018, p. 408, emphasis added).

Despite what might be considered 'global health imperatives' (Evans, 2014, p. 456), the ways in which health knowledges and practices are defined, interpreted and approached in schools are varied (Fitzpatrick & Tinning, 2014). As such, it is important to recognise that policy and practice are rarely straightforward and that policy is enacted amid a multitude of situational and contextual factors (see Ball et al., 2012; Lindsey et al., 2021). The remainder of this chapter will look in detail at how health as part of wider PE policy and curriculum is enacted in both formal and informal schooling, through three phases of education within England (primary, secondary school and early years).

Enactment of health in formal schooling in England

In our discussions above, we outlined both the value laden nature of policy and the burgeoning position of health in the NCPE. We now explore how these issues have influenced the enactment of policy in schools, highlighting the impact of a performative culture within an educational arena dominated by discourses of neoliberalism (Macdonald, 2014). Indeed, despite a growing variety of approaches to the delivery of PE in practice, it is suggested that neoliberalism has pervasively shaped and perhaps even distorted teachers' pedagogic practices (Evans, 2014). From this, a performative culture has been created in

which value is placed on measurable achievements, (self)surveillance, target setting and observable outcomes. The prevalence of this performative culture can
be suggested to be influential in the shaping of PE and the delivery of health
across both primary and secondary schools (Macdonald, 2014). For example,
within the primary context, PE is often seen as giving children a break from the
performative nature of SATs[3] or 'academic' subjects (i.e. English, mathematics
and science). Within secondary schools, the influence of this neoliberal agenda
is perhaps most clearly illustrated in the utilisation of fitness testing measures
(Alfrey & Gard, 2014) and through the influence of examination syllabi on the
shaping of non-examination PE lessons (Harris & Leggett, 2015; Damant, 2020).
Indeed, within secondary education in the UK, it has been suggested that despite
the espoused intentions to engender and promote an understanding and enjoyment of physical activity as part of health (see Cale, 2017), what is often seen
are reductive interpretations of health focused on: promoting vigorous activity
amongst pupils (Cale & Harris, 2009); the indiscriminate use of fitness testing
(Alfrey & Gard, 2014); and the influence of examination PE on 'core' PE lessons
(Harris & Leggett, 2015). The following examples from both primary PE and
secondary PE illustrate how health is often interpreted in practice.

'Health' in primary physical education

As discussed earlier in this chapter, health within the English context sits as part
of the PE curriculum. In primary school, PE is seen as a foundation subject and
is precariously positioned, despite calls from academics and professional bodies to
make PE a core subject within the curriculum (see Harris, 2018). Core subjects
(English, mathematics and science) are generally considered to be of higher status
than other subjects and are usually privileged in terms of their status, preparation
time for teaching and their time and resource allocation in schools. In contrast,
foundation subjects such as PE tend to be marginalised and 'squeezed' in terms
of time and resources (Harris, 2018). In addition, PE tends to be taught by either
generalist teachers with limited training in PE or sports coaches who are seen as
experts but who are not qualified teachers (Smith, 2015).

In response to concerns about the state of PE and school sport, the UK government launched funding for primary PE and sport in 2013. The PE and Sport
Premium (PESP) funding – amounting to £450 million for English schools – was
initially provided for 3 years, although this has been extended to 2021. The funding was intended to support the provision of high-quality PE and school sport
through sustainable investment/improvement. A report from the Department
for Education (2015) suggested that the funding has led to: an upskilled workforce; equipment to support teaching and learning; additional extracurricular
opportunities; and increased participation in inter- and intra-school competitions. However, indications also suggest that the funding has altered the way
PE is delivered. As Smith (2015) indicates, increasingly, the teaching of PE in
England is being undertaken by outsourced sports coaches – many of whom,

whilst possessing National Governing Body (NGB) qualifications, lack professional teaching qualifications and pedagogical skills in relation to curriculum planning and assessment (Griggs, 2016). The notion of outsourcing is discussed in further detail in Chapter 14; however, we feel it is important to touch on it in this chapter. Not least because the nature of the workforce delivering PE (and subsequently health) in primary schools is an important factor when we consider the knowledge that is transmitted and legitimised. Arguably, in this outsourced education system, children are increasingly taught through what Bernstein (2000) termed a performance model, which places emphasis upon 'a specific output of the acquirer, upon a particular text the acquirer is expected to construct, and upon the specialised skills necessary to the production of this specific output, text or product' (p. 44).

A performance model (Bernstein, 1996) is closely aligned with the current dominant discourse in education. It is evident in existing political rhetoric and policy, across all phases of schooling, through the emphasis on the acquisition of predetermined knowledge and skills that are closely managed and assessed against explicit criteria. Pedagogically, this is apparent in strong control over who does what, when and how. Within primary PE, much like secondary, we find that two discourses dominate – sport and health (Griggs, 2015). When looking at the literature on primary PE and legitimised knowledge, we can see that sport tends to be the focus whether that be through the inclusion of fundamental movement skills (Ward, 2017), the focus on sport and competition in curricular PE (Stirrup, 2020) or during extracurricular school sport (Wilkinson & Penney, 2016). The latter two papers certainly highlight the potential influence and impact outsourcing curriculum PE and extracurricular PE/school sport might have on the knowledge transmitted. That is to say, when external coaches assume responsibility, sport, performance and competition tend to dominate lessons. This brings to the fore the question of 'where does health fit'?

Whilst evident in the curriculum for key stage 1 and 2, we might argue that notions of health are perhaps seen more clearly outside of PE within the primary context, particularly in health initiatives and programmes targeted at schools and children. For example, we see the Daily Mile Challenge (DMC) which focuses on improving the physical, social, emotional and mental health and well-being of children through 15 minutes of physical activity in the form of a mile run/walk. However, as Ward and Scott (2019) point out, rather than seeing the DMC as physical activity, children often see it as a time to have a break from their 'academic' school life.

Health in secondary physical education

The dominance of performance models of education have similarly been noted in secondary education (Evans & Penney, 2008). In a performance model, pupils are assessed for what they cannot yet do or do not yet know in relation to a predetermined range of key concepts or content (Bernstein, 2000). Such models are evident in the construction of learning for public examinations – such as that of the GCSE[4] PE – and have been highlighted as being influential in teachers' enactment of health-related curricula (Damant, 2020). Within secondary school PE, performance models have been suggested to result in the hierarchical positioning of abilities and the ascription of different values to different bodies (Evans & Penney, 2008). Notably, it is performance models that dominate in a number of influential PE policy texts, including the NCPE (see Evans & Penney, 2008).

Relatedly, neoliberal discourses and performative cultures in English secondary schools, as in numerous other countries, are concerned with raising standards of academic achievement (Wilkinson & Penney, 2021). In a marketplace dominated by examination league tables, secondary schools have responded by adopting a number of strategies, including: the narrowing of taught curricula; greater uniformity in teachers' practices; and a 'shortening' of key stage 3 to allow additional time to focus on examinable content (Hutchings, 2015). Even as a practical and non-examination subject, core PE in England has not escaped the influence of a performative and outcome-focused culture in schools, and, as highlighted earlier, this has contributed to a number of narrowly conceived responses to the delivery of health-related aspects of the NCPE. Indeed, specifically in relation to the enactment of health-related curricula in PE, Cale, Harris and Duncombe (2016) noted that in those schools where health occupied a particularly marginalised position in practice, teachers expressed a belief that learning about health did not help pupils to gain credible PE examination results.

Examining the expression of health in five case study secondary schools across England and Wales, Harris and Leggett (2015) found that two particular discourses of health predominately shaped teachers' practice in relation to health-related learning. These were discourses of 'fitness for life' and 'fitness for performance'. However, whilst teachers generally articulated a fitness for life discourse within policy, their enactment in practice more often reflected a fitness for performance discourse. This fitness for performance discourse was largely informed by sports performance perspectives – and the bio-medical science discourses and practices associated with them – which emphasise the role of physical activity in increasing fitness and ultimately sports performance. These perspectives resulted in fitness testing and physical conditioning activities being privileged as means through which to teach about 'health' within PE.

Taken together these observations may point towards a position wherein health is predominantly taught in reductive ways – focused on undertaking vigorous physical activity and fitness testing – and understood primarily within the context of sport and performative education. That is, what is relevant for competitive sports performance and what can easily be measured, in terms of fitness test scores or examination outputs, for example. This inevitably positions pupils differently and recognises the predisposition towards particular sports or the possession of a particular body type as valuable forms of physical capital (Evans & Penney, 2008). Ultimately, this may result in the more favourable positioning of some pupils over others and in the recognition of 'ability' as the performance of sports skills or high scores in fitness tests (see Hunter, 2004). The corollary of this, Cale et al. (2020) argue, is that this approach restricts access to those broader educational experiences which might foster more positive engagement with health and physical activity, which may consequently limit learning experiences within PE. Following Harris (2000), Cale et al. (2020) make the call for educators to focus on enacting health-related aspects of the NCPE in a broader sense, drawing attention to the relevance of health across multiple domains of learning, including psychomotor, cognitive, affective and behavioural. In doing so, their call represents a reflection on the salience of the development of more socio-critical approaches to teaching and learning about health in schools.

We now turn our attention to the narrow notions of health which are played out through informal education before children arrive at primary school. We do this recognising that the learning and understanding of health is not confined to the school setting and that children arrive with experiences and knowledge which inevitably shape their experiences of formal schooling.

Health recontextualised in early years education

Although the EYFS has little explicitly to say about health, it reflects neoliberal health discourses circulating in wider society which celebrate the functional (fitness- and health-related), rather than the intrinsic, value of play, PE and sport (Ayo, 2012). Imperatives contextualised, for example, in Public Health England campaigns such as 'Change4Life' encourage families to take greater personal responsibility for their health and well-being (see Chapter 11, this volume). Notwithstanding ideological shifts in the political landscape of early years over the last 30 years, within the EYFS (Department for Education, 2014) play has retained its position as a fundamental aspect of children's development, building their confidence as they 'learn to explore, to think about problems and relate to others' (Department for Education, 2014, p. 8). Through play children putatively are enabled to make sense of their social worlds and engage actively with people and objects (Department for Education, 2014). In the EYFS specifically, regarding health and physical development, play is to cultivate:

1. Moving and handling – (as demonstrated in) children's ability to show good control and coordination in small and large movements, moving confidently in a range of ways
2. Health and self-care – children know the importance for good health of physical exercise and a healthy diet and talk about ways to keep healthy and safe (Department for Education, 2017, pp. 5–8)

Like many education policies, the EYFS is decided by policy makers outside the education system and based on the expectation that practitioners can implement such policies into their settings. Siong Leow, Macdonald, Hay and McCuaig (2014) take this argument further suggesting that many health policies could be considered to sit outside the immediate remit of education completely. Whilst this argument cannot be levelled at early years in the same way it can to formal education, the suggestion that where policies have explicit corporeal dimensions, implementations become moderated by teacher's own biographies, health practices and what they consider the remit of schooling (Vander Schee, 2009) is a valid one.

As with the NCPE in formal schooling, EYFS policy has undoubtedly helped position early years settings as key sites for addressing health issues wherein children are taught from an early age 'the importance for good health of physical activity and a healthy diet' (Department for Education, 2014, p. 8). For example, EYFS policy stipulates that settings should provide healthy meals (Department for Education, 2014, p. 26), although little information is given as to what 'healthy' means. Similarly, practitioners are expected to nurture a 'healthy' individual – essentially through play – in accordance with the expectations of the EYFS. To this end, the EYFS health imperatives are set out in relation to (i) age (e.g. by the age of 3, children should be 'drinking well without spilling') (Department for Education, 2014, p. 26); (ii) pedagogy, essentially child and practitioner-led play; and (iii) key themes (Department for Education, 2014, p. 3) which foreground:

- A unique child
- Positive relationships
- Enabling environments

Government concerns around obesity have nurtured a discourse of health that focuses rather reductively on the notion that 'good' diet and exercise equals fitness and health (Gard & Wright, 2005). This is reflected in early years contexts where efforts are focused on children making the right food choices, with 'snack time' seen by practitioners as an important site for fulfilling the requirements of the EYFS, ensuring children 'understand the importance of physical activity, and … make healthy choices in relation to food' (Department for Education, 2014, p. 8). Furthermore, research has illustrated how definitions of health and health promotion are simultaneously constructed and consolidated in relation to practitioners' expectations of the social class of children within their settings. Stirrup (2018) illustrates that health is at times read through what is considered to be absent from children's (working-class) homes, with practitioners in early years settings taking on the responsibility of providing 'compensatory' education (Stirrup, 2018). Research reveals what can happen when a pathogenic health discourse – explicitly nurturing a deficit view of individuals' health behaviours (McCuaig & Quennerstedt, 2018) – is mediated through play pedagogies which inevitably bring to the fore personal information about children's predispositions and family lifestyles (Stirrup, 2018). Different forms of knowledge and meaning around health are exchanged and valued in relation to perceived social class. Consequently, practitioners, teachers and children are encouraged to survey bodies and food choices, with certain children (and parents) being classified as irresponsible because they do not hold the same 'health' knowledge as practitioners expect them to. This is not to suggest that all children do not have valuable health knowledge, for some their knowledge is just not the kind valued in policy and practice within their early years context. As Ball (2010) argues, many early years influences lie outside the range of policy and are greatly associated with family dynamics, parenting and the home environment. We, therefore, perhaps need to consider how policy can sidestep narrow notions of health to ensure the health discourses of early years do not shape and 'class' the corporeal realities of certain families.

Conclusion

Notwithstanding debates regarding the extent to which PE can, or indeed should, be held accountable for children's health outcomes (see Cale et al., 2020), PE in England is, at present, viewed by many as a useful site for the delivery of health-related learning in the curriculum. In this chapter, we have explored how PE, and subsequently health, are enacted within formal and informal schooling, discussing this in relation to the wider performative context in which PE sits. Key messages arising from this discussion focus on the narrow interpretations of health evident within primary and secondary school PE, as well early years education.

Therefore, whilst doing so with caution, it is perhaps important in concluding this chapter to consider the role that PE, as part of both formal and informal education, *may* play in developing health-related knowledge amongst young people. In an effort to circumvent the narrow and performative interpretations of health outlined in this chapter, and to instead focus on the educative potential of PE in relation to health-related learning, there has been a move to recognise health as applicable to learning across multiple domains (Cale et al., 2020) and to view health as a complex resource. In the UK, these changes have, to some extent at least, been partially mirrored in the call for PE to be considered as planned, progressive learning across multiple domains with learning to occur in terms of both 'learning to move and moving to learn' (Harris, 2020). Whilst beyond the scope of this chapter, we would encourage readers to explore later sections of this volume where a number of recent pedagogical developments which have the potential to contribute to pupils' understanding of health-related issues and their positive engagement with movement in more holistic and educative ways are discussed (see Section IV).

Reflection points

• In this chapter, we discuss the narrow performative interpretations of health that dominate the English context. How does this fit with your own context? In your experience is there a narrow and performative interpretation of health in policy and or practice?

- How might the early years curriculum in your own context influence children's understandings of health as they transition to formal education?
- Have there been any recent curriculum or pedagogical developments in your own context? If so, how have these contributed to young people's understandings of health-related issues?

Notes

1 The Office for Standards in Education, Children's Services and Skills (Ofsted) is a non-ministerial department of the UK government. It is responsible for inspecting a range of educational institutions, including state schools and some independent schools.
2 Within primary school, key stage 1 spans 5–7-year-olds, while key stage 2 spans 7–11-year-olds. At secondary school, key stages 3 and 4 address the learning of 11–14-year-olds and 14–16-year-olds, respectively.
3 SATs are the Standard Assessment Tests used to assess progress at the end of key stages 1 and 2 in English schools.
4 GCSEs are General Certificates of Secondary Education. These are public examinations sat by pupils in England at the end of their secondary schooling.

References

Alfrey, L., and Gard, M. (2014). A crack where the light gets in: A study of Health and Physical Education teachers' perspectives on fitness testing as a context for learning about health. *Asia-Pacific Journal of Health, Sport and Physical Education*, 5(1), 3–18.

Ayo, N. (2012). Understanding health promotion in a neoliberal climate and the making of health conscious citizens. *Critical Public Health*, 22(1), 99–105.

Ball, S. (2010). New class inequalities in education: Why education policy may be looking in the wrong place! Education policy, civil society and social class. *International Journal of Sociology and Social Policy*, 30(3/4), 155–166.

Ball, S. J. (2006). *Education, policy and social class: The selected works of Stephen J. Ball*. Oxon: Routledge.

Ball, S. J., Maguire, M., and Braun, A. (2012). *How schools do policy: Policy enactments in secondary schools*. London: Routledge.

Bernstein, B. (1996). *Pedagogy, symbolic control and identity: Theory, research, critique*. London: Taylor and Francis.

Bernstein, B. (2000). *Pedagogy, symbolic control, and identity: Theory, research, critique*. Lanham, MD: Rowman and Littlefield.

Burrows, L., Wright, J., and Jungersen-Smith, J. (2002). "Measure your belly": New Zealand children's constructions of health and fitness. *Journal of Teaching in Physical Education*, 22(1), 39–48.

Cale, L. (2017). Teaching about healthy active lifestyles. In C. Ennis (Ed.), *Routledge handbook of physical education pedagogies*. London: Routledge, pp. 399–411.

Cale, L. (2019). Young people, social media, physical activity, and health. Final thoughts on the work, the present, and the future. In V. Goodyear and K. Armour (Eds.), *Young people, social media and health*. London: Routledge, pp. 212–224.

Cale, L. (2020). Physical education's journey on the road to health. *Sport, Education and Society*, DOI: 10.1080/13573322.2020.1740979.

Cale, L., and Harris, J. (2009). Fitness testing in physical education – A misdirected effort in promoting healthy lifestyles and physical activity? *Physical Education and Sport Pedagogy*, 14(1), 89–108.

Cale, L., Harris, J., and Duncombe, R. (2016). Promoting physical activity in secondary schools. Growing expectations: Same old issues. *European Physical Education Review*, 22(4), 526–544.

Cale, L., Harris, J., and Hooper, O. (2020). Debating health knowledge and health pedagogies in physical education. In S. Capel and R. Blair (Eds.), *Debates in physical education*. London: Routledge, pp. 256–277.

Damant, E. (2020). *Grade A health: An exploration of the social construction of health and ability within secondary school physical education*. Unpublished Doctoral Thesis. Loughborough University.

Department for Culture, Media and Sport. (2008). *PE and sport strategy for young people*. https://webarchive.nationalarchives.gov.uk/20120505035838/https://www.education.gov.uk/publications/eOrderingDownload/PE_Sport_Strategy_leaflet_2008.pdf.

Department for Culture, Media and Sport. (2015). *Sporting future. A strategy for and active nation*. https://assets.publishing.service.gov.uk/government/uploads/system/uploads/attachment_data/file/486622/Sporting_Future_ACCESSIBLE.pdf.

Department for Education. (2013). *National curriculum in England: Physical education programmes of study*. https://www.gov.uk/government/publications/national-curriculum-in-england-physical-education-programmes-of-study/national-curriculum-in-england-physical-education-programmes-of-study.

Department for Education. (2014). *Early years foundation stage framework (EYFS)*. https://www.gov.uk/government/publications/early-years-foundation-stage-framework–2.

Department for Education. (2015). *The PE and sport premium: An investigation in primary schools Research report*. https://www.gov.uk/government/publications/pe-and-sport-premium-an-investigation-in-primary-schools.

Department for Education. (2017). *Statutory framework for the early years foundation stage*. https://assets.publishing.service.gov.uk/government/uploads/system/uploads/attachment_data/file/596629/EYFS_STATUTORY_FRAMEWORK_2017.pdf.

Department for Education, Department for Digital, Culture, Media & Sport, and Department of Health and Social Care. (2019). *School sport and activity action plan*. https://www.gov.uk/government/publications/school-sport-and-activity-action-plan.

Department for Education and Employment, and Qualifications and Curriculum Authority. (1999). *Physical education. The national curriculum for England*. London: QCA 1.

Department for Education and Science, and the Welsh Office. (1992). *Physical education in the national curriculum*. London: Her Majesty's Stationary Office.

Department of Health. (2016). *Childhood obesity: A plan for action*. https://assets.publishing.service.gov.uk/government/uploads/system/uploads/attachment_data/file/546588/Childhood_obesity_2016 2 acc.pdf.

Evans, J. (2014). Equity and inclusion in physical education PLC. *European Physical Education Review*, 20(3), 319–334.

Evans, J., and Penney, D. (2008). Levels on the playing field: The social construction of physical 'ability' in the physical education curriculum. *Physical Education and Sport Pedagogy*, 13(1), 31–47.

Evans, J., Evans, B., and Rich, E. (2003). 'The only problem is, children will like their chips': Education and the discursive production of ill-health. *Pedagogy, Culture and Society*, 11(2), 215–240.

Evans, J., Davies, B., Rich, E., and De Pian, L. (2013). Understanding policy: Why health education policy is important and why it does not appear to work. *British Educational Research Journal*, 39(2), 320–337.

Fitzpatrick, K., and Tinning, R. (2014). Considering the politics and practice of health education. In K. Fitzpatrick and R. Tinning (Eds.), *Health education: Critical perspectives*, pp. 1–13. Abingdon: Routledge.

Gard, M., add Wright, J. (2005). *The obesity epidemic. Science, morality and ideology*. London: Routledge.

Griggs, G. (2015). *Understanding primary physical education*. Abingdon: Routledge.

Griggs, G. (2016). Spending the primary physical education and sport premium: A West Midlands case study. *Education 3–13*, 44(5), 547–555.

Harris, J. (2018). The case for physical education becoming a core subject in the national curriculum. *Physical Education Matters*, 13(2), 9–12.

Harris, J. (2020). *AfPE health position paper*. AfPE. https://www.afpe.org.uk/physical-education/wp-content/uploads/Health-Position-Paper-2020-Web.pdf.

Harris, J., and Leggett, G. (2015). Influences on the expression of health within physical education curricula in secondary schools in England and Wales. *Sport Education and Society*, 20(7), 908–923.

Harris, J., Cale, L., Duncombe, R., and Musson, H. (2018). Young people's knowledge and understanding of health, fitness and physical activity: Issues, divides and dilemmas. *Sport, Education and Society*, 23(5), 407–420.

Hutchings, M. (2015). *Exam factories? The impact of accountability measures on children and young people*. London: National Union of Teachers (NUT).

Hunter, L. (2004). Bourdieu and the social space of the PE class: Reproduction of Doxa through practice. *Sport, Education and Society*, 9(2), 175–192.

Kirk, D. (2020). Government and physical education. In S. Capel and R. Blair (Eds.), *Debates in physical education*. London: Routledge, pp. 3–17.

Leahy, D., and Harrison, L. (2004). Health and physical education and the production of the at risk self. In J. Evans, B. Davies and J. Wright (Eds.), *Body knowledge and control: Studies in the sociology of physical education and health*. London: Routledge, pp. 130–139.

Lindsey, I., Metcalfe, S., Gemar, A., Alderman, J., and Armstrong, J. (2021). Simplistic policy, skewed consequences: Taking stock of English physical education, school sport and physical activity policy since 2013. *European Physical Education Review*, 27(2), 278–296.

Macdonald, D. (2014). Is global neo-liberalism shaping the future of physical education? *Physical Education and Sport Pedagogy*, 19(5), 494–499.

McCuaig, L., and Quennerstedt, M. (2018). Health by stealth – Exploring the sociocultural dimensions of salutogenesis for sport, health and physical education research. *Sport, Education and Society*, 23(2), 111–122.

Powell, D., and Fitzpatrick, K. (2015). 'Getting fit basically just means, like, nonfat': Children's lessons in fitness and fatness. *Sport, Education and Society*, 20(4), 463–484.

Rich, E., and Evans, J. (2013). Changing times, future bodies? The significance of health in young women's imagined futures. *Pedagogy, Culture & Society*, 21(1), 5–22.

Siong Leow, A. C., Macdonald, D., Hay, P., and McCuaig, L. (2014). Health-education policy interface: The implementation of the Eat Well Be Active policies in schools. *Sport, Education and Society*, 19(8), 991–1013.

Smith, A. (2015). Primary school physical education and sports coaches: Evidence from a study of School Sport Partnerships in north-west England. *Sport, Education and Society*, 20(7), 872–888.

Stirrup, J. (2018). 'How do you feel? What is your heart doing?' … 'It's jumping': The body and health in Early Years Education. *Sport, Education and Society*, 23(6), 547–562.

Stirrup, J. (2020). Performance pedagogy at play: Pupils' perspectives on primary PE. *Sport, Education and Society*, 25(1), 14–26.

Stirrup, J., Duncombe, R., and Sandford, R. (2015). 'Intensive mothering' in the early years: The cultivation and consolidation of (physical) capital. *Sport, Education and Society*, 20(1), 89–106.

Vander Schee, C. (2009). Confessions of the 'unhealthy' – Eating chocolate in the halls and smoking behind the bus garage: Teachers as health missionaries. *British Journal of Sociology of Education*, 30(4), 407–419.

Vincent, C. (2017). 'The children have only got one education and you have to make sure it's a good one': Parenting and parent–school relations in a neoliberal age. *Gender and Education*, 29(5), 541–557.

Ward, G. (2017). Moving beyond sport in primary physical education. In G. Griggs and K. Petrie (Eds.), *Routledge handbook of primary physical education*. London: Routledge.

Ward, G., and Scott, D. (2019). Negotiating the Daily Mile Challenge; looking-like a walking break from the classroom. *Sport, Education and Society*. DOI:10.1080/13573322.2019.1700106.

Wilkinson, S. D., and Penney, D. (2016). The involvement of external agencies in extra-curricular physical education: Reinforcing or challenging gender and ability inequities? *Sport, Education and Society*, 21(5), 741–758.

Wilkinson, S. D., and Penney, D. (2021). Setting policy and student agency in physical education: Students as policy actors. *Sport, Education and Society*, 26(3), 267–280.

2

DEMOCRACY, EQUITY AND SOCIAL JUSTICE

The constitution of 'health' in Swedish physical education and health

Göran Gerdin and Katarina Schenker

Introduction

Like in many countries around the world, such as Australia and New Zealand, a broader notion of 'health' was introduced in the Swedish physical education and health (PEH) curriculum several years ago (Quennerstedt, Burrows & Maivorsdotter 2010). The current Swedish PEH curriculum (Swedish National Agency for Education, 2011) includes not only a focus on physical but also mental health, as well as social well-being, along with aspects of democracy and societal values. Importantly, this broader notion of health is directed towards enhancing pupils' capacity to contribute to the development of society, where the core Swedish societal values of democracy, equity and social justice are particularly emphasised.

The Swedish Education Act (2010) emphasises the importance of the school system being based on fundamental democratic values and equitable access for all. In the Swedish context, social justice is related to social welfare policies involving public health, democracy and solidarity. The ideals of equity and fairness can be traced back to the 1940s, in connection to the reforms of the Swedish school system into a 'school for all' where investing in schooling was seen as important for fostering social cohesion and developing 'good' members of society (Telhaug, Mediås & Aasen, 2004). Equality was a guiding principle in promoting the development of the country and strengthening solidarity while transforming the state into a welfare society (Norberg, 2011). Every child was equally entitled to an education, regardless of where they lived, their parents' socio-economic status, their gender or ethnicity. It was believed that without access to education for all, democratic development and potential social incorporation into society may not occur.

The current Swedish curriculum – including the subject of PEH – is built on these ideals of democracy, equity and social justice. Furthermore, the focus of

Swedish PEH is not only on being physically educated but also enhancing pupils' awareness of, and critical reflection on, how their participation in different physical activity and movement contexts impacts on others' health. However, research continues to show that the 'health' aspect of PEH in Sweden is being marginalised, seemingly unaffected by the adoption of broader notions of health within the curriculum (Quennerstedt et al., 2010). Indeed, it would seem that having fun, sweating and being fit remain the key foci of both content and pedagogical decisions (Öhman, 2010).

In this chapter, we provide an overview and critical interrogation of Swedish PEH with a particular focus on how notions of health underpinned by societal values of democracy, equity and social justice work together to produce PEH curriculum and practice in Sweden. At the same time, we provide a critique of such curricula, and practices related to health within Swedish PEH, by illustrating how this can still, at times, result in pupils being positioned as solely responsible for their own health. Towards the end of the chapter, we report on and discuss an international research project that has explored what PEH that embraces democracy, equity and social justice in relation to health can look like, before offering points for reflection.

Swedish physical education and health – aka 'idrott och hälsa'

During the last century, the subject content in Swedish physical education (PE) has been influenced by different traditions. When PE became a compulsory subject in Swedish primary schools in 1842, the name of the school subject for a long time was simply 'gymnastics'. From the turn of the century, the subject became more and more influenced by physiology and PE was dominated by a physiological discourse (Lundvall & Meckbach, 2004). At that time, the focus on health was mainly around the pupils maintaining good hygiene which, in practice, meant an expectation to get changed before, and shower after, the lesson. Around the mid-20th century, another fundamental idea that developed was that if pupils engaged in a wide range of sports, actively participating in the rapidly growing Swedish sports movement (Sandahl, 2005), they would automatically be/become 'healthy'.

In 1980, when the subject changed its name to 'idrott'[1] (which loosely translates into 'sports'), the content also became influenced by sports performance and social development (Lundvall & Meckbach, 2004). As is the case for the concept of sport, in Sweden, there is a lack of consensus on the meaning of the idrott concept. It may involve – amongst other things – physical activity for health or recreation, aesthetic experience or competitive sports performance. However, the concept of idrott is broader than the international concept of sport (cf. Guttmann, 2004), which makes the situation even more complex.

The meaning of idrott has also been transformed over the years. Larsson (2016), in an overview considering how the concept is used, concludes that idrott may be understood as a social construction, a phenomenon that is constructed and shaped in different contexts and for different purposes, and that there:

> simply does not exist a sport [idrott] phenomenon that you can refer to in all situations. Or, to put it another way, sport [idrott] has no essence, that is, a core or a common denominator that binds together everything that in different contexts is referred to as sport [idrott] (p. 12, authors' own translation).

In Sweden, the introduction of the new 1980 curriculum, and the renaming of the subject to 'idrott', marked the prominent position of the sports movement in society (Annerstedt, 2005). The new curriculum meant greater responsibility for pupils to plan, implement and evaluate participation in sports and other physical activities, taking into account different views of health, movement and lifestyle, as well as requirements related to safety and lifesaving.

Today, PE in Sweden is known as 'idrott och hälsa' ('physical education and health') and Annerstedt (2005) suggests that the change of name from 'sports' to 'physical education and health', together with the new curriculum introduced in 1994, implies that health has become the main focus for PE in Sweden. Health is thus not only part of an imperative argument for legitimising PE in school, but also for the choice of content within the subject. We propose that the Swedish PEH curriculum can be seen as a framework for interpreting the concept of *idrott* – as well as '*hälsa*' ('health') – in this school subject, as discussed in the next section.

The Swedish physical education and health curriculum – providing a framework for 'idrott' and 'hälsa'

According to the Swedish PEH curriculum, the school subject should contribute to the development of a healthy lifestyle. Through positive experiences of movement and outdoor education ('friluftsliv'), pupils should encounter a range of different activities in PEH (e.g. games, dance, swimming and orienteering). They should develop all-round movement competence as well as a belief in their own physical abilities. Pupils should also develop knowledge about how they can maintain good health throughout the lifespan.

In the present 2011 Swedish PEH curriculum, for Years 1–9 (age 7–15), the aim of the subject and its role in education is described as follows:

> Physical activities and a healthy lifestyle are fundamental to people's well-being. Positive experiences of movement and outdoor life during childhood and adolescence are of great importance if we are to continue

to be physically active later on in life. Having skills and knowledge about sports and health is an asset for both the individual and society.

(Swedish National Agency for Education, 2011, p. 48)

Teaching in PEH for Years 1–9 should, for instance, give pupils opportunities to develop their ability to 'plan, implement and evaluate sports and other physical activities based on different views of health, movement and lifestyle' (Swedish National Agency for Education, 2011, p. 48). The aims and scope of the PEH curriculum for Years 10–12, as a progression from earlier years, are described as follows:

> provid[ing] opportunities to experience and understand the importance of physical activities and their relationship with well-being and health … Teaching should raise awareness and challenge stereotypes of what is considered to be masculine and feminine and inform about the consequences of different body ideals.
>
> *(Swedish National Agency for Education, 2012, p. 1)*

Teaching in PEH for Years 10–12 should, for instance, give pupils opportunities to develop the 'ability to take an ethical stand on issues of gender patterns, gender equality and identity in relation to the performance of exercise and sport' (Swedish National Agency for Education, 2012, p. 2).

From an even broader perspective, PEH can be described as a social and cultural meeting place with both the opportunity and the responsibility to strengthen pupils' abilities to understand and empathise with the differing values, beliefs and life circumstances of other pupils. Central values in the Swedish school context are the equal worth of all people, equality between women and men and solidarity between people, as well as the inviolability of human life, individual freedom and integrity. Teaching in school is also to be non-denominational. Schooling should impart a sense of justice, generosity, tolerance and responsibility. No one should be subjected to discrimination and concern for the well-being and development of individuals should permeate all school activities (Swedish Education Act, 2010).

Enhancing the health of all citizens is part of an agenda promoting democracy where people, in different ways, can influence the social well-being of a society (Fernández-Balboa, 1995). Having skills and knowledge about physical activity and health is described as an asset for both the individual and society (Swedish National Agency for Education, 2011). Health inequities are one of the most profound challenges for Sweden, and the country is facing a major task to promote social health by ensuring positive health outcomes for all of its increasingly diverse and multicultural population (Official Reports of the Swedish Government, 2016). Social justice concerns democracy as well as social and political participation and to enact democracy it is therefore necessary to include all pupils in PEH. Thus, the subject of PEH is part of Swedish public health policy.

The subject of PEH may seem ideally placed to contribute to public health policy. Schooling and the subject of PEH are compulsory for 10 years in Sweden, which means that it involves every child for a long period of time in their lives. It requires participation in physical activity, which is perceived to be beneficial for pupils' health and well-being. The subject should also lead to knowledge useful in supporting individuals to make healthy choices throughout life and, in so doing, aid society in enabling a healthier population regardless of socio-economic background. From this perspective, the subject of PEH is part of a policy initiative – much like in other countries such as the UK (see Cale, Harris & Hooper, 2020) – that should lead to a healthier population that lives longer (and results in decreased costs for public health and care services).

These are the good intentions behind the subject of PEH; however, the reality is not always as positive as these intentions. We will now discuss critical research on PEH and the conceptualisation and delivery of health education in Sweden which will interrogate how this school subject is understood and realised in relation to the guiding principles in the current Swedish PEH curriculum.

Critical research on physical education and health and the constitution of health education in Sweden

Research on the Swedish school subject of PEH has shown that it does not appeal to some pupils. In fact, some pupils dislike the subject a lot and some do not even go to the lessons at all (Larsson, 2016; The Swedish Schools Inspectorate, 2018). Critical scholarship on PEH in Sweden continues to highlight that it is still characterised by a strong tradition of sport and games. Despite new curricula in Sweden calling for teachers to address equity (Swedish National Agency for Education, 2011), PEH teachers still have problems catering to the needs of all their pupils (Redelius, Quennerstedt & Öhman, 2015; Ekberg, 2016; Svennberg, 2017; Larsson, Linnér & Schenker, 2018), with achievement and higher grades in PEH often being linked to active participation in sport clubs (Svennberg, 2017). Pupils who do not participate in organised sport in their leisure time often experience feelings of anxiety and inability in PEH (The Swedish Schools Inspectorate, 2018). Research indicates that PEH teachers themselves tend to focus more on making pupils interested in and motivated to do (more) physical activity and sport rather than teaching about health (Schenker, 2018). Further, higher grades in the subject are generally attained by boys with a Swedish background and who have well-educated parents (Svennberg, 2017).

Research on PEH in Sweden, specifically focusing on the conceptualisation and delivery of health education, shows the sustained prevalence of traditional notions and practices. One such notion is that there is a strong connection between physical activity and health, where physical activity is considered as equating to health (Quennerstedt et al., 2010). Health education from this perspective risks being based on a performance logic where it becomes important to be good and active, instead of learning how to feel good through activity. When teaching focuses on high physical activity, learning outcomes risk getting lost or being taken-for-granted (Larsson & Karlefors, 2015).

In Swedish PEH, as in many other countries around the world, the perception of the subject as an important context for physical activity – from a public health perspective – has increased in recent years (see Fröberg, Raustorp, Pagels, Larsson & Boldemann, 2017). Such a view of the subject can help explain why many teachers perceive that discussions, reflections and evaluations displace the practical elements that make pupils (physically) active (Quennerstedt et al., 2010). The concept of health is commonly interpreted from a physiological perspective where taken-for-granted knowledge about what health entails juxtaposes the curriculum's intentions of different approaches to health (Larsson & Karlefors, 2015). Research shows that there are risks associated with uncritically shaping content based on a narrow physical activity focus and that this can even counteract pupils' interest in a physically active lifestyle. Lundvall and Brun Sundblad (2017) highlight that intervention studies with the goal of increasing the physical capacity of young people in the long-term often demonstrate a weak residual effect. The exception being the studies that changed teaching methods and put the pupils' learning in focus (Lundvall & Brun Sundblad, 2017).

Research also suggests that health is often taught as a 'theoretical' subject and that teachers isolate learning about health from practical activities (Karlefors, 2012). The teaching of health and lifestyle is carried out in the form of theoretical lessons or as part of a lesson detached from physical activity or movement. Lundvall and Brun Sundblad (2017) believe that teachers find it challenging to integrate theoretical and practical knowledge – that is, supporting pupils to learn about health through physical activities. Sandahl (2005) further points out a gap between theory and reality, since the curriculum does not necessarily reflect teaching in practice. For instance, in the Swedish Schools Inspectorate's (2018) latest report, it is described that education linked to the strand of health and lifestyle was carried out in less than five per cent of the schools visited. It is believed that the marginal space that health and lifestyle content occupies in Swedish PEH is as a result of teachers' uncertainty as to how this can be put into practice, that is, the teachers do not seem to know what to do with health and lifestyle content in the subject (Schenker, 2018).

The changes in Swedish PEH curricula (both 1994 and 2011) also include a (re)positioning of health whereby the individual is expected to take responsibility for their own health and make the 'right' healthy choices in order to not be a burden on society. In this sense, health as an individual endeavour becomes something that schools should deliver, something that pupils should adhere to and, as responsible citizens, embrace. As such, PEH is influenced by the neoliberal concept of individualism, in which pupils are seen to be responsible for their own health and non-conforming pupils are blamed for their 'failure' to achieve 'health'. Schenker (2018) therefore argues that health education may even risk being 'unhealthy' for those pupils who do not feel that they adhere to normative assumptions of being slim, fit or healthy.

Quennerstedt (2019) recently argued for a move away from teaching young people how to be healthy, through the deployment of ready-made educational packages, towards acknowledging health education as a societal responsibility, where it is recognised that socio-cultural and socio-economic contexts afford diverse opportunities to be healthy and to learn to live healthy lives – a salutogenic approach. A salutogenic approach to what constitutes health means that teachers, for instance, can use the conversations with pupils that take place during a lesson for reflections and discussions about different experiences, without having to isolate health education through theoretical lessons (Brolin, Quennerstedt, Maivorsdotter & Casey, 2018). However, even salutogenic approaches can be problematic if the pedagogical approach utilised draws from an assumption that pupils are solely responsible for their health (Schenker, 2018). For instance, a recent study of a Swedish school found that despite it attempting to enact salutogenic approaches to health, it continued to act, to a significant extent, on individualistic assumptions based on pathogenic notions of health (Brolin et al., 2018). Importantly, these sorts of findings are not confined to the Swedish context but are commonly reported across other contexts, such as within the salutogenic, strengths-based approach of the latest Australian Curriculum for Health and Physical Education (AC:HPE) (Lambert, 2018).

To briefly conclude, research indicates that there is a gap between policy and practice, and it is argued that this is related to tensions between the interests and purposes, political as well as cultural, of different actors. In practice, by adhering to ontologies closely related to bio-medical sciences, socially critical and social justice approaches are lost. Hence, pupils are often positioned as being solely responsible for their own health, and the role of PEH as part of a public health agenda can be questioned.

Within this section, we have not only described and discussed the good intentions of the Swedish PEH curriculum but also engaged with critical scholarship which demonstrates how, even with the best of intentions, problematic practices and understandings of health outcomes still exist. We now report on and discuss an international research project that has explored what PEH that embraces democracy, equity and social justice in relation to health can look like.

The EDUHEALTH project

'Education for Equitable Health Outcomes – the Promise of School Health and Physical Education' (EDUHEALTH) is an international research project involving PEH researchers from Sweden, Norway and New Zealand. In this work, we draw on the World Health Organisation's (WHO) long-standing advocacy for 'equal health' and use the term 'equitable health outcomes' to focus on identifying, highlighting, challenging and ultimately transforming the unequal distribution of power in PEH practice. Achieving health and more equitable health outcomes does not merely relate to the promotion of physical health but goes beyond this to include mental and social well-being. Promoting and striving for equitable health outcomes in and through school PEH is therefore about providing pupils with experiences in various physical activity and movement contexts that develop their abilities/skills to take critical action (Wright, 2004) – both by themselves and in relation to others – underpinned by the values of inclusion, democracy and social justice. The focus on health and health outcomes in PEH is thus not about achieving equal health or equitable health outcomes by the time pupils leave school per se. Rather, it is about instilling a sense of agency in terms of how they, as future citizens, can play an active role in promoting and creating more healthy societies at an individual, group and societal level.

The EDUHEALTH project sought to explore the enactment of PEH teaching practices that address democracy, equity and social justice. Central to this was what qualified as teaching for social justice in PEH, including questions of how teachers could empower rather than marginalise pupils in PEH, regardless of socio-cultural factors such as gender, sexuality, ethnicity and/or social class. Data were gathered through observations of PEH teachers in each of the three countries. The observations were followed by interviews to explore 'captured incidents' within practice which appeared to foreground democracy and social justice.

In the project, we identified both similar and different approaches among the three participating countries. For instance, in all the countries, we noted that teaching for social justice can be described as a way of being for a teacher, where caring and building relationships were important (Mordal Moen et al., 2019). By using body language, the voice, the body, touch etc., the teacher creates a safe and caring environment within which the pupils can develop, learn and grow as individuals and as a group. The data also indicated that socially critical PEH teaching practices may entail teaching about social justice issues in society with an empowering approach. In New Zealand, we observed this more frequently than in the two Scandinavian countries, and an example of this was teaching about Māori culture by highlighting the Māori language and exploring indigenous games. However, it could also be about challenging gender stereotypes or prejudices related to ethnicity to develop increased awareness among pupils. These kinds of approaches have been demonstrated and discussed elsewhere (see Legge, 2010; Fitzpatrick, 2013), but the analysis of the data also revealed other ways of enacting socially critical PEH teaching approaches that have not been noted to the same extent in previous research.

As previously argued, while the school subject is part of an equality project, the pedagogy may embrace an equity approach. However, the equity approach in PEH is mainly needed if there is an injustice in the balance of power among the pupils (e.g. if individual pupils, or groups of pupils, are encouraged to excel/dominate at the cost of other pupils). Embracing teaching content with a non-competitive logic that may focus on participation, cooperation and social responsibility can be one way to adopt an equity approach which is needed when injustices exist. However, as research has shown, different forms of injustice do exist in PEH, and PEH traditions and cultures seem to be strong as well. Therefore, to achieve greater social justice with teaching content associated with PEH, adaptions are commonly needed. Rules and group formations can be used to 'even out' differences in physical ability/skill. Avoiding or 'easing up' on traditional competitive rules can make the game accessible to more pupils. In fact, we have also seen a few cases of what might be termed as 'anti-fair play'. In one case, the teacher made the court bigger for one team (the more physically able/skilled ones) than the other and in another case the teacher choose to participate in the game and he effectively 'disarmed' the most successful players in the other team by marking them. By using this approach, the teacher interfered in an 'anti-fair' way from a game perspective to make the teaching practice more socially just.

Based on the EDUHEALTH project, we can conclude that social justice pedagogies are about ways of recognising social inequities and marginalised groups and at the same time acting on these social inequities in ways that do not further marginalise these groups and that lead to more equitable learning outcomes in PEH. In different PEH contexts, the marginalised groups may differ as well as the strategies for acting on the inequities (Schenker et al., 2019). In teaching for social justice, the teacher has to identify the marginalised groups. In our study, teachers could describe these groups as pupils with less confidence, less skilled pupils, girls and Indigenous pupils (in New Zealand). We could see different approaches towards gender equality, as well as ethnicity, in New Zealand and Scandinavia. In New Zealand, social justice pedagogies start by recognising pupils as raced, gendered and classed individuals, whereas in Sweden and Norway, such pedagogy is deemed problematic. The Scandinavian approach is rather to provide equal opportunities in education regardless of the pupils' backgrounds (Schenker et al., 2019). Interviews with teachers in Sweden also showed that teachers have other ways of labelling marginalised groups. For example, those who are not able to swim, do not have bikes, do not have the kit, are physically injured or do not have a 'normal' body (see also Schenker et al., 2019).

Social justice pedagogies involve teaching for social justice through the actions and embodiments of the teacher. Fernández-Balboa (1995) further argues that a teacher who seeks a social justice agenda begins by recognising and reflecting on social justice issues and examining their own identity, while seeking to understand how they operate within normative, hegemonic structures. In the EDUHEALTH project, we observed the important work of PEH teachers who teach for social cohesion in contexts where it is needed and propose that teaching for social cohesion should be recognised as inherent to social justice pedagogies in PEH. However, we want to stress that teaching for social cohesion as a quest for, or precursor to, social justice must move PEH teachers' practices and pupils' thinking beyond mere social integration. It also needs to address the social conditions that simultaneously privilege and marginalise the values and beliefs of certain groups in society (Smith et al., 2020).

Conclusion

The current Swedish PEH curriculum (Swedish National Agency for Education, 2018) includes not only a focus on physical but also mental health, as well as social well-being, along with aspects of democracy and societal values. This broader notion of health is directed towards enhancing pupils' capacity to contribute to the development of society, where the core Swedish societal values of democracy, equity and social justice are particularly emphasised. Furthermore, the focus of Swedish PEH is not only on being physically able/skilled but also about enhancing pupils' awareness of, and critical reflection on, how their participation in different physical activity and movement contexts impacts on others' health. However, research continues to show that the 'health' aspect of PEH in Sweden is being marginalised, seemingly unaffected by the adoption of broader notions of health in the curriculum (Quennerstedt et al., 2010). Indeed, it would seem that having fun, sweating and being fit remain the key foci of both content and pedagogical decisions (Öhman, 2010). Even though the school system in Sweden should give everyone equal opportunities to participate, problems are to be found in how the subject is taught and realised. As a consequence, those who would benefit from PEH do not seem to want it and those who enjoy the subject might not need it in its present form.

In this chapter, we have problematised the concept of 'idrott' by briefly describing the historical use of the concept and the vague definition(s) it has today. We argue that the use of the idrott concept combined with the health concept ('hälsa') – which also has various interpretations – provides opportunities for strong actors in the field, with vested interests, to influence the values that the subject is passing on. This means that the societal values of democracy, equity and social justice in the Swedish PEH curriculum may not be realised in practice. Instead of a school subject contributing positively to public health policy, notions of idrott and hälsa produce a PEH subject where pupils often end up being solely responsible for their own health. Indeed, research both in Sweden and internationally continues to critique how PEH is both conceptualised and realised in teaching practice despite the good intentions of curricula.

Nevertheless, through the EDUHEALTH project, we have tried to support teachers' practices differently, by instead focusing on the 'good' examples where inclusion and social justice frames practice. The identified practices are not necessarily representative of how all teaching in PEH is (or should be) conducted but, by documenting and analysing these examples, it is hoped that they can provide an alternative to, and a critique of, PEH practice that does not focus on social well-being along with aspects of democracy and societal values. The findings will be used to develop teaching strategies that are intended to assist PEH teachers in refining and developing their practices to enable these to become more inclusive and engaging for all pupils, thus contributing to more equitable health outcomes in PEH. Ultimately, the intention is to provide future PEH teachers with alternatives to traditional ways of becoming and being a PEH teacher (see Section IV, this volume).

Reflection points

- How has the national curriculum for PEH evolved in your country and how can the current curriculum be seen as a socio-historic construct?
- In what ways have broader sport organisations influenced the underpinning values and beliefs of your national PEH curriculum? Are there other organisations that are strong influencers?
- What is the aim and scope of the PEH curriculum in your country and how does this relate to a national public health agenda?
- What are the current inequalities that exist for pupils in PEH in your country? (i.e. who are the privileged and marginalised pupils?)
- How can PEH practices become more inclusive and socially just in your country?

Note

1 Idrott is an old word and can be found in other languages, though not in English, e.g. *idrett* in Norwegian, *idræt* in Danish, *íþrótt* in Icelandic. Originally (in the Viking Age, ranging from the late-8th to the mid-11th century), idrott meant 'competition' (Peterson & Schenker, 2018).

References

Annerstedt, C. (2005). Physical education and health in Sweden. In U. Pühse and M. Gerber (Eds.) *International comparison of physical education – concepts, problems, prospects*, pp. 604–629. Aachen: Mayer & Mayer.

Brolin, M., Quennerstedt, M., Maivorsdotter, N., and Casey, A. (2018). A salutogenic strengths-based approach in practice – an illustration from a school in Sweden. *Curriculum Studies in Health and Physical Education*, 9(3), 237–252.

Cale, L., Harris, J. and Hooper, O. (2020). Debating health knowledge and health pedagogies in physical education. In S. Capel and R. Blair (Eds.) *Debates in physical education*. London: Routledge.

Ekberg, J. E. (2016). What knowledge appears as valid in the subject of Physical Education and Health? A study of the subject on three levels in year 9 in Sweden. *Physical Education and Sport Pedagogy*, 21(3), 249–268.

Fernández-Balboa, J. M. (1995). Reclaiming physical education in higher education through critical pedagogy. *Quest*, 47(1), 91–114.

Fitzpatrick, K. (2018). Brown bodies, racialisation and physical education. *Sport, Education and Society* (2), 135–153.

Fröberg, A., Raustorp, A., Pagels, P., Larsson, C., and Boldemann, C. (2017). Levels of physical activity during physical education lessons in Sweden. *Acta Paediatricia*, 106(1), 135–141.

Guttmann, A. (2004). *Sports: The first five millennia*. Amherst, MA: University of Massachusetts Press.

Karlefors, I. (2012). There are some things we learned – that we hadn't thought of: Experience of and learning in the subject of physical education and health from a student perspective. *Swedish Journal of Sport Research*, 1, 59–82.

Lambert, K. (2018). Practitioner initial thoughts on the role of the five propositions in the new Australian Curriculum Health and Physical Education. *Curriculum Studies in Health and Physical Education*, 9(2), 123–140.

Larsson, H. (2016). Forskning om undervisning och lärande i skolämnet idrott och hälsa. *Svebi Idrottsforskaren*, 1, 5–16.

Larsson, H., and Karlefors, I. (2015). Physical education cultures in Sweden: Fitness, sports, dancing … learning? *Sport, Education and Society*, 20(5), 2–15.

Larsson, L., Linnér, S., and Schenker, K. (2018). The doxa of physical education teacher education – set in stone? *European Physical Education Review*, 24(1), 114–130.

Legge, M. (2010). E noho marae – Transforming learning through direct Māori cultural experience. In C. J. Jesson, V. M. Carpenter, M. McLean, M. Stephenson, & Airini (Eds.) *University teaching reconsidered: Justice, practice, equity*. pp. 139–149. Wellington: Dunmore.

Lundvall, S., and Brun Sundblad, G. (2017). Polarisering av ungas idrottande. I. C. Dartsch, J. R. Norberg, and J. Pihlblad (red.), *De aktiva och De inaktiva. Ungas rörelse i skola och på fritid* (pp. 45–76). Stockholm: Centrum för idrottsforskning.

Lundvall, S. and Meckbach, J. (2004). Physical education in Sweden – (the changing of a subject) from a pedagogical perspective. In P. Jørgenssen and N. Vogensen (Eds.) *What's Going on in the Gym*, pp. 83–86. Odense: University of Southern Denmark.

Mordal Moen, K., Westlie, K., Gerdin, G., Smith, W., Linnér, S., Philpot, R., Schenker, K., and Larsson, L. (2019). Caring teaching and the complexity of building good relationships as pedagogies for social justice in health and physical education. *Sport, Education and Society*. https://doi.org/10.1080/13573322.2019.1683535

Norberg, J. R. (2011). A contract reconsidered? Changes in the Swedish state's relation to the sports movement. *International Journal of Sport Policy and Politics*, 3(3), 311–325.

Official Reports of the Swedish Government (2016). Det handlar om jämlik hälsa ('It is about equal health') SOU 2016:55. Stockholm, Sweden: The Swedish Government [In Swedish].

Öhman, M. (2010). Analysing the direction of socialisation from a power perspective. *Sport, Education and Society*, 15(4), 393–409.

Peterson, T., and Schenker, K. (2018). Social entrepreneurship in a sport policy context. *Sport in Society*, 21(3), 452–467.

Quennerstedt, M. (2019). Healthying physical education – on the possibility of learning health. *Physical Education and Sport Pedagogy*, 24(1), 1–15.

Quennerstedt, M., Burrows, L., and Maivorsdotter, N. (2010). From teaching young people to be healthy to learning health. *Utbildning och Demokrati*, 19(2), 97–112.

Redelius, K., Quennerstedt, M., & Öhman, M. (2015). Communicating aims and learning goals in physical education: Part of a subject for learning? *Sport, Education and Society*, 20(5), 641–655.

Sandahl, B. (2005). *Ett ämne för alla – Normer och praktik i grundskolans idrottsundervisning 1962–2002*. [A Subject for Everyone? – Norms and Practice in the Compulsory School's Physical Education 1962–2002.] Stockholm: Carlssons.

Schenker, K. (2018). Health(y) education in health and physical education. *Sport, Education and Society.* 23(3), 229–243.

Schenker, K., Linnér, S., Smith, W., Gerdin, G., Mordal Moen, K., Philpot, R., Larsson, L., Legge, M., and Westlie, K. (2019). Conceptualising social justice – what constitutes pedagogies for social justice in HPE across different contexts? *Curriculum Studies in Health and Physical Education*, 10(2), 126–140.

Smith, W., Philpot, R., Gerdin, G., Schenker, K., Linnér, S., Larsson, L., Mordal Moen, K., and Westlie, K. (2020). School HPE: its mandate, responsibility and role in educating for social cohesion. *Sport, Education and Society.* DOI: 10.1080/13573322.2020.1742103.

Telhaug, A., Mediås, O., and Aasen, P. (2004). From collectivism to individualism? Education as nation building in a Scandinavian perspective. *Scandinavian Journal of Educational Research*, 48(2), 141–158.

The Swedish Schools Inspectorate (2018). *Kvalitetsgranskning av ämnet idrott och hälsa i årskurs 7–9* ['Quality assessment of the school subject Physical education and health, grade 7–9']. Stockholm: The Swedish Schools Inspectorate.

Svennberg, L. (2017). *Grading in physical education.* Doctoral Thesis. Stockholm, Sweden: Gymnastik-och Idrottshögskolan.

Svennberg, L., Meckbach, J., and Redelius, K. (2014). Exploring PE teachers' 'gut feelings': An attempt to verbalise and discuss teachers' internalised grading criteria. *European Physical Education Review*, 20(2), 199–214.

Swedish Education Act. (2010). Stockholm: Ministry of Education and Research.

Swedish National Agency for Education. (2011). *Curriculum for the compulsory school, preschool class and school-age educare (revised 2018).* Stockholm: Swedish National Agency of Education.

Swedish National Agency for Education. (2012). *Physical education and health curriculum for upper secondary school.* Stockholm: Swedish National Agency of Education.

Swedish National Agency for Education. (revised 2018). *Curriculum for the compulsory school, preschool class and school-age educare.* Stockholm, Sweden: Swedish National Agency for Education.

Wright, J. (2004). Critical inquiry and problem-solving in physical education. In J. Wright, D. Macdonald, and L. Burrows (Eds.) *Critical inquiry and problem-solving in physical education.* London, UK: Routledge, pp. 1–16.

3

PHYSICAL EDUCATION IN THE US

Policy, curriculum and pedagogy

*Dillon Landi, Jennifer L. Walton-Fisette
and Sue Sutherland*

Introduction

In this chapter, we provide an overview of physical education (PE) in the US –
which is, in short, a 'mixed bag.' We use the phrase 'mixed bag', on account of
the lack of continuity and quality control across the 50 states and 16 territories
that comprise the country. While we do not believe that PE should look the same
everywhere, given that the US is very diverse and a 'one-size-fits-all' approach
would not be appropriate, we do believe that all students – no matter their location or socio-economic status – have a right to quality PE. Currently, this is not
the case. We start by outlining the government structure of the US – which is
important as it is a key reason why PE in the US is a 'mixed bag.' We then discuss the role of professional organisations and national standards. In so doing, we
argue that such standards influence the policies of each individual state in the US.
Next, we provide two case studies of PE in the states of Maryland and Ohio. As
part of this, we highlight the different but interconnected nature of policy, curriculum and pedagogy in PE in these two states. We conclude by reflecting on
why PE is a 'mixed bag' and consider how we might transform that reputation.

Government structure in the US

From the founding of the US to the 1950s, control over educational policies
and practices rested in the hands of local communities – by way of over 80,000
locally elected school boards (Fuhrman et al., 2007). This is because the US
has a decentralised system of government, that is, a government that transfers
authority from central to local control (at state and/or city level). While we do
have a national government (colloquially, the Federal government), laws within
the US divest educational authority to local communities. In 1952, however,

a landmark case in the US (Brown v. Board of Education of Topeka, Kansas) forced a community school board to stop segregating schools based on race. Since then, state governments (and, to a lesser extent, the Federal government) have gained authority over education (Center of Education Policy, 1999). Given this, there are three major levels of government that influence policy, curriculum and pedagogy in the US: federal, state and local.

Whilst it is easy to consider these governments in a hierarchical relationship, their relationship is perhaps better described as being 'intra-active' (Barad, 2007). Intra-active is different from interactive. Intra-active shifts our thinking from conceptualising things as independent, to things existing *because* they connect with other things (as networks). Interactive, on the other hand, starts with the assumption that things exist independently before coming into contact with one another. So, instead of thinking of these governments as discrete and independent, we start from the assumption that each of these governments, their policies and their functions, exist *because* of their connections with one another (see Figure 3.1). Thus, it is not a hierarchical relationship, but rather a mutually productive relationship where each influences the expansion and production of the other.

The Federal government's role in education is primarily concerned with issues of equity and ensuring people from disadvantaged groups are protected (Hill, 2000). Federal legislation targets specific equity issues (usually race, sex and dis/ability) in order to ensure equal access. This function of the Federal government was produced because state and local governments were not addressing these issues, resulting in lawsuits from citizens. According to the US Constitution – the foundational law of the US – individual states have ultimate authority over their respective education systems, not the Federal government. In order to exercise their authority, each state government has established a Department of

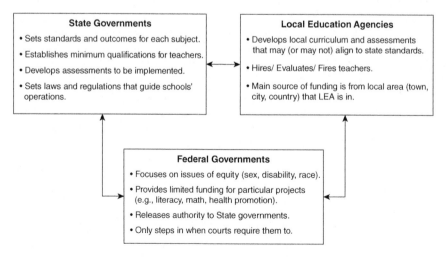

FIGURE 3.1 Intra-active relationship between different governments

Education. The main purpose of state Departments of Education is to develop and enforce regulations around teaching licensure (who can teach), academic standards (what should be taught), school accreditations (maintaining standards), state-wide student assessments (measuring student learning) and school finance (providing *some* financial support) (Fuhrman et al., 2007).

Although state Departments of Education set regulations, they further divest authority for education to local communities. These local governments are referred to as Local Education Agencies (LEAs) – of which the US currently has over 13,500. While the state government's role is to develop regulations, standards and policies, it is the responsibility of LEAs to develop ways to comply with these. As such, LEAs are (usually) a group of locally-elected community members that oversee the operations, finances, policy and curricular agendas of local schools. Accordingly, they are responsible for curriculum development, assessments, teacher evaluations, hiring/firing employees and various other compliance matters. While some LEAs are larger, for example, New York City (New York) has over 1,700 schools, others are much smaller, with Guttenberg (New Jersey) having but a single school. LEAs are primarily funded by taxes derived from local towns and cities, and this inevitably leads to discrepancies in budgets between more or less affluent neighbourhoods. Given that curricula, assessments, evaluations, hiring practices and budgets are very different, PE instruction can also vary significantly between LEAs.

There are multiple intra-active relationships occurring between the Federal government, state governments and LEAs. To start, the Federal government's expanding role in education is due to a lack of attention being paid to equity and diversity by state governments and LEAs. As such, Federal oversight itself is a product of the relationship between the three entities. The state Departments of Education were produced based on an intra-active relationship between the Federal government (establishing authority to states) and LEAs (needing guidelines to manage and operate schools). LEAs, on the other hand, were historically produced because the state and Federal governments divested authority to them – with there being over 80,000 school boards at one point. As state and Federal authority increased, the number of LEAs has decreased to around 13,500 and their autonomy has been heavily diminished by regulations. So, the current format of LEAs is continually being produced because of the intra-active relationship between the Federal government, state governments and local communities. Thus, these entities are intra-active and continually produce and evolve as they come into contact with one another. Yet, the ways they intra-act are different depending on the communities. Given that the Federal government has deferred authority to states, there is no 'National Curriculum' that guides PE as such. This has led to further intra-actions with professional organisations in the US context.

National standards and the US physical education policy

The Society of Health and Physical Educators of America (SHAPE) is the oldest and largest health and PE professional organisation in the US. We consider SHAPE to be a part of the intra-active relationship that exists between Federal, state and local governments. Evidence of this intra-active relationship can be found in the fact that SHAPE has over 200,000 members and has affiliate organisations within each state (e.g. SHAPE New Jersey, SHAPE Maryland). SHAPE has considerable influence over PE in the US through its five broad functions: (a) develop professional standards, position statements and resources, (b) organise and provide professional development, (c) distribute grants, awards and funding, (d) provide advocacy and lobby with governments and (e) support scholarship. Evidently, SHAPE performs various functions, having a wide-reaching and intra-active network that yields considerable influence over all things related to PE in the US context.

SHAPE's standards documents have particular relevance to this chapter. SHAPE has developed two documents that both implicitly and explicitly influence the US PE policy: (a) *National Standards & K-12 Grade-Level Outcomes for Physical Education* (SHAPE America, 2014) and (b) *National Standards for Initial Physical Education Teacher Education* (SHAPE America, 2017). As Walton-Fisette and Sutherland (2020) have stated, while these documents are not explicit policies, they often intra-act with the different policymakers and governmental task forces that develop state-wide standards. Given this, SHAPE standards play a considerable role in the production of state-level policies across the country. In addition, the initial teacher education (ITE) standards have an intra-active relationship with teacher preparation programmes. In other words, these documents directly influence what happens in schools and the university programmes that prepare the teachers who staff them.

While these documents are evidently influential, that is not to say they are without critique. Indeed, we have each been responsible for critiquing them in one way or another. Walton-Fisette and Sutherland (2020) argued that although SHAPE has been influential in curriculum reform in the US for the past 25 years, in their examination of the K-12 (Years 1–13) and ITE standards, they documented a regressive trend in addressing issues of social justice. Although they claim social justice *is* addressed, it is minimal and therefore reproduces inequity. Meanwhile, Landi and colleagues (2021), claimed the behaviourist orientation of the K-12 standards seeks to minimise cultural issues. As such, these fail to make reference to race and sexuality in any meaningful way and make only tangential connections to gender. Landi and colleagues (2021) further argued that SHAPE is happy to use the term 'physical literacy,' but fails to represent any of the theoretical and pedagogical advancements of the concept (Whitehead, 2010). Our critiques aside – for the time being – having discussed these national standards, we now consider the effects of the intra-active relationship between policy, curriculum and practice in the US.

Policies in physical education in the US

Each state's Department of Education is tasked with developing policies that guide PE. These policies account for teaching standards, minimum time expectations for teaching PE, graduation requirements, teacher certifications and teacher evaluations. However, state Departments of Education often divest authority to LEAs. Such a decentralised approach – letting each LEA decide their own requirements – leads to a 'mixed bag' and little continuity. While we do not believe that PE should be standardised, nor look the same everywhere (PE in California *should* look different to PE in Alaska), we do believe in having minimal expectations. This can be similar to having minimum safety regulations in restaurants. Restaurants should not develop their menus *based* on safety regulations, but they should meet those regulations while preparing food. Within PE in the US, LEAs often develop curricula (menus) by aligning them directly to standards (safety regulations), or they develop their own standards not connected to the state. In so doing, PE programmes are either aiming low (minimum safety regulations) or completely neglecting them and making up their own!

Teacher certification (registration/licensure/qualification) provides another example of the lack of continuity within the US PE. Each state establishes minimum requirements to be a teacher. For example, the New Jersey Department of Education (2020) requires teachers to pass a *national* test (Praxis II), basic skills test, minimum 3.0 GPA[1] (B average), hygiene test and meet one of these requirements:

a.   successfully graduate from an undergraduate ITE programme;
b.   successfully graduate from an alternative ITE programme (e.g. post-bachelors, masters); or
c.   have an undergraduate degree in any subject and 30 credit hours (10 classes) in PE (provisional license).

Although it is preferable that teacher candidates graduate from an accredited programme, the third option allows for persons to come back to university and take classes in *PE* and do an 'on the job' internship. However, each state may do this differently. For example, the Florida Department of Education (2020) requires teachers to pass a *statewide* subject test, minimum 2.5 GPA (C average), and meet one of these requirements:

a.   successfully graduate from an undergraduate ITE programme;
b.   successfully graduate from an alternative ITE programme (e.g. post-bachelors, masters); or
c.   have an undergraduate degree in any subject and have 12 credit hours (4 classes) in kinesiology, coaching, exercise science and/or PE (provisional license).

The requirements to be a PE teacher differ greatly here. Within the state of New Jersey, candidates had to take at least 10 classes specifically in PE. While in Florida, candidates only had to take four classes from a broad range of fields inclusive of sport, sport medicine, physiology and sport psychology (as examples).

Candidates in New Jersey needed to graduate with a 3.0 GPA (B), but in Florida this was reduced to a 2.5 GPA (C). There are stark differences between these qualifications, potentially leading to discontinuity amongst the quality of physical educators in the US.

The lack of continuity is further evidenced by the amount of time PE is allocated in schools. Some states require *more* PE than others through credit and time mandates. Within California, there are strict rules on PE. Students in grades 1–6 (Years 2–7) must have 200 minutes per 10 school days (roughly 100 minutes per week), while students in grades 7–12 (Years 8–13) must have 400 minutes of PE for every 10 school days (roughly 200 minutes per week) (Kohl & Cook, 2013). Contrastingly, in Delaware, the law states PE is required for K-8 (Years 1–9) but does not require a minimum number of minutes devoted to instruction. Indeed, students in Delaware are only required to enrol in one credit (one class) of PE over 4 years of high school (Instructional Program Requirements, 2017). Again, there is much variability from state to state in terms of who is required to take PE and how much is required, in what is evidently a 'mixed bag'.

Given the lack of time allocated to PE, and the low bar for entry as a teacher of the subject, much of the research examining policy has tried to prove the usefulness of the subject in schools – especially with regard to obesity. As such, researchers in PE – and public health more broadly – have analysed the relationship between policy mandates and obesity levels (e.g. Cawley et al., 2007; Chriqui et al., 2013; Lounsbery et al., 2013). Much of this research has resulted in ambivalent findings, typically evidencing no causal relation between increased PE time and decreased obesity levels (Cawley et al., 2007). Despite this, SHAPE generates a *Shape of the Nation* report every 4 years that seeks to 'grade' individual state governments on PE policies (SHAPE America, 2016). They make grandiose claims such as, if states align to their recommendations, they will likely reduce obesity (SHAPE America, 2016). The focus on obesity has obscured and stunted other scholarly work on PE policy. For example, unlike in other countries (e.g. Culpan, 2004; Penney, 2008; MacLean et al., 2015), nobody in the US has conducted examinations on the relationship between policy, curriculum and pedagogy. As such, we now seek to reflect on this potential relationship within the US context.

Policy, curriculum and pedagogy: An intra-active approach

Tinning (2010) previously argued that the US PE has been oriented towards a technocratic perspective. Through a technocratic fashion, topics like policy, curriculum and pedagogy have been separated out and treated as distinct. Such distinctions, however, have been disrupted for some time (Kirk, 1993). An example of this disruption is 'models-based practice'. Models often serve to package theory, curriculum and pedagogy into digestible formats. Within this chapter, we conceptualise policy, curriculum and pedagogy as having an 'intra-active' relationship (Barad, 2007). From this perspective, policy, curriculum and pedagogy are inseparable as they exist because of each other. In this section, we take two specific cases, the states of Maryland and Ohio, and examine the intra-active relationship between policies, curriculum and pedagogy within them. Subsequently, having outlined these two cases, we consider what occurs in PE across these spaces.

Maryland physical education

The state of Maryland has adopted the *National Standards & K-12 Grade-Level Outcomes for Physical Education* (SHAPE America, 2014) as their state standards. Within Maryland, there are 24 LEAs that correspond with the 24 counties that comprise the state. State law in Maryland requires that students in K-8 (Years 1–9) receive PE each year with 'sufficient frequency and duration to meet the requirements of the state curriculum' (Program in Physical Education, 2016). Each of the 24 counties locally decides how much time they want to devote to PE. Within some LEAs (e.g. Howard County), each school is required to provide the same amount of time for PE, while other LEAs (e.g. Baltimore City) leave that decision up to individual principals in schools. Therefore, students' experiences of PE may vary greatly depending on where they go to school. Meanwhile, in high schools, Maryland law mandates students complete one-half credit prior to graduation – which equates to half of a school year.

As you can see, curriculum and pedagogy already have an intra-active relationship with state policy as LEA's are required to provide enough instructional time for K-8 students in Maryland to meet the requirements of the state curriculum. Thus, curriculum, policy and pedagogy all combine to produce specific time allotments of instruction. Under Maryland Code, all LEAs are required to provide a PE curriculum guide for schools within their jurisdiction. Some LEAs adopt SHAPE outcomes outright and place them in a curriculum map (e.g. Frederick County). Other LEAs create their own curriculum standards that go beyond SHAPE's document – for example, to integrate a focus on biophysical foundations (e.g. Montgomery County). Given this, in some cases, the intra-active relationship between SHAPE-LEAs-teachers works to produce different PE curricula depending on the particular place and time allotment. This is because the actors (e.g. standards, LEAs, administrators) within this network bring some form of agency and power that influences curriculum development. Notably, because of the decentralised organisation of the government, outside and/or private organisations (e.g. FitnessGram) also intra-act and produce changes in PE.

The Montgomery County LEA has a historic relationship with the University of Maryland. On account of this, Ennis and Chen (2015), based at the University of Maryland at this time, created and implemented the 'Science and PE' curriculum in the Montgomery County LEA. The Science and PE curriculum is a specific packaged curriculum that integrates science-based concepts into activities. The goal of integrating the science-based knowledge is to increase cognitive outcomes and hopefully lead to 'healthier lifestyles'. Thus, locally-driven agendas and partnerships affect the intra-active relationship between policies, curriculum and schools. Importantly, this curriculum development project was *federally* funded by the National Institute of Health – which shows how Federal priorities can affect the 'decentralised' local agenda.

The SHAPE standards (and the goals of PE) in the US are often dictated by 'where the money is' (Hawkins, 2008). The Montgomery County LEA is the wealthiest county in the state and, given its financial flexibility, is able to choose who to establish partnerships with. In other areas, like Baltimore City, much of what happens is driven by Federal agendas in conjunction with private institutions (like Johns Hopkins University, which does not have a PE programme) that bankroll PE such that it is solely about physical activity promotion (Menschik et al., 2008). In other words, the Baltimore City LEA is often underfunded and therefore at the whim of organisations that promise funding. Such opportunities do not exist for more rural LEAs like Garrett County. Thus, what happens in the name of PE is a 'mixed bag' within the state, because the intra-active relationships are connected to other factors that are omitted in simple policy analyses like those undertaken by SHAPE.

Reflecting on the above, PE in Maryland is a 'mixed bag' that has little continuity across LEA lines. The decentralised nature of government, which is meant to provide local responsiveness, allows private and/or external organisations to influence PE. Within this system, wealthier LEAs have greater freedom and opportunity than those with little money. Notably, much of what happens in Maryland PE is driven by political agendas and wealth. Given the intra-active relationship between all of these entities, other aspects like social justice issues are not addressed. As such, the purpose of PE across the state varies, PE is taught differently, and schools are funded at disparate levels – leading to mass inequities.

Ohio physical education

Within Ohio, there are 931 LEAs that correspond with the 88 counties that comprise the state. State law in Ohio requires that students in K–8 (Years 1–9) receive PE each year, although there are no time expectations stipulated. Ohio Code mandates that students complete one-half unit (equivalent to 60 hours of instruction) of PE in high school prior to graduation (Ohio Revised Code, 2019). However, the state allows LEAs – locally referred to as school districts – to grant student 'waivers' from PE class by showcasing subject matter competency or by participating in a school sport, marching band, cheerleading or other extracurricular activities. Since 2013, the state has required that individuals teaching K-12 PE hold a valid license in PE. However, teachers were also 'grandfathered in' as, if they were already teaching PE before 2013, they were allowed to continue teaching without a PE license.

In addition to the Ohio law and policies, PE is also guided by national and state standards. Ohio adopted the national standards as their state standards in

2007 (NASPE, 2004; SHAPE America, 2014; Ohio Department of Education, 2020). At that time, there were six national standards that guided PE curriculum; however, these standards did not include specific grade-level outcomes or indicators. Thus, in 2009, Ohio formulated benchmarks and indicators for all six standards across the K-12 (Years 1–13) grade levels. This prompted many school districts to revise their PE curricula, though it was for each school district and/or the individual teachers within schools to determine whether they were offering instruction that was standards-based and aligned with this policy or not. That is, the standards offered guidance to PE teachers, but the decisions to utilise the standards to frame curriculum, instruction and assessment was not a state requirement at that time.

The following year, in 2010, state policies were passed to establish a measure of student achievement with regard to meeting the benchmarks contained in the PE Academic Content Standards that was to be included on the state report card (Ohio Department of Education, 2020). To measure whether students were 'meeting' these benchmarks, PE assessments were developed, with there being two benchmarks for each standard, resulting in 12 assessments for each grade band: K-2, 3–5, 6–8 and 9–12. Beginning from the 2012–2013 academic year, school districts had to submit data to the state indicating how many K-12 (Years 1–13) students were: advanced (3), proficient (2) or limited (1) across each of the standards and benchmarks. In 2016, Ohio aligned their standards to the new SHAPE standards document bringing the number of standards to five and corresponding assessed benchmarks to 10. Data are tracked and submitted via formulated Excel scoring sheets provided by the Ohio Department of Education.

Whilst these assessment and reporting procedures might seem fairly robust, in practice it would seem that they are anything but. Within the Kent City School District, for example, there were 3,423 K-12 students in the 2019–2020 academic year (NCES, 2020). The school district only has to perform the PE evaluations on students in grades 2, 5 and 8 (Years 2, 6 and 9, respectively), as well as high school (Years 10–13), which is approximately 1,053 students. Therefore, we only gain a narrow understanding of how many students are achieving the standards per year. Each student is expected to complete 10 assessments to measure their achievement of the standards and benchmarks. Yet, instead of each student having 10 data points to report (i.e. a total of 10,530), the score being submitted is an average across all of these, to decide if the students *collectively* meet *all* of the standards and benchmarks. As such, a student may be successful in one standard (e.g. fitness and physical activity), but struggle with other areas (e.g. motor skills, tactics and strategies) – but this would not be evident based on the school's reporting. Therefore, the Ohio Department of Education would be unaware since they will only represent one data point – that is, if they are advanced, proficient or limited across all of the standards and benchmarks. The total number of students within each category is subsequently submitted to the state. This means that the Kent City School District will submit a total of 12 numbers to the state (three for each of grades 2, 5 and 8 and high school) out of a possible 10,530. Although the assessments are a state requirement, it is up to the PE teachers in each district to provide a curriculum that is standards-based and includes an authentic implementation of the PE evaluations.

Therefore, conceivably, it would seem that Ohio has a positive intra-active relationship with policy, curriculum and pedagogy. There are standards and evaluations that guide PE curriculum across the state – regardless of the size or affluence of the school district. Yet, PE teachers are not held accountable for the quality of instruction, alignment to standards or implementation of assessments, making Ohio PE no less of a 'mixed bag.' This, of course, does not even consider the minimal focus on social justice issues within this intra-active relationship of PE in the state of Ohio. An overhaul of policies, curriculum and pedagogical practices is necessary for a more just and equitable educational experience for all students who receive PE in Ohio – as is the case in Maryland.

Conclusion

In a 1984 Wendy's® commercial, there were three elderly women looking at a non-Wendy's burger that had a huge bun but a very small patty. This prompted one of the ladies to quip, 'Where's the beef?' The beef, of course, being the most important part of the hamburger (not the bun). When we consider curriculum, policy and pedagogy as intra-active, we understand each of these elements as influencing and producing the other. It seems, however, that the intra-action between these three factors has produced an imbalance. As policies expand and become more stringent, curricula swell to meet these increased needs, and aspects such as accountability and assessment become privileged. In this situation, addi- tional stress and expectations are placed on teachers and students. Yet, when these policies are formed, the actors often neglect these important elements: students, teachers and pedagogy. In other words, policy and curriculum may have swelled but, when it comes down to it, we know very little about how those things intra- act with students, teachers and pedagogy. So, one might ask, 'Where's the beef?'

What is more concerning is that while policies mandate particular standards (minimum safety regulations) and curricula are aligned to those mandates (ham- burger menu) – what actually happens in practice could be completely different (where's the beef?). Not to mention, the way PE is experienced by students is dependent on the LEA, their school and the local community. So, despite being a mile away from each other, one school may be providing an excellent PE expe- rience (filet mignon), whilst a school down the road might be getting a rubbish experience (spam), or they may not be getting PE at all (by means of a waiver system).

The point to note is that the decentralised system of government has created a situation where PE is vastly different depending on the communities that offer it. As such, wealthy communities get programmes aligned to some privileged forms of knowledge (e.g. Montgomery County). Poorer districts become 'lab subjects' for public health strategies aimed at increasing physical activity for urban youth (e.g. Baltimore City). Others are restricted by assessments but, because they are not audited, enforced or held accountable, schools may offer one thing and submit something else to the state (e.g. Kent City). In any case, there is a consistent lack of engagement with students, teachers and communities in the development of policies and curricula. As a result, the intra-actions between them produce an inequitable system in the US where PE becomes a 'mixed bag.'

To reiterate, we are not suggesting that PE should look the same everywhere. We do argue, however, that PE should be developed with students, teachers and communities in mind. There is a residual belief in the US that making a policy, or national standards, can act as a 'silver bullet' for solving problems. As such, policies, standards and assessments are produced without actually engaging with those who experience them. This is why assessments are produced that teachers may (or may not) follow. It is also why universities feel they are able to enter school districts and tell teachers 'what is right' for their programmes. Such an approach puts students (and their lived experiences) last in PE – when they should be first.

We conclude by claiming that PE in the US will only change when it is not seen as an intervention. Too many times, PE is proffered as the solution to obesity, social and emotional health problems or as a means of developing skilled athletic performers. We argue that such approaches are not educative, but are training *for* the physical. Training *for* the physical decides what is best for students prior to meeting them. Instead, we call for our subject to shift towards education *about* the physical. In this way, students would learn *about* the biophysical, psychological, socio-cultural and historical dimensions of human movement. By shifting away from training *for* the physical – and towards education *about* the physical – policy, curriculum and pedagogy are produced in relation to each other. This is markedly better than the 'ad hoc' system that exists currently. If we were to realise such a shift, things would not be a 'mixed bag' because content and expectations would be the same – but the way they are achieved and connected to students' lives would be different. Such an approach would leave room for diversity of thought, cultures and communities. Importantly, it would place students at the centre of pedagogy and not the political and financial agendas that rob our field of its soul (Hawkins, 2008).

Reflection points

- In this chapter, we illustrated how policy, curriculum and pedagogy are interconnected and intra-act. How does policy, curriculum and pedagogy intra-act in your country?
- What are the benefits of a decentralised government system? What are the limitations? Is there a way to strike a balance and what would this look like for PE?
- Assessments and standards are becoming more commonplace across the world. What should we be assessing in PE to demonstrate student learning? Should these scores be used to evaluate teachers and schools?

Note

1 GPA stands for grade point average and it is the averaged total of all grades. It is equivalent to the 'classification' system, whereby 3.0 (B) GPA is equivalent to 2:2 degree, and a 2.5 (C) GPA is equivalent to third class honours.

References

Barad, K. (2007). *Meeting the universe halfway: Quantum physics and the entanglement of matter.* Durham, NC: Duke University Press.

Cawley, J., Meyerhoefer, C., and Newhouse, D. (2007). The impact of state physical education requirements on youth physical activity and overweight. *Health Economics, 16*(12), 1287–1301.

Center of Education Policy. (1999). *A brief history of the federal role in education: Why it began and why it's still needed.* Washington, DC: Center on Education Policy.

Chriqui, J. F., Eyler, A., Carnoske, C., and Slater, S. (2013). State and district policy influences on district-wide elementary and middle school physical education practices. *Journal of Public Health Management and Practice: JPHMP, 19*(3 Suppl 1), S41–S48.

Culpan, I. (2004). Physical education curriculum: A humanistic positioning. In A.-M. O'Neill, J. Clark, and R. Openshaw (Eds.), *Reshaping culture, knowledge and learning: Policy and content in the New Zealand curriculum framework.* New Zealand: Dunmore Press, pp. 225–243.

Ennis, C., and Chen, A. (2015). *Perfect partnership: Science enriched physical education.* National Institute of Health. https://nihsepa.org/project/perfect-partnership-science-enriched-physical-education-phase-i/.

Florida Department of Education. (2020). *Educator certification. Educator certification.* http://www.fldoe.org/teaching/certification/.

Fuhrman, S. H., Goertz, M. E., and Weinbaum, E. E. (2007). Educational governance in the United States: Where are we? How did we get here? Why should we care? In S. H. Fuhrman, D. K. Cohen, and F. Mosher (Eds.), *The state of educational policy research.* Mahwah, NJ: Lawrence Erlbaum Associates, pp. 41–61.

Hawkins, D. (2008). Pragmatism, purpose, and play: Struggle for the soul of physical education. *Quest, 60*(3), 345–356.

Hill, P. T. (2000). The federal role in education. *Brookings Papers on Educational Policy, 2000,* 11–40.

Instructional Program Requirements. (2017). *Pub. L. No. 20 DE Reg. 971, Title 14 Delaware administrative code.* https://regulations.delaware.gov/AdminCode/title14/500/503.shtml.

Kirk, D. (1993). Curriculum work in physical education: Beyond the objectives approach? *Journal of Teaching in Physical Education, 12,* 244–265.

Kohl, H. W., and Cook, H. D. (Eds.). (2013). *Educating the student body: Taking physical activity and physical education to school.* NW Washington, DC: The National Academies press.

Landi, D., Blackshear, T., and McFadden, C. (2021). SHAPE America and physical literacy: An event horizon? *Curriculum Studies in Health and Physical Education.* doi: 10.1080/25742981.2021.1908835.

Lounsbery, M. A. F., McKenzie, T. L., Morrow Jr., J. R., Monnat, S. M., and Holt, K. A. (2013). District and school physical education policies: Implications for physical education and recess time. *Annals of Behavioral Medicine, 45*(Suppl. 1), S131–S1141.

MacLean, J., Mulholland, R., Gray, S., and Horrell, A. (2015). Enabling curriculum change in physical education: The interplay between policy constructors and practitioners. *Physical Education and Sport Pedagogy, 20*, 79–96.

Menschik, D., Ahmed, S., Alexander, M. H., and Blum, R. W. (2008). Adolescent physical activities as predictors of young adult weight. *Archives of Pediatrics & Adolescent Medicine, 162*(1), 29–33.

National Association for Sport and Physical Education. (2004). *Moving into the future: National standards for physical education* (2nd ed.). Reston, VA: Author.

NCES (2020). *Public school districts 2019–2020*. https://nces.ed.gov/ccd/districtsearch/district_detail.asp?Search=2&details=1&ID2=3904416&DistrictID=3904416.

New Jersey Department of Education. (2020). *Physical education certificate of eligibility*. New Jersey Department of Education. https://nj.gov/education/license/endorsements/1630CE.pdf.

Penney, D. (2008). Playing a political game and playing for position: Policy and curriculum development in health and physical education. *European Physical Education Review, 14*, 33–49.

Ohio Department of Education. (2020). *Physical education*. http://education.ohio.gov/Topics/Learning-in-Ohio/Physical-Education.

Ohio Revised Code. (2019). *3313.603. Requirements for high school graduation; workforce or college preparatory units.* http://codes.ohio.gov/orc/3313.603.

Program in Physical Education. (2016). *13a.04.13.01. Code of Maryland Regulations § Maryland State Board of Education.* http://mdrules.elaws.us/comar/13a.04.13.01.

SHAPE America. (2014). *National standards and grade-level outcomes for K-12 physical education.* Champaign, Illinois: Human Kinetics.

SHAPE America. (2016). *2016 Shape of the nation: Status of physical education in the USA.* Reston, VA: Author.

SHAPE America. (2017). *National standards for initial physical education teacher education.* http://www.shapeamerica.org/accreditation/upload/National-Standards-for-Initial-Physical-Education-Teacher-Education-2017.pdf.

Tinning, Richard. (2010). *Pedagogy and human movement: Theory, practice, research.* Abingdon: Routledge.

Walton-Fisette, J. L., and Sutherland, S. (2020). Time to SHAPE up: Developing policies, standards and practices that are socially just. *Physical Education and Sport Pedagogy, 25*(3), 274-287. https://doi.org/10.1080/17408989.2020.1741531.

Whitehead, M. (2010). *Physical literacy: Throughout the life course.* London: Routledge.

4

EXPLORING THE ROLE OF ASSESSMENT POLICY IN SECURING AN EDUCATIVE HEALTH AND PHYSICAL EDUCATION IN SCHOOLS

Louise McCuaig

Introduction

Assessment, if not a 'dirty' word in health and physical education (HPE), is certainly one that attracts advocacy, critique and consternation in equal measure across the field. Indeed, assessment matters within school HPE programmes have long been a source of tension for the field's educators, policymakers and key stakeholders. As vexatious as assessment might be for the HPE profession, in the current neoliberal climate of surveillance, audits and accountability (Lingard, Martino & Rezai-Rashti, 2013), there has been both an urgent need for, and growing engagement with, this privileged practice within physical education (PE) (Macdonald & Brooker, 1997; MacPhail, 2007; Thorburn, 2007; Hay & Penney, 2013; Brown & Penney, 2018). Considerably less attention has been directed towards assessment in health education, although this is attracting an increasing interest amongst researchers (Leahy, Burrows, McCuaig, Penney & Wright, 2016). While often mirroring issues faced by the broader education community, HPE assessment literature demonstrates the unique impact of the field's emphasis on movement and physical performance (Brown & Penney, 2018), as well as its relationship with national health agendas (Leahy et al., 2016). Notwithstanding this distinction, less attention has been paid to the role that high-stakes assessment plays in addressing the enduring gap between curriculum policy and classroom practice (Kirk, 2009).

In response, this chapter explores how assessment policy can strengthen or inhibit the potency and purchase of new philosophies, content and practices in school HPE programmes. Two 'stories' of Australian HPE curriculum reform – that inspired the author's interest in the critical role that assessment can play in securing an innovative, sustainable and educative school HPE – are documented within the chapter. The first of these curriculum reforms occurred at a national level and resulted in the construction of a nationally consistent HPE curriculum framework for the first 10 years of compulsory Australian schooling. The second took place as part of a review of the Australian senior school phase which accompanied the national reform agenda (Australian Council for Educational Research, 2014), and subsequently underpinned the reform of the HPE senior (or examinable) subjects in the Australian state of Queensland. Harnessing the theoretical contributions of Basil Bernstein (1990), this chapter demonstrates the ways in which the powerful message system of assessment shaped Australian teachers' investment in adopting innovative and sustainable approaches to curriculum and pedagogy. This analysis informs some concluding thoughts on how assessment might contribute to an educative HPE.

Assessment in health and physical education

A broad review of the history of approaches to HPE assessment in Queensland, a state of Australia, provides initial insight into the challenges facing educators and policymakers on the 'what' and 'why' of assessment in HPE. Curriculum policy and implementation in Australia is a complex affair due to the multiple levels of public policy governance informing schooling and education. While the states and territories have ultimate responsibility for schooling, since the early 1990s there has been popular and political enthusiasm for a cohesive, national curriculum for years Preparatory-10, which includes the compulsory phases of primary (5–11-year-olds) and secondary (12–15-year-olds) schooling. Australia's first attempts to create a national junior curriculum resulted in a formalised integration of health education, PE and personal development into one subject area – and this unification of health education and PE was maintained in the reform programme presented later in this chapter. Meanwhile, efforts to unify the curriculum delivered to students in the non-compulsory and examinable senior phase of schooling (16–18-year-olds) failed to gain traction.

In the state of Queensland, advice on assessment by syllabus authors of the 1950s noted that PE 'has much broader aims than the achievement of physical skills; indeed, the more significant aspects of PE do not lend themselves to objective measurement' (Department of Education Queensland, 1952, p. 14). However, the introduction of compulsory secondary schooling in the 1970s was to trouble this perspective. Securing a highly prized place in the new, compulsory junior high school curriculum inspired considerable debate about the purpose and rigour of testing amongst the Queensland HPE profession. HPE leaders of the day advocated for the use of knowledge and skill tests that were emerging within sport science communities (Thompson, 1980) including: written tests; standardised and teacher-designed physical skills tests; and behaviour rating scales that assess social skills and attitudes (Board of Secondary School Studies Queensland, 1975). Notwithstanding this momentum, Queensland educators continued to question the rationale and impact of assessment in HPE.

By the late 1990s, endeavours to produce an inaugural Australian Curriculum offered little clarity on assessment practices for HPE teachers. While the Queensland HPE Key Learning Area (KLA) materials encouraged teachers *and* students to evaluate their learning (Queensland School Curriculum Council, 1999), there was scant information on the preferred techniques of student assessment or advice to teachers on reflective practices. Not surprisingly, research exploring HPE KLA implementation in Queensland highlighted the 'need for clear procedures for assessment and reporting' (Macdonald, Glasby & Carlson, 2000, p. 7). Meanwhile, the burgeoning enrolment of students in the junior phase of secondary schooling during the 1970s provoked demand for, and implementation of, senior (or examinable) HPE courses in 1978. Some 50 years of Queensland Senior HPE curriculum delivery drove considerable innovation, as the profession responded to the demands of high-stakes assessment regimes that determined students' entry into university and career pathways (Hay, 2008). Advocacy for the inclusion of senior examinable subjects in HPE were, once again, wedded to questions concerning the validity of assessment practices. As early as 1997, Macdonald and Brooker (1997) raised issues about performance-based assessment in PE. Echoing the concerns of their predecessors, they concluded that 'it remains to be answered whether performance-based subjects should reject the structures of assessment and accountability and simply concentrate on providing students with experiences that characterise the chosen subject area (such as the joy of movement)' (p. 99).

A decade on, Thorburn (2007, p. 179) continued the debate about issues of performance-based assessment in Scottish examinable PE, arguing that 'PE is being studied but only occasionally experienced'. He warned physical educators to resist being 'trapped by certification' and that assessment of physical performance should emerge from learning environments that are 'true to the practical essence of PE' (Thorburn, 2007, p. 181). Such concerns are shared by HPE researchers who have focused on health education in school settings. As Quennerstedt, Burrows and Maivorsdotter (2010) argue, the possibilities that 'new curricula afford for learning health are traded for the notion that teaching young people how to be healthy should be the penultimate goal of health education' (p. 103). Either implicitly or explicitly, assessment practices consequently promote 'slippage between monitoring health-related behaviours and assessment in health education' (Leahy et al., 2016, p. 91). As a result, school health education programmes can escape their educational foundations to align more with an interventionist intent. Such concerns are neither surprising nor exclusively Australian. Aligning the rationales of school health education curricula with national public health agendas offers status, funding and much needed resources. Steeped in the language of health promotion, some programmes can be reduced to 'specific, short-term interventions that produce "visible" changes in pupils' health-related behaviours' (Inchley, Muldoon & Currie, 2006, p. 66).

Within the following sections of this chapter, I outline two Australian Curriculum reform 'stories' to examine how the purpose, practice and accountability of assessment plays a critical role in securing an educative, as opposed to an interventionist, intent for school HPE. Although not claiming to provide an accurate account of the complexity of decisions informing the construction of the Australian Curriculum: HPE (AC:HPE) (Australian Curriculum, Assessment and Reporting Authority, 2014), and Queensland General Senior Health syllabus (Queensland Curriculum and Assessment Authority, 2018), I draw on personal experience as a curriculum writer and information garnered from publicly available curriculum and policy documents to weave a reflective, but inevitably partial, curriculum reform narrative.

Constructing the Australian Curriculum in Health and Physical Education

Established in 2008, the Australian Curriculum, Assessment and Reporting Authority (ACARA) was responsible for the development of Australia's second attempt at a national curriculum (Australian Curriculum, Assessment and Reporting Authority, 2012a). ACARA was charged with making 'clear to teachers what has to be taught' and 'what achievement standards are expected of them', while teachers were considered best placed to 'make decisions about the pedagogical approach that will give the best learning outcomes' (National Curriculum Board, 2009, p. 15). Note here that formal guidance on pedagogical matters is therefore beyond the remit of ACARA's agenda. ACARA adopted an extensive and collaborative curriculum development process that involved four phases of activity: shaping, writing, implementation and monitoring and evaluation (Australian Curriculum, Assessment and Reporting Authority, 2012a). Work in the shaping phase produced a broad outline of the Foundation to Year 12 (F–12) curriculum for a subject. Initially, the subject of HPE struggled to gain a place in the early phases of this reform process. As such, health and education stakeholders argued that the 'well-being of our young people is under threat from a wide range of health problems' (Daube et. al., 2010, p. 1), drawing on national public health reports that strongly supported the inclusion of health literacy skills as a core element of the Australian Curriculum (National Health and Hospitals Reform Commission, 2009; National Preventative Health Taskforce, 2009). Responding to this groundswell of advocacy, ACARA was directed to begin constructing a course of study for HPE.

Competing perspectives on the purpose of compulsory HPE in schools are evident in the scholarship dedicated to the promotion and critique of the propositions (or 'big ideas') that were to shape the new AC:HPE (Australian Curriculum, Assessment and Reporting Authority, 2012b). The AC:HPE was explicitly identified as having an educative intent (Macdonald, 2013), a proposition that emphasised the teaching of knowledge and skills that underpin active, healthy living as opposed to 'fixing' health behaviours or producing sporting excellence. Four additional propositions, including adopting a strengths-based approach to HPE (McCuaig, Quennerstedt & Macdonald, 2013), teaching health literacy

(Alfrey & Brown, 2013), enacting socio-critical inquiry (Leahy, O'Flynn & Wright, 2013) and valuing movement (Brown, 2013), were incorporated into an orienting framework intended to drive innovative HPE practice in Australian schools.

As McCuaig, Atkin and Macdonald (2019) report, settlement of the AC:HPE was not easily achieved. Contestation was rife, with the Australian sport and exercise research community particularly vocal in their critique of the proposed AC:HPE's philosophical underpinnings. Indeed, the lead writer of the AC:HPE acknowledged that the AC:HPE's strengths-based approach, drawing on saluto-genic theory, was possibly a world first and therefore somewhat 'risky business' in curriculum-making (McCuaig et al., 2013). It was perhaps not surprising to discover that, following the release of the AC:HPE, research confirmed teachers' variable understandings, confidence and engagements with the AC:HPE's new philosophies and content (Hogan, Enright, Stylianou & McCuaig, 2018; Lambert, 2018). As Lambert (2018, p. 137) insightfully summarises, the AC:HPE's 'big ideas' are 'conceptually challenging, making teachers apprehensive, Australian academics nervous and international observers dubious'.

Systemic complexity also played a considerable role in teachers' diverse implementation of the AC:HPE. As McCuaig and colleagues (2019) reveal, by 2018, five of the eight Australian jurisdictions had implemented versions of the AC:HPE. The three states who had not implemented the AC:HPE chose instead to incorporate the Australian Curriculum into local frameworks or established syllabus structures. A further complication to this messy landscape emerged when the Australian Government instigated a review of the Australian Curriculum in response to conservative critiques. HPE experts contributing to this review noted that teachers would need considerable ability and aptitude to successfully trans-late learning goals into engaging, cohesive programmes (Donnelly & Wiltshire, 2014). Matters of assessment, however, were rarely a focus of commentary sur-rounding the AC:HPE. Yet, as shall be discussed later, the practicalities of assess-ment can offer a unique insight into the realisation (or otherwise) of the field's aspirations for an educative HPE. Evidence of this can be found in the second of our curriculum reform 'stories' that occurred at a state level.

Constructing the Queensland Senior Health subject

As a result of renewed enthusiasm for a cohesive Australian Curriculum, a review of the final phase of schooling was also undertaken at numerous levels of federal and state government (Australian Council for Educational Research, 2014). In the state of Queensland, this review led to the return of external assessment in the final semester of senior studies, demanding the construction of highly prescriptive syllabuses for some 50 subjects. A systemic imperative for those involved in this senior schooling reform was to ensure that new courses of study aligned with the underpinning principles of the Australian Curriculum. The Queensland Curriculum and Assessment Authority (QCAA) began the process of curriculum redevelopment in January 2016, with a view to having all subjects ready for implementation in January 2019.

Clearly, the defining feature of this curriculum reform agenda was the reintroduction of external examination practices which, the QCAA argued, offered a significant transition towards more rigorous quality assurance processes (Queensland Curriculum and Assessment Authority, n.d.). This transition would be secured through three new assessment protocols in Queensland's senior phase of schooling:

- School-based assessment instruments, previously attracting little scrutiny, now require endorsement by the QCAA before use in schools
- Students' results in these assessments are externally confirmed by independent teacher assessors trained and accredited by the QCAA
- Results from school-based tasks are combined with one external assessment developed and marked by the QCAA (Queensland Curriculum and Assessment Authority, n.d.)

A striking implication of this suite of assessment policies and practices is the dramatic increase in Queensland teachers' and schools' accountability to external agents. Without question, the return of external examinations raised concern amongst HPE teachers that many of the ruthlessly pursued and highly prized attributes of their current senior HPE programmes would be eroded. Previous iterations of these programmes had successfully retained assessment tasks that evaluated students' application of knowledge and skills in authentic sport and health-related contexts (Hay, 2008), but these valued attributes were now perceived to be 'at risk'. Feedback gathered during the reform by the Queensland branch of the peak professional body, the Australian Council for Health, Physical Education and Recreation (ACHPER), indicated that HPE teachers were most troubled by the impact that external examinations would have on students' motivation, participation and performance in physical activities. Few teachers raised the matter of alignment with the newly released AC:HPE, and there was generally little attention paid to health education.

Alignment with the AC:HPE's 'big ideas' was, however, strenuously emphasised by the QCAA in formal design briefs. With consideration of Senior Health, writers were informed that the AC:HPE's three health-related 'big ideas' of a strengths-based approach, health literacy and critical inquiry should be included in the redeveloped syllabus (Queensland Curriculum and Assessment Authority, 2016). As part of the resulting Senior Health syllabus (Queensland Curriculum and Assessment Authority, 2018), the salutogenic model of health was established as the conceptual foundation for the course's Health Inquiry model (see Figure 4.1). Design of the Health Inquiry Model was in direct response to the QCAA's requirement that teachers and stakeholders would be provided clarity on the pedagogical approaches to be used in the

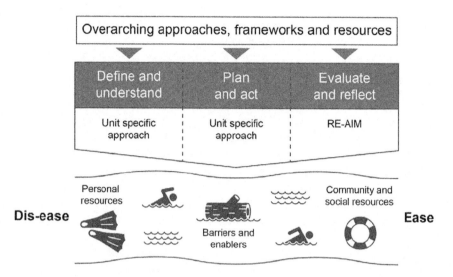

FIGURE 4.1 Health Inquiry Model, Senior Health syllabus (Queensland Curriculum and Assessment Authority, 2018)

teaching of each subject. Explicitly embedding a pedagogical approach represented a significant divergence from approaches to the Australian Curriculum and inevitably strengthened the interplay between the curriculum, pedagogy and assessment dimensions of the senior subjects.

Just prior to the implementation of these senior subjects in 2019, and in stark contrast to the AC:HPE reform, Queensland HPE teachers demonstrated substantially more engagement with the content, pedagogical approaches and assessment implications of the two new senior HPE courses. While the Queensland branch of ACHPER struggled to attract teachers to AC:HPE professional development events before 2016, later masterclasses on the theoretical underpinnings of the new senior courses 'sold out' quickly. As a co-presenter of the Senior Health masterclass, it was truly remarkable to witness teachers' investment in grasping a deep understanding of the 'new' theoretical perspectives and innovative approaches that had, more than 5 years ago, been introduced to the profession through the AC:HPE (Australian Curriculum, Assessment and Reporting Authority, 2012b). Indeed, as late as October 2019, Queensland Education Department officers were devising HPE conference presentations to allay teachers' concerns that curriculum reform timelines had not allowed for an alignment of rationales, content and approaches between junior and senior HPE curricula.

How might we understand these two conflicting 'stories' of curriculum reform in Australian HPE? There can be little question that the divergent approaches to student assessment, pedagogy and accountability undertaken by national and state authorities accounted for these contrasting tales of curriculum reform and implementation. In seeking to explore these dynamics, Bernstein's theoretical contributions are particularly helpful.

Discussion

Drawing on Bernstein's theoretical contributions enables an interrogation of the factors that contribute to teachers' diverse responses to new philosophical orientations and innovative practices in HPE. According to Bernstein (1990), the selection, classification, transmission and assessment of educational knowledge can be viewed as occurring through the three *interrelated* message systems of pedagogy, curriculum and evaluation (or we could say, assessment). Bernstein's emphasis on the interrelated nature of these message systems alerts us to how effective educational work in schools is dependent on the *alignment and coherence* of the three message systems (Penney, Brooker, Hay & Gillespie, 2009). However, as Broadfoot (1996) observes, 'assessment procedures are so closely bound up with the legitimization of particular educational practices' (p. 87) that assessment is typically considered the most important of the three message systems.

Assessment as a message system in schooling essentially operates to define, communicate and ascribe value. This operation is evident at every level of the education system. For example, in the Senior Health curriculum reform outlined above, the official assessment policies stipulate those learning objectives that warrant accountability and accordingly the knowledge and skills that are valued (Ranson, 2003). Knowledge and skills that do not attract assessment or robust accountability are consequently considered less significant. As Hardman and Marshall (2000) argue, this valuing of some knowledge and skills over others influences schools' choices on what and how curriculum is implemented in their classrooms.

Assessment, and the disparate accountability measures within the context of these two Australian HPE curriculum reforms, also appears to play a critical role in driving teachers' investment in closing the curriculum policy-practice gap. Of particular interest are the ways in which assessment became a primary mechanism through which the Australian HPE profession could evaluate the realisation (or otherwise) of the AC:HPE's educative intent. As Hay and Penney (2009, p. 88) explain, 'two critical tasks of assessment are the collecting of information and the making of interpretations, both of which are shaped by the purpose of the assessment'. In the first instance, the simple presence of an assessment item in a school's HPE unit, the outcomes of which are formally reported to parents and carers, offers a 'litmus test' of the educative intent of any HPE programme. In the case of the AC:HPE, however, there has been little in the way of policy to suggest that teachers, schools and/or systems are held accountable for the delivery and reporting of HPE assessment tasks commensurate with this fundamental facet of educational practice.

A further determinant of a HPE programme's educative intent concerns the nature of student data gathered through assessment and used to establish student achievement levels. If this information only includes or privileges students' bio-physical attributes or behaviour, such as body weight, caloric intake and output, step count or fitness test results, then it is highly unlikely that the unit of work values knowledge and skills commensurate with an educative remit. Moreover, research suggests that in response to teachers' concerns regarding their HPE experience and expertise – particularly at the primary school level – schools readily and strategically outsource their HPE programmes to external providers (Williams, Hay & Macdonald, 2011; Hogan et al., 2018, Chapter 14, this volume). Scholars exploring these outsourcing practices have found that, in their efforts to demonstrate impact and evidence-based practice, external providers often emphasise the collection and evaluation of health behaviour data (McCuaig, Woolcock, Stylianou, Ng & Ha, 2020), as opposed to learning outcomes.

Such latitude of curriculum delivery is not afforded to those teaching the senior phase of Queensland schooling. Highly prescriptive syllabus documents that explicitly outline what is to be taught, how it is to be taught and when, what and how student performance is assessed, leave little room for interpretation or ad-hoc implementation. Should teachers stray from these prescriptive instructions, external and mandated audits of their assessment practice have been designed to address inexperience or recalcitrance. Even teachers' interpretation of student data attracts an exacting scrutiny through the process of confirmation, designed to 'maximise public confidence in the reliability of the grades awarded by teachers … [as] QCAA will independently review a representative sample of assessments in every subject in every school' (Queensland Curriculum and Assessment Authority, n.d.).

Conclusion

For those tasked with promoting the uptake of curricula emerging from these Australian HPE reform agendas, the role of high-stakes assessment has thus proven to be a 'double-edged sword' in closing the enduring curriculum policy-practice gap. In their discussion on the interactions between curriculum innovation and assessment, Leahy and colleagues (2016, p. 92) provide us with some insight into these dynamics when they observe that:

> official texts that offer possibilities for creative interpretation and new approaches to health education curriculum, also offer the possibility for established approaches to be reaffirmed with new requirements being accommodated within existing, largely unchanged, health education curriculum programmes.

Put succinctly, in the absence of quality assessment and rigorous accountability, innovative curricula emerging from reform endeavours can simply get lost on the policy and practice 'pathways' to HPE classrooms. This is where tensions for many might emerge, as high-stakes assessment is by no means a benevolent educational practice (Lingard et al., 2013). Yet, reflection on the Australian HPE curriculum reform journey affirms scholars' calls for a comprehensive engagement with the theory and practice of assessment in education settings.

Over the past decade, numerous scholars have begun this vital work, with Hay and Penney (2009) notably proposing four conditions for promoting assessment efficacy in HPE: learning-oriented; authentic; valid; and socially just. Assessment tasks aligned with these conditions would be constructed to demand students' development and use of particular knowledges and skills; provide sufficiently rich, accessible and decipherable information and data to students and teachers as to current states of learning; be connected to the world beyond the classroom and require the 'life-wide' and 'life-like' utility of the knowledges and skills; meet the widely recognised conditions of construct validity; and be accessible and achievable by all students within a learning field (be it a classroom, school or system). For those who envision an innovative, sustainable and, most significantly, educative HPE, engagement with assessment must be a 'contact sport'.

Reflection points

- How is assessment embedded into HPE curricula and programmes within your own context?
- What are the potential benefits and costs of assessment practices within HPE programmes?
- What accountability exists with regard to assessment in HPE and to what ends?
- To what extent are assessment practices within your own context driving an educative orientation to HPE?

References

Alfrey, L., and Brown, T. D. (2013). Health literacy and the Australian Curriculum for Health and Physical Education: A marriage of convenience or a process of empowerment? *Asia-Pacific Journal of Health, Sport and Physical Education*, 4(2), 159–173.

Australian Council for Educational Research. (2014). *Redesigning the secondary–tertiary interface: Queensland Review of Senior Assessment and Tertiary Entrance*. Available at: https://www.acer.org/files/Redesigning_the_secondary-tertiary_interface_Ed_2. pdf. Accessed January 13th 2020.

Australian Curriculum, Assessment and Reporting Authority. (2012a). *Curriculum design process: Version 6*. Sydney: ACARA. Available at: https://docs.acara.edu.au/resources/ ACARA_Curriculum_Development_Process_Version_6.0_-_04_April_2012_-_ FINAL_COPY.pdf. Accessed January 13th 2020.

Australian Curriculum, Assessment and Reporting Authority. (2012b). *The shape of the Australian Curriculum: Health and Physical Education.* Sydney: ACARA.

Australian Curriculum, Assessment and Reporting Authority. (2014). *Australian Curriculum: Health and Physical Education.* Sydney: ACARA. Available at: https://www. australiancurriculum.edu.au/f-10-curriculum/health-and-physical-education/. Accessed January 13th 2020.

Bernstein, B. (1990). *The structuring of pedagogic discourse, Vol IV: Class, codes and control* London: Routledge.

Board of Secondary School Studies Queensland. (1975). *Syllabus in Health and Physical Education Years 8–12.* Brisbane: Author.

Broadfoot, P. M. (1996). *Education, assessment and society.* Buckingham: Open University Press.

Brown, T. D. (2013). 'In, through and about' movement: Is there a place for the Arnoldian dimensions in the new Australian Curriculum for Health and Physical Education? *Asia-Pacific Journal of Health, Sport and Physical Education,* 2(4), 143–157.

Brown, T. D., and Penney, D. (2018). *Examination physical education: Policy, practice and possibilities.* London: Routledge.

Daube, M., Quelch, G., Roberts, L., Moodie, R., Pesce, A., Oliver, I, and Stanley, F. (2010). *100413 HPE letter Gillard.* Available at: http://www.achper.org.au/_ files/f/27376/100413 HPEletter Gillard.pdf. Accessed July 20th 2011.

Department of Education Queensland. (1952). *Physical education: Introductory handbook.* Brisbane: Author.

Donnelly, K., and Wiltshire, K. (2014). *Review of the Australian Curriculum: Final report.* Canberra: Australian Government. Available at: https://docs.education.gov.au/ system/files/doc/other/review_of_the_national_curriculum_final_report.pdf. Accessed January 13th 2020.

Hardman, K., and Marshall, J. J. (2000). *World-wide survey of the state and status of school physical education.* Manchester: University of Manchester.

Hay, P., and Penney, D. (2013). *Assessment in physical education: A sociocultural perspective.* London: Routledge.

Hay, P. J. (2008). *Social construction of abilities and conduct of assessment in senior PE.* The University of Queensland, School of Human Movement Studies.

Hay, P. J., and Penney, D. (2009). Proposing conditions for assessment efficacy in physical education. *European Physical Education Review,* 15(3), 389–405.

Hogan, A., Enright, E., Stylianou, M., and McCuaig, L. (2018). Nuancing the critique of commercialisation in schools: Recognising teacher agency. *Journal of Education Policy,* 33(5), 617–631.

Inchley, J., Muldoon, J., and Currie, C. (2006). Becoming a health promoting school: Evaluating the process of effective implementation in Scotland. *Health Promotion International,* 22(1), 65–71.

Kirk, D. (2009). *Physical education futures.* London: Routledge.

Lambert, K. (2018). Practitioner initial thoughts on the role of the five propositions in the new Australian Curriculum Health and Physical Education. *Curriculum Studies in Health and Physical Education,* 9(2), 123–140.

Leahy, D., O'Flynn, G., and Wright, J. (2013). A critical 'critical inquiry' proposition in health and physical education. *Asia-Pacific Journal of Health, Sport and Physical Education,* 4(2), 175–187.

Leahy, D., Burrows, L., McCuaig, L., Penney, D, and Wright, J. (2016). *School health education in changing times.* London: Routledge.

Lingard, B., Martino, W., and Rezai-Rashti, G. (2013). Testing regimes, accountabilities and education policy: Commensurate global and national developments. *Journal of Education Policy*, 28(5), 539–556.

Macdonald, D. (2013). The new Australian Health and Physical Education Curriculum: A case of/for gradualism in curriculum reform? *Asia-Pacific Journal of Health, Sport and Physical Education*, 4(2), 95–108.

Macdonald, D., and Brooker, R. (1997). Assessment issues in a performance-based subject: A case study of physical education. *Studies in Educational Evaluation*, 23(1), 83–102.

Macdonald, D., Glasby, T, and Carlson, T. (2000). The HPE statement and profile Queensland style. *The ACHPER Health Lifestyle Journal*, 47(1), 5–8.

MacPhail, A. (2007). Teachers' views on the construction, management and delivery of an externally prescribed physical education curriculum: Higher grade physical education. *Physical Education and Sport Pedagogy*, 12(1), 43–60.

McCuaig, L., Quennerstedt, M., and Macdonald, D. (2013). A salutogenic, strengths-based approach as a theory to guide HPE curriculum change. *Asia-Pacific Journal of Health, Sport and Physical Education*, 4(2), 109–125.

McCuaig, L., Atkin, J., and Macdonald, D. (2019). In pursuit of a critically oriented physical education: Curriculum contests and troublesome knowledge for transformations. In Richard Pringle, Håkan Larsson and Göran Gerdin (Eds.), *Critical research in sport, health and physical education: How to make a difference*. London: Routledge.

McCuaig, L., Woolcock, L., Stylianou, M., Ng, J. Y., and Ha, A. S. (2020). Prophets, pastors and profiteering: Exploring external providers' enactment of pastoral power in school wellbeing programs. *Discourse: Studies in the Cultural Politics of Education*, 41(2), 223–237.

National Curriculum Board. (2009). *The shape of the Australian Curriculum*. Sydney: Commonwealth of Australia. Available at: https://docs.acara.edu.au/resources/The_Shape_of_the_Australian_Curriculum_May_2009_file.pdf. Accessed January 13th 2020.

National Health and Hospitals Reform Commission. (2009). *A healthier future for all Australians*. Canberra: Commonwealth of Australia.

National Preventative Health Taskforce. (2009). *Australia: The healthiest country by 2020. National preventative health strategy –A roadmap for action*. Canberra: Commonwealth of Australia.

Penney, D., Brooker, R., Hay, P., and Gillespie, L. (2009). Curriculum, pedagogy and assessment: Three message systems of schooling and dimensions of quality physical education. *Sport, Education and Society*, 14(4), 421–442.

Queensland Curriculum and Assessment Authority. (n.d.). Introducing Queensland's new senior assessment system: From syllabus to subject result. Available at: https://www.qcaa.qld.edu.au/downloads/senior/snr_new_assess_syllabus_to_subject.pdf. Accessed January 13th 2020.

Queensland Curriculum and Assessment Authority. (2016). *Health education senior syllabus 2016: Design brief*. Brisbane: Author.

Queensland Curriculum and Assessment Authority. (2018). *Health 2019 V1.2. General senior syllabus*. Brisbane: Author. Available at: https://www.qcaa.qld.edu.au/downloads/senior-qce/syllabuses/snr_health_19_syll.pdf. Accessed January 13th 2020.

Queensland School Curriculum Council (1999). *Health and Physical Education: Initial in-service materials*. Brisbane: Publication Services, Education Queensland.

Quennerstedt, M., Burrows, L., and Maivorsdotter, N. (2010). From teaching young people to be healthy to learning health. *Utbildning och demokrati*, 19(2), 97–112.

Ranson, S. (2003) Public accountability in the age of neo-liberal governance. *Journal of Education Policy*, 18(5), 459–480.

Thompson, T. I. (1980). Developments in physical education in Queensland—1940s to 1980's: Oral history; Mr. T. Thompson. Transcript of Tape Recorded Interview October 8, 1980.

Thorburn, M. (2007). Achieving conceptual and curriculum coherence in high-stakes school examinations in physical education. *Physical Education and Sport Pedagogy*, 12(2), 163–184.

Williams, B. J., Hay, P. J., and Macdonald, D. (2011). The outsourcing of health, sport and physical educational work: A state of play. *Physical Education and Sport Pedagogy*, 16(4), 399–415.

SECTION II

Exploring constructions of health within (physical) education

INTRODUCTION

Shirley Gray

The three chapters in this section are all connected through the theme of health, or more specifically, how health is conceptualised and how it is taught in schools. Although the chapters are set in different geographical locations and focus on different educational settings, they present many common ideas which, taken together, highlight the problems with the way in which health is understood and enacted in schools. The chapters focus their attention on a particularly dominant conceptualisation of health and reveal the ways in which this is influencing school curricula, pedagogy and student learning. They highlight the prevalence of a deficit understanding of health, where the health of students is perceived as something that needs to be 'fixed'. Furthermore, this view of health means engaging in practices that aim to reduce the risk of illness and to shape bodies towards normative standards. As you will learn from your engagement with these chapters, this can have severe consequences for young people's learning and health.

In Chapter 5, Petrie and Thompson give an account of how health is understood in the context of primary schools in New Zealand. They explore what this means from the perspective of the students (referred to in the chapter using the Māori word for children – tamariki) and consider what health education could be in the future. Throughout this chapter they write H/health, using H/h to acknowledge that young people learn about health not only through the formal curriculum, but also through their day-to-day experiences in schools and the wider community.

Petrie and Thompson begin this chapter by setting the scene globally, demonstrating how H/health education has become a key feature of curricula around the world. In doing so, they highlight the various ways in which health is conceptualised noting that although some countries – including New Zealand – have adopted a holistic and strengths-based approach, many continue to adopt a medicalised approach that has little regard for local context or culture. However, the authors state that, regardless of the approach adopted, as public health agendas intersect with education agendas, the prevalence of health promotion in schools becomes more evident. This can result in approaches that focus on physical health, addressing perceived deficits, regulating behaviour and monitoring results against standardised 'norms'. This can have damaging effects for some young people, especially those tamariki for whom the types of behaviours and bodies that they are encouraged to achieve lack cultural relevance.

Petrie and Thompson then explore the impact that H/health education might have on the practices of teachers and draw from their own research to exemplify how teaching may be constrained by various factors, including teacher knowledge – or lack thereof. This has led to the proliferation of outsourcing within health education in primary schools in New Zealand, where external agencies enter schools to deliver activities that are centred on informing young people about how to lead a healthy lifestyle.

The authors recognise that tamariki learn about health through various means – physically, socially, culturally and digitally – and, as noted, that such learning is not confined to the school context. This has resulted in a common conceptualisation of health by young people, where health is related to making and monitoring the 'right' or healthy choices. To highlight this point, Petrie and Thompson present images drawn by children to depict how being healthy (or not) is perceived to be related to behaviours and lifestyle choices. It is very clear from these drawings that the young people understand health in relation to either following or deviating from rules for preventing illness. This can be problematic for many children as they struggle to abide by the 'rules' of health in their own contexts.

In making suggestions about what H/health education could be, Petrie and Thompson propose an approach that acknowledges the range of ways in which young people experience health. Central to this approach is that health is viewed as a process, not a fixed end point. The authors conclude by suggesting that a more critical and contextualised approach is necessary, where teachers recognise health as a dynamic, social and culturally mediated concept. Finally, readers are encouraged to consider these ideas from their own perspectives and reflect upon the needs of their learners, their current practice and what they could do to develop an approach that focuses on learning about health, rather than seeking to 'fix' the health of young people in primary schools.

In Chapter 6, the authors Hooper, Harris and Cale examine the concept of health, or more specifically health-related learning, within the context of physical education (PE) in England. They do so against a historical backdrop that demonstrates the relationship between PE and health since the early20th century. They highlight that this relationship has prevailed over time and that its prominence in schools in England in the 1980s seemed to be closely aligned with public health concerns related to inactivity among children. This is reflected in some of the changes that have been made over time to the terminology used to describe health in the context of PE, initially described as health-related fitness, then health-related exercise and more recently health-related learning. However, despite issues of nomenclature, there remains some uncertainty about how 'health' should be taught in PE, resulting in significant variability in health-related teaching and learning across schools in England. This is augmented by the fact that many PE teachers have insufficient knowledge about health-related learning, something that is also highlighted by Petrie and Thompson in the first chapter of this section. Consequently, many PE teachers draw on their knowledge of fitness for sports performance to guide their curricula and pedagogies related to health. Regardless of which conception of health is adopted (public health or fitness for sports performance), both focus largely on the body and what needs to be done to improve physical health, address perceived deficits and avoid risks.

This ambiguity about what health means in PE and how it should be taught is also reflected in the ways in which young people understand health. To demonstrate both how young people understand health and how this understanding has remained stable over time, the authors turn to the work of Harris (1994) to show that very little has changed since the early 1990s. Then, children almost exclusively described health in relation to the body, diet and exercise. The authors give some indication of the prevalence of this conception by reviewing literature from around the world, all presenting similar findings. This research also demonstrates that young people have a very clear idea about what is good and bad for their health, yet a poor understanding of the more complex issues surrounding the concept and what it means to be healthy. In 2018, Harris and colleagues returned to this research to explore once more how young people understand health. Rather disappointingly, little had changed (Harris, Cale, Duncombe & Musson, 2018). However, this 2018 study was conducted before the most recent iteration of the National Curriculum for PE (NCPE) in England which focuses more explicitly on healthy, active lifestyles. It was of interest, therefore, to explore the extent to which this may have impacted on how children and young people conceptualise health. In taking up this challenge, Hooper (2018) adopted participatory methods – similar to those adopted by Petrie and Thompson – to initiate discussions around health with young people aged 11–12. However, once again, the same (misconstrued) conceptualisations emerged, with young people making reference to diet and exercise and describing bodies they deemed to be healthy and unhealthy, expressing in particular how appearance was a significant indicator of health (specifically that being fat was both unhealthy and undesirable). It seems that, despite changes to the health-related discourses presented in policy texts, the ways in which young people understand health remain unchanged. This is similar to the claims by Petrie and Thompson who found that children had a narrow conception of health, even when policy described a broad and holistic notion of health. Hooper, Harris and Cale conclude by suggesting the need for further work to be carried out to develop PE-for-health pedagogies that support a holistic notion of health, something that, as Petrie and Thompson allude to, might begin when teachers interrogate and challenge their own understanding of health. Readers are encouraged to consider what such pedagogies might look like, something that is explored further in the final chapter of this section.

In Chapter 7, the final chapter in this section by Laura Alfrey and Rosie Welch, the authors offer an interesting insight into how health is commonly conceptualised and taught within the context of health and PE (HPE) in Australia. They begin by providing contextual detail about the Australian HPE curriculum, highlighting the framework, or five propositions, that guide teachers' planning, pedagogy and assessment. This framework appears to offer HPE teachers opportunities to develop and enact a school HPE curriculum that is both progressive and critical, one based on a broad and inclusive conception of health. However, similar to the other chapters in this section, a key issue noted is that how teachers teach health within HPE is significantly influenced by how they understand the concept. This leads the authors to identify three key problems that influence how teachers understand health, namely: (i) valued knowledge in HPE; (ii) the contested purpose of HPE; and (iii) privileged and marginalised bodies in HPE. The authors then consider how the curriculum framework in Australia, one that offers potential for transformation, might be used to respond to these problems.

In addressing the first problem, 'valued knowledge in HPE', the authors, like others in this section, highlight the fundamental role that teacher knowledge plays in shaping the way that they teach health. They suggest that teachers often have a very objective and scientific understanding of health, viewing physical activity and sport as a means to manage bodies and prevent risks. However, while acknowledging the challenges of teacher change, they suggest that, over time, with consistent messages from initial teacher education (ITE) and schools, teachers may begin to develop a broader and more socially just conception of health and health pedagogies. In addressing the second problem, 'the contested purpose of HPE', they report that HPE as a subject is often justified as a means to solve wider social 'problems', for example, declining levels of physical activity and poor mental health among young people. They demonstrate how this is manifest in the regulative and surveillance practices of teachers, and the impact that this can have on the way that young people view themselves and their bodies. To attempt to 'solve' this problem, the authors refer to critical inquiry and strengths-based approaches, something that might be considered in response to Hooper, Harris and Cale's call for the development of PE-for-health pedagogies. These approaches encourage teachers and students to challenge taken-for-granted assumptions about health and to explore alternative conceptions and practices. In attending to the final problem, 'privileged and marginalised bodies in and beyond HPE', the authors consider how health is understood as it intersects with gender, class and race. Similar to the claims of Petrie and Thompson, they highlight the role of the wellness industry in shaping which bodies are deemed healthy and therefore socially valued. In doing so, they make the point that not all bodies are valued or equal, and those that fall outside the acceptable 'norm' are often marginalised in HPE. In summary, this chapter, like the other chapters in this section, skilfully highlights the problems with the way in which health is conceptualised within HPE, while simultaneously encouraging teachers to be more self-aware about how they understand and teach health. Readers are encouraged to reflect upon their students' experiences and bodies, as well as their own, and consider the ways in which they might begin to create equitable and inclusive experiences that make all pupils feel a sense of belonging in HPE.

All three chapters in this section highlight the problems with the ways in which health is conceptualised in schools. Each demonstrates how health is typically conceptualised in a narrow and limited way, related to diet, exercise and the body, something that has to be worked on or to be 'fixed' – regardless of social, cultural, environmental or personal circumstances. This can lead to health experiences in PE that are negative and even damaging for some young people. Importantly, the authors also guide the reader to consider alternative, broader conceptualisations of health. In doing so, they highlight the critical role of the teacher in changing the way health is understood, focusing on health as a learning process, one that is broad, (culturally) relevant and inclusive. Key to this transformation is teachers' engagement with critical, reflective practice and professional learning, and the authors pose important questions that encourage the reader to begin this process.

References

Harris, J. (1994). Young people's perceptions of health, fitness and exercise: Implications for the teaching of health-related exercise. Physical Education Review, 17(2), 143–151.

Harris, J., Cale, L., Duncombe, R. & Musson, H. (2018). Young people's knowledge and understanding of health, fitness and physical activity: Issues, divides and dilemmas. *Sport, Education and Society*, 23(5), 407–420.

Hooper, O. (2018). *Health(y) talk: Pupils' conceptions of health within physical education.* Doctoral thesis, Loughborough: Loughborough University.

5

H/health EDUCATION IN PRIMARY SCHOOLS

Teachers, learners and initiating change

Kirsten Petrie and Kylie Thompson

Introduction

H/health education practice in primary schools is experienced by tamariki[1] (children) in a multitude of ways. Some of these include: Health Education as a curriculum subject; health–oriented physical education (PE); school-wide health promotion activities; and the social discourses of health embodied in the every-day practices of classrooms and school communities. Acknowledging the blurring of boundaries that occurs between these experiences, we have chosen to use H/h within this chapter to illustrate the points of intersection or overlap between Health Education as a formal curriculum subject and health education as practice in schools and communities that is not framed in relation to official curriculum policy. Following a critical examination of primary school-based H/health education as theory, policy, curriculum and practice, we examine how H/health education is framed in the primary school with a particular focus on the competing conditions that shape teacher practices. This is followed by a discussion of empirical findings around how tamariki think, talk and practice health and, to a lesser extent, wellbeing. Within the final section of this chapter, we draw on the voices of tamariki and teachers to consider what H/health education could be, where it could go and what steps schools and teachers could take in order to move towards meaningful change in practice.

H/health education in primary schools

H/health education as policy manifests as a mandated curriculum subject/learning area under various guises across different country contexts, including: Health and Physical Education in Aotearoa New Zealand (NZ); Health and Wellbeing in Scotland; Personal, Social, and Health Education in England; and the Swedish equivalent in the form of Health, Sexuality and Family Education. Within countries such as Aotearoa NZ, Australia and Scotland, there has been recognition of the need to adopt a holistic, strength-based (and/or salutogenic) approach to thinking about Health Education, at least in aspects of their curricula. Yet, the historical tenants of narrow, deficit, medicalised approaches to health are still evident across curricula in other countries (e.g. Singapore, South Korea and Chile) where the focus remains on risk minimisation and personal responsibility. At the same time, the importance of wellbeing, and associated aspects such as social and emotional learning, has also come to prominence in national curricula beyond the realm of Health Education (e.g. Aotearoa NZ, Australia and Scotland).

For low income countries, it appears that Health Education curricula can become narrowly framed in relation to a combination of World Health Organisation (WHO) objectives and/or practice influenced by 'colonial' understandings of health and interventionist approaches with little respect for culture and context (Taylor, Quinn, Littledyke & Coll, 2012). For example, research undertaken in the Solomon Islands by Petrie and Tehe (2011) highlights how international 'experts' adopt deficient and medicalised approaches to Health Education curriculum development and resourcing, with little regard for socio-cultural understandings. In doing so, there has been a colonising history, a narrowing of the curriculum and little opportunity for Solomon Island educators to utilise self-determination models during the process of curriculum development.

Practices in schools can also reflect *health promotion as health education* in and amongst the school 'curriculum'. As a result of intersecting education and public health agendas, schools have become breeding grounds for health promotion activities. This is not surprising given the tendency for health promotion advocates to adopt a 'catch them while they are young' mentality. Alongside, or as part of, more formalised health promotion activities, schools adopt policies to reinforce representations of health, and what is 'right' or 'wrong'. For example, it is not uncommon for schools to have rules stipulating that children are not allowed sweets, that they are only allowed to drink water and not soft drinks or flavoured milk, and that they must follow a 'no hat, no play' policy. More draconian policies and practices include the act of teachers conducting lunch box 'checks' (Pluim, Powell, & Leahy, 2018) or measuring and displaying children's BMI within the classroom, often as part of public 'health promotion' initiatives (e.g. 'Planet Health', a programme in the US (Carter, Wiecha, Peterson, Nobrega & Gortmaker, 2007) or 'Change4Life', an initiative in the UK (National Health Service, 2020)).

As detailed in Chapter 1, this volume, primary schools often frame *health-oriented PE* as a way to imprint the notion of healthy lifestyles on impressionable tamariki and to address perceived deficits in their physical health. PE as a curriculum subject also appears to be a site for health education as it relates to physical health (see Powell, 2017), and less formally mental health (and cognitive development). Tied to health-related fitness and physical activity agendas in PE are bio-pedagogies and the reinforcement of traditional norms of size, shape, muscularity and weight that can have detrimental effects on tamariki (Burrows, Wright & McCormack, 2009; Welch, McMahon & Wright, 2012).

It is difficult to deny the ubiquitous nature of 'health' initiatives currently saturating primary schools around the world. An analysis of global education policies and practices demonstrates that despite the potential for H/health education to be everywhere there is also a very real risk that in the end it is nowhere. That is to say, a global preoccupation with health promotion, wellbeing, social and emotional learning and health literacy[2] initiatives does not necessarily result in improved H/health education policy or practice. We now shift our focus to what this means for how generalist teachers make sense of and practice H/health education and the resulting implications for learners and their learning.

Primary school teachers' practices around H/health education

It's all great, we have the Life Education[3] van coming into school this week to teach about making friends. What's the point? I am feeling really discouraged. I have taught the 9-10-year-olds, the wee young ones (5-6-year-olds) and have my own teenage kids and I see all the health-related stuff they are dealing with. Now I'm watching two kids in my class in the middle of their parents' break up and seeing how quickly this has changed who they are, I really question what we are doing in our school to help all these kids manage their lives. Lots don't have a 'safe base' to return to, the framework of the family as a stable platform to help them navigate the complex stuff they are all dealing with, and yet we think the 'Life Ed' van coming for one week, 'teaching' these kids for two or three hours is going to be enough. Between this and a few lessons of Keeping Ourselves Safe[4] we really aren't equipping them with the knowledge and skills they need to manage the everyday, let alone the more challenging moments in life. So, we are doing more and more numeracy and literacy, but these kids are struggling with life, and we just don't do enough.

(Rachel, primary school teacher in a rural community of Aotearoa NZ – personal communication, 2019)

How we determine what should be included as part of H/health education and what we should spend time on in primary school settings is to some extent determined by individual teachers. However, as Rachel's frustrations evidence, more commonly decisions about curriculum and pedagogy in the name of H/health Education are not necessarily being framed by the needs of the learners in any specific context. Instead, what happens in classrooms may be constrained by traditional notions of what constitutes H/health Education, legacy programming, competing priorities, teacher confidence, teacher workloads and resource availability (Formby, 2011; Petrie et al. 2013a).

In Aotearoa NZ, the recent National Monitoring Study of Student Achievement (NMSSA) (Young et al., 2019) indicated that about two-thirds of teachers at both Year 4 (age 7–8) and Year 8 (age 11–12) levels reported that their students spent 10 hours or less *per term* focused on explicit learning related to Health Education. Given the lack of time dedicated to Health Education, it also appears that many schools and teachers deliver *health promotion as health education* and use external providers and their resources (Williams, Hay, & Macdonald, 2011; Petrie, Penney, & Fellows, 2014; Hogan, Enright, Stylianou, & McCuaig, 2018; Chapter 14, this volume), or develop 'on-the-spot' H/health education opportunities as incidents occur in classrooms and playgrounds (Powell, 2019). Therefore, it is not surprising that H/health education becomes saturated by a focus on food and nutrition, physical health, hygiene, puberty and relationships. A multitude of well-intended teaching activities centred around the presentation of 'healthy lifestyle' rules and knowledge to make the 'right' decisions are continually being developed within schools in Aotearoa NZ. However, as Wright (2014) suggests, the teacher-centred approaches that are commonly paired with these types of activities typically fail as students believe they are simply being told what to do, how to behave or scared into making 'healthy' decisions.

In contrast to the planned learning that is privileged in the priority areas of numeracy and literacy, H/health education can instead be seen as reactionary, spasmodic and opportunistic. For teachers, the disconnect between what they view as important learning and what actually happens in their classes and schools becomes apparent through their everyday practices and this can have a significant influence on tamariki's constructions of health.

Am I healthy? Tamariki's perspectives on being healthy and constructions of health

As previously noted, tamariki's constructions of health are not solely framed by the teaching of H/health Education in school settings. Health messages are abundant across all aspects of their lives, be it in classes, at home, in social and print media, when they visit their doctor, when shopping for clothes/food and all manner of other aspects. This makes it difficult to frame what explicit 'learning' occurs from H/health education in primary school settings. Further, it is apparent that, internationally, tamariki appear to be making sense of health in much the same way (see Chapter 6, this volume). That is to say, they appear to understand that they are expected to be individually responsible and accountable for making 'good' choices and behaving/acting in ways that demonstrate they have control over and are managing their health (Burrows & Wright, 2004; Burrows, 2008, 2010). Tamariki make their engagement with such notions evident through the surveillance and monitoring of the behaviours and choices of themselves, their peers, their families and all those around

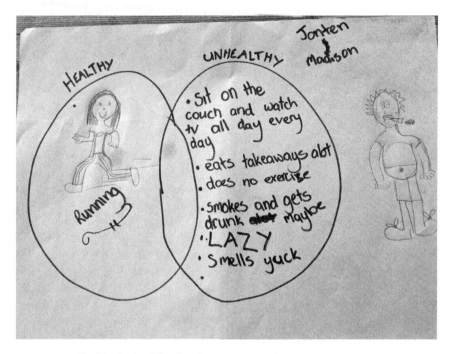

FIGURE 5.1 Healthy/unhealthy drawings

Images from children involved in EveryBody Counts (EBC) research project (Petrie et al., 2013a)

them (Burrows & Wright, 2007; Webb & Quennerstedt, 2010; Cosgriff et al., 2013, Powell & Fitzpatrick, 2015).

Figures 5.1 and 5.2, drawn by children aged 8–9, depict how discourses associated with being 'healthy' and 'unhealthy' are framed in relation to behaviours and lifestyle 'choices' that are deemed appropriate or not. The 'healthy' individual and their family follow the 'rules' for good health – underpinned primarily by medicalised illness prevention logic. The 'healthy' person does exercise to get 'fit' and lose weight, and they eat 'healthy foods' whilst limiting 'treat' foods. They do not engage in 'bad' behaviours such as smoking or spending too much time on the couch.

Comparably, when asked about 'wellbeing', the responses from students reflected understandings of the social (relationships), psychological (self) and physical (body) dimensions, with recognition that wellbeing was fluid and constantly changing dependent on the situation or context at any given point in time (Kostmann & Nilsson, 2012). It may be that the terms educators use, be it 'health' or 'wellbeing', contribute to how tamariki understand and experience H/health education in school settings. Within our work with primary school children who were exposed to the notion of hauora[5], we started to see a developing understanding of wellbeing following a 2-year reframing of H/health

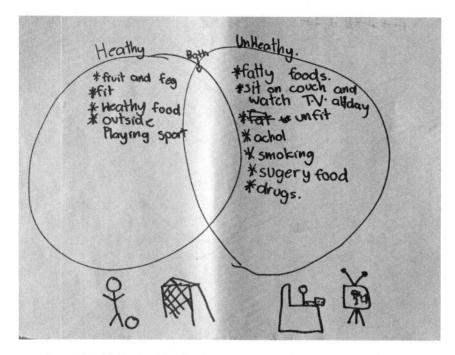

FIGURE 5.2 Healthy/unhealthy drawings

Images from children involved in EveryBody Counts (EBC) research project (Petrie et al., 2013a)

education. This is evidenced by David (age 7), a participant in the EBC project (Petrie et al., 2013a):

> Being healthy means having company with your family, friends and pets because you feel happy and that's good. It also means playing and feeling useful. If people are being mean, use your WITS[6]. It can mean being active like running around or rock climbing, playing with friends, doing a cross-country, limboing and rope climbing. Plus eating right like fruit, but if you eat junk food it doesn't mean you're unhealthy.

David's broadening understanding of health, in alignment with the notion of hauora, was representative of his peers and was also reflected nationally within the findings of the NMSSA (2017) report. When asked to draw pictures or write words to show the things that people can do or have in their life to keep themselves feeling well and happy – which is sometimes referred to as hauora or wellbeing – 'the majority of Year 4 and Year 8 students identified physical, mental/emotional and social aspects of well-being but relatively few identified spiritual aspects' (Young et al., 2019, p. 32). However, in the same report, the influence of health promotion activities was equally apparent. When students were asked to identify one health message they thought was important for their school community, students across Year 4 and Year 8, variously referred to the following:

> Help each other ... Look out for texting drivers ... Eat healthy food ... Be inclusive in the playground ... Keep in shape ... Encourage friendship ... Keep healthy – wash your hands ... No drugs ... No knives ... Look after the environment ... Be sunsmart ... Use the pedestrian crossing ... Don't bully ... Stop smoking ... Respect people.
>
> *(Young et al., 2019, p. 31)*

In contrast to responses from an in-class activity associated with wellbeing that demonstrated broadening understanding of health, key messages propagated by the wider school community reinforced students' sense that there were 'rules' that framed 'good' and 'bad' health practices. These messages very much mirror a range of health promotion initiatives and messages that have circulated through schools and communities in Aotearoa NZ in recent years.

While internationally formal curricula have expanded the brief of H/health Education to include more holistic notions of health (and wellbeing), the above examples demonstrate there is still a tendency for tamariki to make sense of health in line with narrow, deficit, medicalised approaches to health. Their responses are reflective of school policies, classroom practices and pre-packaged resources and programmes focused on food, nutrition and physical activity, all of which are underpinned by broader public health discourses influenced by economic imperatives, neoliberalism and healthism (see Chapter 8, this volume). As Leahy and Harrison (2008) have highlighted, tamariki (like adults) face the constant challenge of navigating day-to-day life amidst a myriad of health 'rules', especially when they have very little control over their life and choices. School policies and learning activities that set out to support children to make 'better' health-related choices and resist 'risky' behaviours may seem well-intended. However, research by Welch, McMahon and Wright (2012) reveals that they can also end up negating pleasure, shutting off alternative knowledges and closing down the social and cultural benefits of foods. Yet, despite these concerning outcomes, many health promotion programmes also explicitly aim to position tamariki as the family health educator (Burrows, 2017).

The tamariki's responses also illustrate how teachers/schools are not delivering Health Education as a broad area of learning – which is not surprising if they are only allocating 10 hours of learning per term. Instead, H/health education in the form of health promotion dominates. Therefore, what we do in primary schools in the name of H/health education appears to have little impact amongst the extensive health messaging that swirls around tamariki as part of their everyday lives. Until schools, and individual teachers, are able to acknowledge that goals underpinned by healthism are deeply flawed, we will no doubt see a continuation of 'risky and shameful pedagogies' (Leahy, 2014, p. 171), focused on trying to make children healthy as opposed to teaching them about health (Gard & Leahy, 2009).

Moving towards meaningful change in H/health education

In this section, and in line with the work of Quennerstedt, Burrows and Maivorsdotter (2010), we explore the idea that instead of adopting a 'fix them' and 'teach them to be healthy' approach, we should acknowledge the range of ways in which young people 'do' health and how they learn to make sense of themselves as healthy (or not). Such a stance is framed by the aim of supporting tamariki to conceive health as a learning process that takes place in the context where they as young people (and later as adults) live, learn, love and flourish. In line with salutogenic notions, learning health then is something one continuously does, a practice situated in one's life rather than an outcome of any health education practice (Quennerstedt et al, 2010).

Schools, and teachers, are caught between the aim of the state to ameliorate health problems and the intentions of curriculum documents to approach the teaching of health as an educational discipline (Fitzpatrick & Tinning, 2014). At the same time, there are wider discourses and influences at play that no doubt impact on teachers' ability to make meaningful changes to how they think about and practice H/health education. Nevertheless, educators who recognise this tension to be problematic, and who are motivated to initiate change, are already asking how what they are currently doing with/to young people in the name of H/health education, meets the needs (or not) of these diverse children (see Fitzpatrick & Tinning, 2014; Leahy, Burrows, McCuaig, Wright & Penney, 2016). To instigate change, we believe further research is needed to develop clear and digestible examples of 'good' practice for schools looking to re-imagine their existing approaches. With this in mind, this final section offers some provocations to help educators in primary schools begin re-imagining their approach.

Initiating change

For any primary school teacher committed to approaching teaching as inquiry, pedagogical decision-making requires that they ask themselves, 'What matters most and is important for my students' learning?' and therefore 'What should we spend time on?'. Such questions are philosophical as well as pedagogical, and while finding 'quick fixes' in pre-packaged resources and programmes or adapting existing pedagogical approaches may seem more pragmatic, more meaningful change will require a philosophical shift. As Grootenboer, Edwards-Grove and Rönnerman (2020, p. 42) suggest:

> one way to prompt reflective thought about current practices is to take time to stop and consider what is happening, and this needs to occur

outside the usual pressures of teaching in day-to-day school life ... we need to step outside the routine and consider how these sedimented ways of doing things are working.

The following vignette is an example of an attempt to do just that. It has been crafted by the authors of this chapter – based on their work in primary schools – and highlights the thinking of a middle school leader we have named Rata. Here, we see Rata opening the dialogue about H/health education in her school as part of a meeting focused on H/health education:

> I'm not so sure about our current approach. I'm sick of seeing kids feel ashamed and targeted because of their size or shape in the activities we're doing. We don't like it when people judge us, but sometimes I think we are oblivious to the damage we do when we try to 'fix' our students or shape their bodies to try and make them all look the same. We're also making some pretty big assumptions about what counts as 'healthy'. Too often we come at it from very white, Western, privileged, middle class perspectives – me included. I think we need to be a little bit careful with what we're planning here and consider what our purpose is when it comes to health education.
>
> I mean, do any of us really believe our job is to actually change the body types and eating habits of our students. I'm not convinced. We're talking about complex things here and lots of them are outside of our students' control. Maybe we need to think about approaching this in a different way - instead of just focusing on how we want our students to behave, let's start a conversation about what we want them to learn.

As Rata expresses, she has found herself frustrated and concerned by what we might view as practices reflective of moralistic approaches to health influenced by healthism. Her comments problematise the enduring belief reflected in practice that responsibility for bodily vigilance lies within the individual. Tinning and Glasby (2002) suggest that perceiving health in this way can lead to schools adopting big lofty goals tied to making children 'healthy'. However, as Rata identifies, such an approach fails to recognise the complex social and cultural determinants that sit outside of the child themselves.

At the beginning of this dialogue, Rata foregrounds the opportunity for her colleagues to reflect on the questions 'What are we doing here?' and 'What are we concerned about?'. Any progression of this opportunity for change will require an ongoing interrogation of personal assumptions along with the development of strategies and support systems that enable teachers to critique and resist mainstream health messaging.

Brave educators – like Rata – will need to stand against problematic 'fix them' goals and challenge the beliefs and practices that continue to perpetuate the idea that children can and should take responsibility for their own health. The power and influence of healthism make this no easy feat. If we accept that many teachers may have entered their careers driven by a desire to 'make a difference' and have a transformative contribution to the lives of 'at risk' children, then the seductiveness of a 'fix it' approach to H/health education becomes even clearer. We need to ensure that our practices as teacher educators, researchers and policy writers better support teachers to interrogate their beliefs and practices (see Petrie et al., 2013b).

Changing the pedagogy

Philosophical change needs to be coupled with an openness to explore pedagogical approaches that will encourage tamariki to become critical health consumers, knowledge interrogators and problem solvers. This also requires teachers to engage with more critically-aligned, student-centred pedagogies. The scenario below has been adapted from activities outlined in a NZ food and nutrition learning progressions toolkit (Ministry of Education, n.d.). It provides an example of a teacher (Mr Thomas) facilitating a semi-structured conversation to challenge his Year 4 students' conceptions that food can simply be categorised as 'good' or 'bad':

Mr Thomas: Ok, you all have a picture in front of you of something we might eat. I want you to come up and choose where to put your picture on this continuum.

[Students undertake activity]

Mr Thomas: This is the 'good' end and the other end is 'bad'. Jordan you put birthday cake at the bad end of the continuum, why do you think it belongs there?

Jordan: Easy – it has heaps of sugar, especially in the icing and I know that blue food colouring is really bad too.

Mr Thomas: Jazz, I notice you had a picture of a birthday cake too but you chose to put yours more towards the middle.

Jazz: Yeah, that's because birthdays are fun. We always share our cakes and I love it when everyone sings to me.

Mr Thomas: Tai and Laura – you both had vegetables and put them right at the good end of the continuum, why was that?

Tai: It's obvious, everyone knows vegetables give you lots of energy.

Mr Thomas: What else do you know about vegetables? Does everyone always get to eat lots of vegetables?

Laura: Mum always says they're expensive and most of them are disgusting. Actually, I want to move mine down the line a bit.

Sione: But my Nana grows her own vegetables and sometimes I help her. She gives us lots of yummy carrots.

Mr Thomas: That sounds like a fun way to spend time with your Nana, Sione. So food can bring people together too. Can anybody else find a picture that doesn't fit neatly into just one category?

In the way that Mr Thomas presents food and nutrition education, students are not only encouraged to view food as it relates to holistic notions of wellbeing, but they are also supported to recognise that diverse perspectives are valued and there are no fixed 'rules'. Student input is valued, differences are celebrated and a strengths-based approach is adopted. A clear message is also being sent to the students that they will need to think critically because the teacher uses questioning in a way that disrupts the notion that there is one 'right' answer. Similarly, it became clear in the EBC project (Petrie et al., 2013a, p. 7), that "applying approaches such as scaffolding, differentiated activities, guided questioning, and ensuring every student was engaged in active learning, teachers provided learning opportunities that were challenging, inclusive and safe". In this way, teachers were also able to take risks and use alternative strategies in order to explore complex ideas, grapple with the interpersonal dimensions of health and challenge taken-for-granted assumptions.

Resisting the 'fix them' mentality in H/health education

If schools are serious about moving beyond traditional, narrow, 'fix them' approaches to H/health education, then they will also need to consider a more localised, contextual approach to their curricula and pedagogies. In doing so, teachers need to reflect on how they can respond to diverse communities and settings, changing national and global politics and the unique learning needs of their own students. Further, educators need to be able to consider mana whenua (the indigenous people of the land) and other indigenous peoples' concepts of wellbeing (Fitzpatrick et al., 2019). The changing demographics in our communities, and welcoming of refugees and migrants, will also require all educators to consider what constitutes health for the diverse members of our primary school classrooms.

Questions relating to how young people come to acquire the skills to participate in so-called healthy practices and how they come to form positive or negative dispositions towards themselves and their own bodies, as well as questions about the ways health can be practised in diverse settings and situations, need to be prioritised (Quennerstedt et al., 2010). A more holistic understanding of wellbeing, one that is multidimensional and interrelated, moves beyond promoting narrow health-related protocols focused on bodily surveillance and which carefully considers social determinants of health will be necessary. This approach requires a reconceptualisation of health as a dynamic, socio-cultural process in which tamariki are encouraged to flourish in ways that are meaningful to them, not just ways that align with public discourses of health. An acceptance of this thinking would also suggest that there is no one answer to the question, what could quality H/health education look like? For teachers and schools committed to ensuring a quality H/health education experience for their tamariki, a disruption of the dominant discourses as discussed in this chapter will go a long way to progress health as a learning process instead of a mechanism for 'fixing' children.

Reflection points

- On finishing primary school, what would be the key learning (knowledge, skills, attitudes and dispositions) that would help tamariki maintain and enhance their own wellbeing, and that of others and their communities?
- How does this align with what is currently happening in the name of H/health education in your own context?
- How effectively does current H/health education meet the *learning* needs (or not) of your diverse tamariki and school communities?
- What could be done in your own context to move towards a focus on learning about health as opposed to 'fixing' tamariki (and their families) who are perceived to be 'unhealthy'?

Notes

1 Tamariki is the Māori (indigenous people of Aotearoa New Zealand) word for children and is preferred when discussing children in education settings in Aotearoa New Zealand.
2 *Health literacy* is a fairly new concept and is defined by the WHO as 'the cognitive and social skills which determine the motivation and ability of individuals to gain access to, understand and use information in ways which promote and maintain good health' (WHO Commission on the Social Determinants of Health, 2007).
3 Life Education is an external provider that primary schools in Aotearoa NZ use as part of their health education programme. Life Education, through the medium of *Harold the Giraffe*, focuses on teaching children about self-esteem, social relationships, body systems, food and nutrition and substances (see https://www.lifeeducation.org.nz/).
4 Keeping Ourselves Safe is a programme of ready-made resources schools in Aotearoa NZ use as part of their Health Education programmes (New Zealand Police, 2011).
5 In health and physical education, in the NZ Curriculum, the word *hauora* is based on Mason Durie's Te Whare Tapa Whā model (Durie, 1994). This is one of a number of holistic Māori models of health and includes the four mutually-supporting dimensions: taha hinengaro (mental and emotional); taha whānau (social); taha tinana (physical); and taha wairua (spiritual).
6 WITS is a school acronym representing 'Walk Away, Ignore, Tell Someone'.

References

Burrows, L. (2008). "Fit, fast, and skinny": New Zealand school students 'talk' about health. *Journal of Physical Education in New Zealand*, *41*(3), 26–36.
Burrows, L. (2010). 'Kiwi kids are Weet-Bix™ kids'—body matters in childhood. *Sport, Education and Society*, *15*(2), 235–251.
Burrows, L. (2017), Children as change agents for family health. *Health Education*, *117*(5), 498–510.
Burrows, L., and Wright, J. (2004). 'Being Healthy' – Young New Zealanders' ideas about health. *Childrenz Issues*, *8*(1), 7–12.
Burrows, L., and Wright, J. (2007). Prescribing practices: Shaping healthy children in schools. *International Journal of Children's Rights*, *15*, 83–98.
Burrows, L., Wright, J., and McCormack, J. (2009). Dosing up on food and physical activity: New Zealand children's ideas about 'health'. *Health Education Journal*, *68*(3), 157–169.

Carter J., Wiecha J., Peterson K., Nobrega S., and Gortmaker S. (2007). *Planet health: An interdisciplinary curriculum for teaching middle school nutrition and physical activity* (2nd ed.). Champaign, IL: Human Kinetics.

Cosgriff, M., Burrows, L., Petrie, K., Keown, S., Devcich, J., Naera, J., and Duggan, D. (2013). "You'll feel fat and no one will want to marry you": Responding to children's ideas about health. *Set: Research Information for Teachers, 2013*(1), 21–28.

Durie, M. (1994). *Whaiora Maori health development.* Auckland: Oxford University Press.

Fitzpatrick, K., and Tinning, R. (2014). *Health education: Critical perspectives*: Oxon, UK: Routledge.

Fitzpatrick, K., Leahy, D., Webber, M., Gilbert, J., Lupton, D., and Aggleton, P. (2019). Critical health education studies: Reflections on a new conference and this themed symposium. *Health Education Journal, 78*(6), 621–632.

Formby, E. (2011). 'It's better to learn about your health and things that are going to happen to you than learning things that you just do at school': findings from a mapping study of PSHE education in primary schools in England. *Pastoral Care in Education, 29*(3), 161–173.

Gard, M., and Leahy, D. (2009). Dicing with death: Tensions, contradictions and awkward positions in school health education. In M. Dinan-Thompson (Ed.), *Health and physical education: issues for curriculum in Australia and New Zealand* (pp. 183–197). Melbourne, Australia: Oxford University Press.

Grootenboer, P., Edwards-Groves, C., and Rönnerman, K. (2020). *Middle leadership in schools: A practical guide for leading learning.* Oxon, UK: Routledge.

Hogan, A., Enright, E., Stylianou, M., and McCuaig, L. (2018). Nuancing the critique of commercialisation in schools: Recognising teacher agency. *Journal of Education Policy, 33*(5), 617–631.

Kostmann, E., and Nilsson, L. (2012). Children's perspectives on health: What makes children feel good according to themselves? *International Journal of Education, 4*, 1–11.

Leahy, D. (2014). Assembling a health[y] subject: Risky and shameful pedagogies in health education. *Critical Public Health, 24*(2), 171–181.

Leahy, D., and Harrison, L. (2008). Weighing it up: Thinking about the implications of school based obesity prevention initiatives. *HPER Healthy Lifestyles Journal, 55*(1), 19–22.

Leahy, D., Burrows, L., McCuaig, L., Wright, J., and Penney, D. (2016). *School health education in changing times: curriculum, pedagogies and partnerships.* London, UK: Routledge.

Ministry of Education. (n.d.). Food and Nutrition. *Health and Physical Education: Learning Progressions.* Retrieved 30 March 2020 from http://hpeprogressions.education.govt.nz/

National Health Service. (2020). *Change 4 Life.* Retrieved January 6 2020 from https://www.nhs.uk/change4life

New Zealand Police. (2011). Keeping Ourselves Safe (KOS) Youth Education Programme. *Youth Education Services.* Retrieved 29 October 2019 from http://www.police.govt.nz/keeping-ourselves-safe-kos

Petrie, K., and Tehe, M. (2011). Making sense of health education in the Solomon Islands. *Waikato Journal of Education, 16*(2), 31–42.

Petrie, K., Penney, D., and Fellows, S. (2014). Health and physical education in Aotearoa New Zealand: An open market and open doors? *Asia-Pacific Journal of Health, Sport and Physical Education, 5*(1), 19–38.

Petrie, K., Burrows, L., Cosgriff, M., Keon, S., Naera, J., Duggan, D., and Devcich, J. (2013a). *Everybody counts? Reimagining health and physical education in primary schools.* Retrieved from Wellington: http://www.tlri.org.nz/tlri-research/research-progress/school-sector/every-body-counts-understanding-health-and-physical

Petrie, K., Burrows, L., Cosgriff, M., Keown, S., Naera, J., Duggan, D., and Devcich, J. (2013b). *An Everybody Counts approach to HPE: Considering our teaching practices.* Retrieved 12 May 2020 from http://www.tlri.org.nz/sites/default/files/projects/EBC%20reflective%20questions_1.pdf.

Pluim, C., Powell, D., and Leahy, D. (2018). Schooling lunch: Health, food, and the pedagogicalization of the lunch box. In S. Rice and A. G. Rud (Eds.), *Educational dimensions of school lunch: Critical perspectives* (pp. 59–74). Cham, IL: Springer International Publishing.

Powell, D. (2017). Primary physical education and health. In G. Griggs & K. Petrie (Eds.), *Handbook of primary physical education* (pp. 9–19). London, UK: Routledge.

Powell, D. (2019). The 'will to give': Corporations, philanthropy and schools. *Journal of Education Policy, 34*(2), 195–214.

Powell, D., and Fitzpatrick, K. (2015). 'Getting fit basically just means, like, nonfat': Children's lessons in fitness and fatness. *Sport, Education and Society, 20*(4), 463–484.

Quennerstedt, M., Burrows, L., and Maivorsdotter, N. (2010). From teaching young people to be healthy to learning health. *Utbildning och demokrati, 19*(2), 97–112.

Taylor, N., Quinn, F., Littledyke, M., and Coll, R. K. (2012). *Health education in context an international perspective on health education in schools and local communities*: Rotterdam: Sense Publishers.

Tinning, R., and Glasby, T. (2002). Pedagogical work and the 'cult of the body': Considering the role of HPE in the context of the 'new public health'. *Sport, Education and Society, 72*(2), 109–119.

Webb, L., and Quennerstedt, M. (2010). Risky bodies: Health surveillance and teachers' embodiment of health. *International Journal of Qualitative Studies in Education, 23*(7), 785–802.

Welch, R., McMahon, S., and Wright, J. (2012). The medicalisation of food pedagogies in primary schools and popular culture: A case for awakening subjugated knowledges. *Discourse: Studies in the Cultural Politics of Education, 33*(5), 713–728.

Williams, B. J., Hay, P. J., and Macdonald, D. (2011). The outsourcing of health, sport and physical educational work: A state of play. *Physical Education & Sport Pedagogy, 16*(4), 399–415.

World Health Organization Commission on the Social Determinants of Health. (2007). *Achieving health equity: From root causes to fair outcomes.* Retrieved 21 November 2019 from: https://www.who.int/social_determinants/resources/csdh_media/cdsh_interim_statement_final_07.pdf.

Wright, J. (2014). Beyond body fascism. *Health education: Critical perspectives.* New York, NY: Routledge.

Young, S., Liau, A., Jones, L., White, J., Gilmore, A., Asil, and M., Pohatu. (2019). *Insights for Teachers: NMSSA Health & Physical Education 2017 [National Monitoring Study of Student Achievement (NMSSA)]* (16-IN). Retrieved from https://www.educationcounts.govt.nz/publications/series/nmssa/all-nmssa-publications.

6

HEALTH-RELATED LEARNING IN PHYSICAL EDUCATION IN ENGLAND

Oliver Hooper, Jo Harris and Lorraine Cale

Introduction

The role of physical education (PE) in health has long been recognised in many countries and, arguably, this is increasingly the case on account of growing concerns over the health and well-being of children and young people. However, whilst schools have been recognised for the role that they might play in promoting health to children and young people, concerns have been expressed regarding the status and position of health in PE and the approaches and practices used to support health-related learning. In addition, concerns have been raised in relation to the knowledge, understandings and conceptions of health promoted by and through PE, with a growing body of research suggesting that children and young people's health-related knowledge and understandings are worrying and problematic.

Within this chapter, we explore health-related learning within the PE curriculum in England, outlining how the status and position of health has changed in recent decades. As part of this, we consider the various challenges reportedly faced in relation to health-related teaching within PE, which have given rise to calls for an increased emphasis on the pedagogies of health-related learning. Subsequently, we explore the evidence pertaining to children and young people's health-related knowledge and understandings, highlighting findings that have been noted consistently over time and across different contexts. Following this, new evidence is presented on young people's conceptions of health in the context of healthy, active lifestyles within PE in England, providing a current 'picture of health'.

Health-related learning within the physical education curriculum in England

Health has been associated with PE since the subject was introduced as part of the education system, though its prominence was somewhat diminished by the 1940s, when alternative objectives such as skill development were prioritised (Kirk, 1992). However, during the 1980s, health experienced a resurgence as a priority within the subject, with Almond (1989) noting a rising interest in the area in schools across England. This resurgence has been argued by Tinning (2010, p. 177) as being fuelled by PE being positioned as 'a solution to the problem of improving the unhealthy lifestyles of children'. Strong, renewed interest in the area was witnessed during this period when health-related fitness (HRF) became popular within PE in England. Health-related exercise (HRE) was considered by some to be a more favourable term than HRF because it was felt that it better reflected the subject's relationship with health (Harris, 1997) and has tended to be the most commonly used term to refer to the delivery of health within PE in England for some time since (Cale & Harris, 2005; Harris, 2010). That said, there have been many terms used internationally to refer to this component of the PE curriculum, from HRF, to health-based PE, to health-oriented PE (Harris, 2000; Harris, 2010).

Harris (2000, p. 2) describes HRE as 'the teaching of knowledge, under-standing, physical competence and behavioural skills, and the creation of positive attitudes and confidence associated with current and lifelong participation in physical activity'. Within the National Curriculum for PE (NCPE), HRE was initially identified as a theme to be delivered through the different activity areas, such as athletics, games and gymnastics, rather than as a separate area in its own right. However, concerns were expressed that such an approach may lead to it being marginalised and not adequately addressed within the curriculum (Cale, 1996). Harris (1997) confirmed this to be the case, noting widespread uncertainty amongst teachers with regard to the delivery of HRE and considerable variation in approaches and practices within schools. Subsequently, Cale (2000) explored how schools were delivering HRE and found that combined approaches were most commonly used, involving integration within the various activity areas, teaching through discrete, distinct units of work within PE, as well as through delivery within other curriculum subjects. This arguably demonstrated a more explicit, structured and comprehensive approach to the teaching of health within PE. However, Ward (2010) highlighted that, whilst combined approaches con-tinued to be most commonly used to deliver HRE, there was much disparity between how these were employed and, consequently, children and young peo-ple's experiences of HRE were variable.

Whilst it is important to consider the approaches employed in the delivery of HRE, it is also important to consider the pedagogies. Accordingly, attention has shifted more recently to the pedagogies that support children and young people's health-related learning within PE (Cale, Harris & Hooper, 2020). This represents a response to concerns expressed by Armour and Harris (2013) regarding the lack of appropriate pedagogies for effectively supporting health-related learning within PE. They claim that, despite there being much interest in the area, little attention has been paid to the development of 'PE-for-health' pedagogies, call-ing for further work to be done (Armour & Harris, 2013). These calls have been echoed by many others (e.g. Haerens, Kirk, Cardon & De Bourdeaudhuij, 2011;

Hodges, Kulinna, van der Mars & Lee, 2016; Hastie, Chen & Guarino, 2017) who equally recognise the need for such work, particularly given the persistent challenges PE has faced in working towards effective health-related teaching.

Challenges within health-related teaching and learning in physical education

Calls to consider the pedagogies employed for health-related teaching have resulted from concerns being expressed with regard to the status and position of health in PE and the approaches and practices used to support health-related learning (Cale, Harris & Duncombe, 2016; Cale et al., 2020). Despite PE teachers professing health to be an important and valued learning area within the subject, their approaches and practices might not necessarily reflect this (Alfrey, Cale & Webb, 2012; Cale et al., 2016). For example, Alfrey and colleagues (2012) identified that sport dominated many teachers' approaches to health-related teaching while Harris and Leggett (2015a, 2015b) highlighted that PE teachers' preoccupation with sport often resulted in health-related learning being conceptualised through a 'fitness for sports performance' lens, with fitness training and testing commonly being employed to facilitate health-related learning. Evidently, research would suggest that health-related learning within PE is often addressed through a narrow, sport-focused and fitness-oriented approach (Alfrey et al., 2012; Harris & Leggett, 2015a, 2015b).

A potential reason for PE teachers' adoption of such approaches and practices may be their limited health-related knowledge. Over the past few decades, several studies have reported PE teachers to have limited and even insufficient knowledge with regard to health (e.g. Miller & Housner, 1998; Stewart & Mitchell, 2003; Castelli & Williams, 2007; Kulinna, McCaughtry, Martin, Cothran & Faust, 2008; Puhse et al., 2011; Alfrey et al., 2012; Harris & Leggett, 2015a, 2015b). The study by Castelli and Williams (2007) provides particularly concerning findings, highlighting that when PE teachers completed a test of HRF knowledge – designed for 14–15-year-old pupils in the US – only 38% met the standard expected of the young people for whom it was designed. It is perhaps unsurprising, therefore, that Stewart and Mitchell (2003) have questioned PE teachers' capacity to effectively contribute to children and young people's health-related learning.

Despite the reported limitations with regard to PE teachers' health-related knowledge, it has been suggested that teachers themselves do not necessarily recognise such shortcomings (Cale & Harris, 2011; Alfrey et al., 2012). Within their study, Alfrey and colleagues (2012) noted that, although there was limited health-related learning provision within PE initial teacher training (ITT) programmes and limited engagement with relevant continuing professional development (CPD) in this area, the majority of PE teachers felt confident in their abilities to effectively deliver health-related teaching. On this, Harris (2010) suggests that PE teachers may consider themselves to be knowledgeable about health on account of the experiences they are likely to have had prior to commencing ITT, with many having backgrounds in sport science. Tinning (2010) concurred with such a suggestion and argued that the traditionally science-oriented programmes of study that PE teacher education (PETE) students access at university prior to their ITT are likely to be responsible for PE teachers' beliefs that they are well equipped to deliver health-related teaching. However, and as Tinning (2010) notes, such programmes are arguably unlikely to have sufficiently prepared PE teachers for health-related teaching, given their (predominantly) physiological foci. Given the aforementioned concerns regarding the approaches and practices employed in the delivery of health-related teaching and PE teachers' health-related knowledge, it is perhaps unsurprising that concerns have also been raised with regard to children and young people's knowledge and understandings of health within PE.

Children and young people's knowledge and understandings of health within physical education

Harris (1994) was an early proponent of research into children and young people's knowledge and understandings of health, conducting a study with young people (aged 11–14) in England during the early 1990s. She identified that they described health almost exclusively in the physical sense and were typically preoccupied with food and exercise as moderators of health. Further, she highlighted that young people often had to manage conflicting messages about health, which proved problematic when trying to make sense of the concept. As a result, Harris (1994) called for further research into children and young people's knowledge and understandings of health, stating that 'if healthy practices have their roots in childhood, it is important for educators to increase their understanding of the ground in which they sow their seed, as well as the processes which might help or hinder germination and growth' (p. 149). The call by Harris (1994) for further research has, until very recently, largely gone unanswered within England, though related research has emanated from countries such as the US, Australia, New Zealand and Canada (e.g. Placek et al., 2001; Burrows, Wright & Jungersen-Smith, 2002; Stewart & Mitchell, 2003; Burrows & Wright, 2004; Wright & Burrows, 2004; Wright, O'Flynn & Macdonald, 2006; Beausoleil, 2009; Burrows, Wright & McCormack, 2009; Keating et al., 2009; Lee & Macdonald, 2009; Rail, 2009; Burrows, 2010; Lee & Macdonald, 2010; O'Shea & Beausoleil, 2012; Powell & Fitzpatrick, 2015).

Placek and colleagues (2001) conducted research with young people aged 11–12 in the US exploring what they perceived to be the purpose of exercise and how they might go about 'getting fit'. They noted that young people considered fitness as equating to looking good and being thin, and that they held several misconceptions related to exercise, for example, that sweating 'burns off' fat and that performing specific exercises could 'burn off' fat in a particular area. Further, Placek and colleagues (2001) suggested that although young people considered exercise to be 'good for them', they often had difficulty in articulating why they thought so. Stewart and Mitchell (2003) conducted further research in the US, with their study involving high school-aged young people completing a test comprising various questions relating to health-related fitness. The findings of their study highlighted that young people had limited knowledge pertaining to health-related fitness and were only able to score on the more basic elements of the test, with it being noted that young people had particular difficulty in applying fitness concepts, especially when this required them to make links between different concepts (Stewart & Mitchell, 2003). This led Stewart and Mitchell (2003) to conclude that young people's knowledge of fitness concepts was 'narrow, vague and often incorrect' (p. 550). Such findings were echoed by Keating et al. (2009) who identified inadequate and erroneous HRF knowledge as a major issue in their study of HRF in PE programmes from kindergarten through to the 12th grade in the US. Whilst such studies are somewhat limited in that they focus on fitness as opposed to health, their findings are nonetheless a cause for concern.

In New Zealand, Burrows et al. (2002) drew upon data obtained from the National Education Monitoring Project (NEMP) – generated through various interactive tasks and interviews/focus groups – to explore the health-related knowledge and understandings of children and young people aged 8–9 and 12–13. They identified that, in keeping with various other studies, children and young people predominantly described health physically (or, corporeally), stating that 'according to the majority of the students [health] meant eating the right food, drinking lots of water, being active and keeping oneself clean' (Burrows et al., 2002, p. 44). Burrows and colleagues (2002) noted that, in their definitions of what it meant to be healthy, children and young people made reference to exercise and diet as the key moderators of health and frequently conflated health with fitness. Further, they highlighted that children and young people often described fitness in relation to weight, which many assumed to be a measure of an individual's fitness. Appearance was closely connected to both fitness and weight and 'looking good' was a particular concern for many children and young people (Burrows et al., 2002). Findings such as these are also corroborated by studies in Australia (e.g. Lee & Macdonald, 2009, 2010), which similarly identified appearance to be a significant feature within young people's conceptions of health.

Subsequent work by Burrows and colleagues (2002), which also drew on the NEMP data (Burrows & Wright, 2004; Wright & Burrows, 2004; Burrows et al., 2009; Burrows, 2010), revealed two further noteworthy findings. Firstly, Burrows and Wright (2004) highlighted that children and young people 'talk' about health with much certainty, proposing that they 'delineated a remarkably clear line between healthy and unhealthy practices', with a healthy person being someone who 'doesn't smoke, drink, or take drugs, eat junk food, or too much food, stress out, watch too much TV, be lazy [or] think bad thoughts' (p. 201). Secondly, Wright and Burrows (2004) described how, when discussing health, children and young people frequently used the word 'don't' and outlined behaviours that should be avoided with much fervour. Burrows et al. (2002) supposed that the responses elicited from the children and young people within their study were indicative of 'the effectivity of the health and fitness discourses which are circulating in … society' (p. 46).

Rail (2009) conducted a study using interviews and focus groups to explore the ways in which young people (aged 13–16) in Canada conceptualised health. She noted that, in keeping with various other studies, young people were particularly concerned with appearance when discussing health and, specifically, 'not being fat'. Rail (2009) proposed that young people's concerns in this regard were typically related to the negative consequences associated with 'fatness' (i.e. bullying). Similar findings within the Canadian context have been reported by Beausoleil (2009) and O'Shea and Beausoleil (2012) who noted the prominence of appearance within young people's conceptions of health. The work undertaken by Powell and Fitzpatrick (2015) in New Zealand is also noteworthy in this regard. They used photo elicitation interviews to explore the health-related knowledge and understandings of children (aged 9) and, likewise, they highlighted that children regarded fatness as something to be avoided, with fitness being equated to non-fatness.

To summarise, research suggests that children and young people's health-related knowledge and understandings are rather limited, somewhat superficial and, at times, erroneous – with these findings being consistent over time and across different contexts. However, as noted above, within the English context, the call of Harris (1994) for further research in this area has largely gone unanswered. Therefore, until very recently, there was little evidence with regard to how children and young people's health-related knowledge and understandings might have changed (or not). Recently though, Harris, Cale, Duncombe and Musson (2018) conducted a study involving young people aged 12–15 within secondary schools in England. Despite more than two decades having passed since Harris' early study in the 1990s (Harris, 1994), Harris and colleagues (2018) found that, rather disappointingly, little had changed. Indeed, the study concluded that 'young people generally have simplistic knowledge and somewhat confused understandings of health, fitness and physical activity' (Harris et al., 2018, p. 418). Whilst the study by Harris and colleagues (2018) provided a useful update on children and young people's health-related knowledge and understandings within the English context, the data were collected prior to the introduction of the most recent version of the NCPE which reframes health-related learning through a focus on healthy, active lifestyles (see Chapter 1, this volume). As such, a study conducted by Hooper (2018) sought to address this gap by exploring the ways in which young people conceptualised health in the context of healthy, active lifestyles within PE in England.

Conceptualising 'health' within the context of healthy, active lifestyles

The Healthy, Active Lifestyles (HAL) study by Hooper (2018) provides the most recent evidence on young people's conceptions of health within PE in England. As part of the study, Hooper (2018) conducted focus groups with young people (aged 11–12) within which he employed creative and innovative participatory methods to explore the ways in which they conceptualised 'health'. These methods involved young people: drawing what 'health' meant; responding to true/false statements about leading a healthy, active lifestyle; and discussing cartoon images representing a range of lifestyle contexts related to health and physical activity. Data were subsequently analysed and revealed various findings with regard to the ways in which young people conceptualised 'health'. Several key findings from the study – related to 'getting physical' and 'looking the part' – are presented below.

Getting physical

The physical dimension of health was prominent in young people's conceptions, with most conceptualising 'health' *exclusively* in the physical sense. Given this prominence, it is perhaps to be expected that diet and exercise featured heavily within young people's talk, with almost all referring to these when describing what 'health' meant, as exemplified in the following quotations:

> You need to do lots of exercise to be healthy, and you need to not eat bad foods. (Faz, 11)
> A healthy person eats the right foods and drinks enough water … they'll do exercise as well, like, they'll play sports. (Rhys, 12)
> You can't eat bad foods, like fatty foods, if you want to be healthy … and you have to exercise a lot, you can't be lazy. (Chloe, 11)
> If you're going to be healthy, you need to make sure that you're getting enough exercise and that you're not eating the wrong foods. (Alisha, 12)

Young people tended to refer to diet and exercise as key moderators of 'health' – with limited references made to wider dimensions of health such as the mental, social and emotional domains. However, whilst frequent reference was made to diet and exercise, that is not to say that these aspects – and the role they played in health – were well understood. Conceptual confusion was evident, at least to some extent, for most young people. For example, many were confused about the role that diet and/or exercise played in their health and/or fitness, describing how eating healthily would make them fitter:

> If you eat fruits and veg[etables], they'll make you fitter. (Harry, 11)
> You need to make sure that you eat healthily to get fit, so having enough of each food is important. (Divya, 12)

Most young people also had difficulty in distinguishing between the concepts of health and fitness and, in trying to do so, often conflated them. Further, whilst some were able to distinguish between these concepts, they typically considered health to be associated with diet, and fitness to be associated with exercise. Allied to this, young people often demonstrated rather dichotomous views with regard to health – positioning a person as either 'healthy' or 'unhealthy' according to their health-related behaviours (typically taken as their diet and exercise), as exemplified in Figures 6.1 and 6.2.

The 'healthy/unhealthy' dichotomy evidenced within young people's conceptions of health is somewhat concerning, particularly given the certainty with which this was constituted. These findings are somewhat akin to those of Burrows and Wright (2004) who, as noted above, highlighted how children and young people 'delineated a remarkably clear line between healthy and unhealthy practices' (p. 201). Such conceptions are inherently limited given that very few, if any, will attain a 'perfect' state of health, with there being a risk that those who are positioned as 'unhealthy' are marginalised as a result of their health status (Hooper, 2018).

The dichotomous ways in which young people conceived health also meant that they were relatively prescriptive in terms of how a person should *do* health. Young people were typically able to provide extensive lists of what a person should and should not do to be 'healthy' but, interestingly, many described considerably more behaviours that should be avoided and talked more about the things that they should *not do*, to be 'healthy', than the things that they should do. For example, young people stated:

> You shouldn't eat junk food if you want to stay healthy. You shouldn't have fatty foods and things, they're really bad for you. (Ewan, 12)
>
> It's not good for you to sit down on the sofa and not do anything but like play on your PlayStation or your Xbox, you shouldn't do that. (Khush, 12)
>
> You can't have sugary drinks … they'll make you all unhealthy. (Rosie, 11)
>
> You shouldn't smoke or drink, or do drugs, they're all really bad for you, like, really bad. (Amira, 12)

Whilst it is encouraging that young people were found to be able to distinguish between what might be considered 'healthy' or 'unhealthy' behaviours, the certainty with which they did so may be problematic. Indeed, most young people within Hooper's (2018) study seemed to assume that engaging in, or avoiding, certain behaviours *would* make them 'healthy'. However, as Burrows and colleagues (2002) assert, there can be much uncertainty in the pursuit of 'health' and children and young people must be cognisant of this.

The corporeal notions within young people's conceptions of health are particularly evident in the data presented above, as has been found in a number of previous studies (e.g. Burrows et al., 2002; Burrows & Wright, 2004; Beausoleil, 2009; Burrows et al., 2009; Lee & Macdonald, 2009; Rail, 2009; Burrows, 2010;

Lee & Macdonald, 2010; O'Shea & Beausoleil, 2012; Powell & Fitzpatrick, 2015; Harris et al., 2018). However, young people's conceptions also had aesthetic orientations, as discussed below.

Health

FIGURE 6.1 Health drawing (Connor, 11)

Health

FIGURE 6.2 Health drawing (Bethany, 11)

Looking the part

It is perhaps to be expected that, with young people conceiving 'health' as a pre-dominantly corporeal concept, appearance – taken as a person's shape, size and weight – was prominent within the majority of their conceptions. Young people

typically expressed that a person's appearance was indicative of their health sta
tus, as exemplified in the following quotations:

> A healthy person has a fit body, like they'll be a good shape, maybe with muscles. (Makary, 12)
> Fat people aren't very healthy, like if you're fatter, it's not good for you. (Jess, 11)
> Healthy people have a thinner body, like they're not fat or anything, they're just a good shape. (Joshua, 12)
> If you're fat, you're going to be unhealthy, you can't be anything else really. (Harpreet, 12)

Young people placed particular emphasis on how a person 'looked' within their conceptions of health. Allied to this, many demonstrated rather simplistic associations, namely equating thinness with healthiness and fatness with unhealthiness. Whilst there were some young people who problematised the notion that 'fat was bad' and 'thin was good', such talk was somewhat contradictory in that, whilst these young people acknowledged that being thin did not necessarily mean that a person was 'healthy', most attested that it was better to be thin than to be fat. For example, two young people stated:

> If you're too thin, that's not good … but it is better than being too fat. (Jasmine, 12)
> It's not always good to be thin, like it can be bad for you, but it's better to be thin than fat, that's worse. (Malaika, 12)

Weight was a key determinant of whether a person was considered to be 'healthy' or not for the vast majority of young people – though typically this was not judged by conventional means (for example, weighing scales). Rather, this was judged by the eyes as young people variously described how it could be 'seen' whether a person was 'unhealthy' or not:

> You can just see if someone is healthy or not; if they're unhealthy, they'll be all fat and things. (Tommy, 11)
> If you look at a person, and they're bigger, well, fatter … you can just tell that they're not healthy. (Kayleigh, 12)

Young people made rather superficial judgements about a person's health status based on their shape, size and weight. Similar findings have been highlighted in studies by Burrows and colleagues (2002) and Beausoleil (2009) who identified that young people 'looked' to see whether a person was 'healthy' or not, constituting health as something that can be 'read off' the body. Therefore, as well as being based on corporeal notions, young people's conceptions of health have aesthetic orientations.

Taken together, the findings outlined above present an all too recognisable 'picture of health'. It would seem that despite policy and curricular developments in the area of health-related learning in PE, little has changed with regard to children and young people's conceptions of health. Findings from the work of Hooper (2018) reiterate those of earlier studies which have similarly identified the corporeal notions that pervade young people's conceptions of health and the aesthetic orientations inherent within these. Indeed, as Harris and colleagues (2018) concluded, children and young people's conceptions of health are, for the most part, reductive, limited and limiting.

Conclusion

Within this chapter, we have explored health-related learning and the PE curriculum in England, outlining how the status and position of health has changed and become increasingly prominent in recent years. We have discussed several of the challenges reportedly faced in relation to health-related teaching within PE – from problematic approaches and practices to shortcomings with regard to teachers' health-related knowledge – which have given rise to calls for an increased emphasis on the pedagogies of health-related learning (Cale et al., 2020). We have explored the evidence pertaining to children and young people's health-related knowledge and understandings, revealing these to be rather limited, somewhat superficial and, at times, erroneous – with these findings being consistent over time and across different contexts. Finally, we have presented new evidence on young people's conceptions of health in the context of healthy, active lifestyles within PE, which suggests that little has changed (Hooper, 2018). These findings arguably provide further evidence of the need to develop new 'PE-for-health' pedagogies (Armour & Harris, 2013) which better support children and young people to develop holistic conceptions of health. To do so, consideration must be given not only to the PE context but also to the wider contexts within which children and young people live their lives, such as the home and digital spaces and the influences these have on health-related learning (see Chapters 9 and 10, this volume). Further, attention must be paid to the social and cultural factors which mediate health-related learning, as pedagogies must be sensitive and responsive in this regard (see Chapter 13, this volume). By developing new 'PE-for-health' pedagogies, which are relevant and responsive, we might hope for a brighter picture of health in the future.

Reflection points

- In what ways does the status and position of health within PE impact health-related teaching and learning?
- How might PE teachers' knowledge, approaches and practices influence children and young people's health-related knowledge and understandings?

- What wider influences could impact on children and young people's conceptions of health?
- What might new 'PE-for-health' pedagogies look like?

References

Alfrey, L., Cale, L. and Webb, L. (2012). Physical education teachers' continuing professional development in health-related exercise. *Physical Education and Sport Pedagogy*, 17 (5), 477–491.

Almond, L. (1989). New wine in a new bottle – implications for a national physical education curriculum. *British Journal of Physical Education*, 20 (3), 123–125.

Armour, K. and Harris, J. (2013). Making the case for developing new PE-for-health pedagogies. *Quest*, 65 (2), 201–219.

Beausoleil, N. (2009). An impossible task? Preventing disordered eating in the context of the current obesity panic, in J. Wright and V. Harwood (Eds.) *Biopolitics and the 'Obesity Epidemic': Governing bodies*. London: Routledge.

Burrows, L. (2010). Push play every day: New Zealand children's constructions of health and physical activity, in M. O' Sullivan and A. MacPhail (Eds.). *Young people's voices in physical education and youth sport*. London: Routledge.

Burrows, L. and Wright, J. (2004). The good life: New Zealand children's perspectives of health and self. *Sport, Education and Society*, 9 (2), 193–205.

Burrows, L., Wright, J. and Jungersen-Smith, J. (2002). "Measure your belly": New Zealand children's constructions of health and fitness. *Journal of Teaching in Physical Education*, 22 (1), 39–48.

Burrows, L., Wright, J. and McCormack, J. (2009). Dosing up on food and physical activity: New Zealand children's ideas about 'health'. *Health Education Journal*, 68 (3), 157–169.

Cale, L. (1996). Health related exercise in schools – PE has much to be proud of! *British Journal of Physical Education*, 27 (4), 8–13.

Cale, L. (2000). Physical activity promotion in secondary school. *European Physical Education Review*, 6 (1), 71–90.

Cale, L. and Harris, J. (2005). (Eds.) *Exercise and young people: Issues, implications and initiatives*. Basingstoke: Palgrave Macmillan.

Cale, L. and Harris, J. (2011). Learning about health through physical education and youth sport, in K. Armour (Eds.) *Sport pedagogy: An introduction for teaching and coaching*. Harlow: Prentice Hall, 53–64.

Cale, L., Harris, J. and Duncombe, R. (2016). Promoting physical activity in secondary schools. Growing expectations: same old issues. *European Physical Education Review*, 22 (4), 526–544.

Cale, L., Harris, J. and Hooper, O. (2020) Debating health knowledge and health pedagogies in physical education, in S. Capel and R. Blair (Eds.) *Debates in physical education*. London: Routledge.

Castelli, D. and Williams, L. (2007). Health-related fitness and physical education teachers' content knowledge. *Journal of Teaching in Physical Education*, 26 (1), 3–19.

Haerens, L., Kirk, D., Cardon, G. and De Bourdeaudhuij, I. (2011). Toward the development of a pedagogical model for health-based physical education. *Quest*, 63, 321–338.

Harris, J. (1994). Young people's perceptions of health, fitness and exercise: Implications for the teaching of health-related exercise. *Physical Education Review*, 17 (2), 143–151.

Harris, J. (1997). *Physical education: a picture of health? The implementation of health-related exercise in the National Curriculum in secondary schools in England*, unpublished doctoral thesis. Loughborough: Loughborough University.

Harris, J. (2000). *Health-related exercise in the national curriculum*. Leeds: Human Kinetics.

Harris, J. (2010). Health-related physical education, in R. Bailey (Eds.) *Physical education for learning: A guide for secondary schools*. London: Continuum.

Harris, J. and Leggett, G. (2015a) Testing, training and tensions: The expression of health within physical education curricula in secondary schools in England and Wales. *Sport, Education and Society*, 20 (4), 423–441.

Harris, J. and Leggett, G. (2015b). Influences on the expression of health within physical education curricula in secondary schools in England and Wales. *Sport Education and Society*, 20 (7), 908–923.

Harris, J., Cale, L., Duncombe, R. & Musson, H. (2018) Young people's knowledge and understanding of health, fitness and physical activity: issues, divides and dilemmas. *Sport, Education and Society*, 23 (5), 407–420.

Hastie, P., Chen, S. and Guarino, A. (2017). Health-related fitness knowledge and development through project-based learning. *Journal of Teaching in Physical Education*, 36 (1), 119–125.

Hodges, M., Kulinna, P., van der Mars, H. and Lee, C. (2016). Knowledge in action; fitness lesson segments that teach health-related fitness in elementary physical education. *Journal of Teaching in Physical Education*, 35, 16–26.

Hooper, O. (2018). *Health(y) talk: Pupils' conceptions of health within physical education*. Doctoral thesis, Loughborough: Loughborough University.

Keating, X., Harrison, L., Chen, L., Xiang, P., Lambdin, D., Dauenhauer, B., Rotich, W. and Castro Pinero, J. (2009). An analysis of research on student health-related fitness knowledge in K-16 physical education programs. *Journal of Teaching in Physical Education*, 28, 333–349.

Kirk, D. (1992). *Defining physical education: The social construction of a school subject in post-war Britain*. London: Farmer Press.

Kulinna, P., McCaughtry, N., Martin, J., Cothran, D. and Faust, R. (2008). The influence of professional development on teachers' psychosocial perceptions of teaching a health-related physical education curriculum. *Journal of Teaching in Physical Education*, 27, 292–307.

Lee, J. and Macdonald, D. (2009). Rural young people and physical activity: Understanding participation through social theory. *Sociology of Health and Illness*, 31 (3), 36–374.

Lee, J. and Macdonald, D. (2010). "Are they just checking our obesity or what?" The healthism discourse and rural young women. *Sport, Education and Society*, 15 (2), 203–219.

Miller, M. and Housner, L. (1998). A survey of health-related physical fitness knowledge among pre-service and in-service physical educators. *Physical Educator*, 55 (4), 176–186.

O'Shea, J. and Beausoleil, N. (2012). Breaking down 'healthism': Barriers to health and fitness as identified by immigrant youth in St. John's, NL, Canada. *Sport, Education and Society*, 17 (1), 97–112.

Placek, J., Griffin, L., Dodds, P., Raymond, C., Tremino, F. and James, A. (2001). Middle school students' conceptions of fitness: The long road to a healthy lifestyle. *Journal of Teaching in Physical Education*, 20, 314–323.

Powell, D. and Fitzpatrick, K. (2015). 'Getting fit basically just means, like, non-fat': Children's lessons in fitness and fatness. *Sport, Education and Society*, 20 (4), 463–484.

Puhse, U., Barker, D., Brettschneider, W., Felmeth, A., Gerlach, E. … (2011). International approaches to health-oriented physical education: Local health debates and differing conceptions of health. *International Journal of Physical Education*, 3, 2–15.

Rail, G. (2009). Canadian youth's discursive constructions of health in the context of obesity discourse, in J. Wright and V. Harwood (Eds.) *Biopolitics and the 'Obesity Epidemic': Governing bodies.* London: Routledge.

Stewart, S. and Mitchell, M. (2003). Instructional variables and student knowledge and conceptions of fitness. *Journal of Teaching in Physical Education*, 22 (5), 533–551.

Tinning, R. (2010). *Pedagogy and human movement: Theory, practice, research.* Oxon: Routledge.

Ward, L. (2010). *Physical education teachers' engagement with 'health related exercise' and health related CPD: A healthy profile?* Doctoral thesis, Loughborough: Loughborough University.

Wright, J. and Burrows, L. (2004). "Being Healthy": The discursive construction of health in New Zealand children's responses to the national education monitoring project. *Discourse*, 25 (2), 211–230.

Wright, J., O'Flynn, G. and Macdonald, D. (2006). Being fit and looking healthy: Young women's and men's constructions of health and fitness. *Sex Roles – A Journal of Research*, 54 (9–10), 1–15.

7

AUSTRALIAN HEALTH AND PHYSICAL EDUCATION TEACHERS' PHILOSOPHIES AND PEDAGOGIES OF HEALTH

Laura Alfrey and Rosie Welch

Introduction

Focusing largely on the Australian context, this chapter explores the role of health and physical education (HPE) teachers' philosophies and pedagogies of health. We draw upon research findings and existing literature to provide insight into how health is often conceptualised by both generalist and specialist HPE teachers, and the implications this might have for student learning. After making reference to the Australian policy and education contexts, we introduce the concept of 'philosophies' as a means to understand teachers' perspectives and pedagogies as they relate to 'health' in HPE. We next illuminate three key 'tensions' that can impact the ways in which HPE teachers come to understand and teach about health, including: (i) valued knowledge in HPE; (ii) the contested purpose of HPE; and (iii) privileged and marginalised bodies in HPE. Finally, we make suggestions about how teachers and teacher educators can respond to these tensions, and thus find small and nuanced ways in their teaching practice to challenge dominant discourses of health and the body. We finish with some concluding thoughts and reflection points for consideration.

The Australian health and physical education policy and education contexts

The forging of health education and physical education has brought with it opportunities, challenges and debates related to what content is taught, how and by who. The formal HPE curriculum in Australia for Levels F–10 (age 6–16) is organised around two strands – 'Personal, Social and Community Health' and 'Movement and Physical Activity' – with the intention that they will be integrated within lessons, units and programmes where possible and relevant. Lynch's (2017) paper entitled

'How does a physical education teacher become a Health and Physical Education teacher?' shared the observation of a primary generalist teacher who remarked:

> The health part of it ... we don't, like I hardly even touch on it, which is really sad because I am very passionate about that as well. It is just a whole time thing for us, there's just no time.
>
> *(Lynch, 2017, p. 358)*

This quote speaks to our experiences as HPE teacher educators whereby it is not uncommon for students in initial teacher education (ITE) programmes to be 'prepared' to teach primary HPE as a generalist through one 24-hour unit or subject. Lynch's (2017) research provides evidence on this, confirming that not all states and territories in Australia have prepared generalist teachers to teach HPE, and the content included in ITE programmes and F–10 classrooms varies between institutions and schools.

Who teaches health and physical education?

In referring to 'HPE teachers' in this chapter, we include primary and secondary generalist teachers as well as specialist teachers. We do so because the curriculum configuration in Australian states and territories requires both generalists (at primary level) and specialists (at primary and secondary levels) to teach, assess and report on HPE learning outcomes. Whilst there is an overarching Australian Curriculum guiding content and learning outcomes, it is the mandate of states and territories to moderate and mobilise the enactment of curriculum as they see fit. Thus, we are cautious to collectivise the Australian context. However, it is fair to say that primary generalist teachers (Levels F–6) are typically responsible for teaching HPE in primary schools in conjunction with, or replaced by, external providers, specialists, organisations and associations, such as 'Life Education' (Burrows & Wright, 2004; Lynch, 2015). In secondary schools (Levels 7–12), while there are exceptions, it is most common that HPE is taught by specialist teachers.

In the state of Victoria, the evolution of the relationship between health education and physical education (PE) means that more experienced teachers have often qualified as specialists in either the former or the latter. More recently, and similarly to what has happened in New South Wales for some time, graduates are now qualifying to teach both HPE disciplines with efforts to integrate where possible (Penney, 2020). We also have a continuum between primary generalists who have responsibilities for HPE in some form, and specialist teachers, operating across both primary and secondary sectors in either health education, PE or HPE. Depending on where teachers are positioned on these axes of education, and context-based differences, their philosophies on the purpose of HPE and how it is best taught will vary (Green, 2003; Alfrey, Cale & Webb, 2012). We will explore the notion of HPE teachers' philosophies and biographies as part of how they approach health within HPE shortly, but first we share a little more about the Australian policy context as it relates to HPE.

Contemporary curriculum: The five 'propositions'

The Australian Curriculum for HPE (AC:HPE) includes five 'propositions' that transcend the binary of the two aforementioned strands of learning outcomes aligned with either 'Personal, Social and Community Health' or 'Movement and Physical Activity'. The propositions, or 'key ideas', are unique to the AC:HPE and are foregrounded in the rationale and aims of it (Australian Curriculum, Assessment and Reporting Authority, 2014). They serve to describe and underpin the desired implementation of the curriculum, and are expected to feature as part of HPE teachers' planning, pedagogy and assessment. Based on research for a futures-orientated curriculum, two of the five propositions are intended to guide all teaching across HPE. They include: (i) focus on educative purposes (see DinanThompson, 2013); and (ii) take a strengths-based approach (see McCuaig, Quennerstedt & Macdonald, 2013). The other three propositions are intended to inform pedagogies depending on the desired knowledge and skill learning outcomes. These include: (iii) value movement (see Brown, 2013); (iv) develop health literacy (see Alfrey & Brown, 2013); and (v) include a critical inquiry approach (see Leahy, O'Flynn & Wright, 2013). The propositions are informed by historical debates in the literature about quality HPE pedagogy and offer the impetus for reimagining approaches that are dynamic and responsive to the needs of contemporary learners (Macdonald, 2013). In this chapter, we consider the propositions for the role they can play in responding to three broad 'tensions' that relate to the purposes and constructions of health within HPE: (i) valued knowledge in HPE; (ii) the contested purpose of HPE; and (iii) privileged and marginalised bodies in HPE.

The propositions that characterise the AC:HPE are designed to help HPE teachers shift their focus towards the educational importance of learning about movement and health, and away from pedagogies of health and fitness promotion that are oriented towards behaviour change for a predefined health outcome (e.g. 'fitness', 'diet', 'weight' or 'well-being'). While teachers are not responsible (at least in Australia) for measuring students' health and/or fitness outcomes, their role in HPE and how this is integrated in school curricula and practices for different purposes has been a topic of ambiguity and contestation for some time (Charlton, 1981; Leahy, Burrows, McCuaig, Wright & Penney, 2016). The propositions in the Australian context offer guidance on the role of HPE as educative, strengths-based and anchored to developing skills and knowledge in health literacy, valuing movement and critical inquiry. However, in seeking to enact curriculum policy, such as that represented by these HPE propositions, there is always interplay between teachers' own knowledge, skills and philosophies about HPE, health and the body.

Health and physical education teachers' philosophies: A means of understanding their perspectives and pedagogies

The ways in which HPE teachers construct and teach about health are influenced by their philosophies on teaching HPE more generally (Green, 2003). The notion of 'philosophies' is a valuable conceptual tool to consider how lifelong personal and professional biographies go some way to informing teachers' dispositions regarding how they think about and teach HPE (Green, 2003; Dowling, 2006; McEvoy, Heikinaro-Johansson & MacPhail, 2017). Existing scholarship on specialist HPE teachers, for example, suggests that they have often experienced success and enjoyment through a sport-focused HPE curriculum as a student (biography), remain heavily 'entangled' in sport-orientated networks (e.g. sporting clubs) and are exposed to prevailing and 'residual ideologies' (Kirk, 1988) at work (e.g. sport is the best way to teach HPE) and via the media (e.g. playing sport will make you healthy). This combination of factors can mean that HPE teachers are more likely to reproduce a sport-focused curriculum which 'retains traditions of the past' and marginalises other topics and areas of the curriculum (Keay, 2005, p. 139). The intention of this chapter is to provide an opportunity to explore and critically reflect upon teaching philosophies, with a view to developing pedagogical approaches related to HPE that challenge the status quo and reach out to wider resources and disciplines to enhance the enactment of contemporary HPE.

Constructions of 'health' in health and physical education and socio-critical pedagogies: 'Tensions' and 'Circuit-Breakers'

In this section, we draw upon existing literature to highlight three broad 'tensions' that relate to the purposes and constructions of health within HPE and responses to these. The tensions we explore are: (i) valued knowledge in HPE; (ii) the contested purpose of HPE; and (iii) privileged and marginalised bodies in HPE. We have synthesised each tensions from existing scholarship and, drawing on this scholarship and our own experiences as researchers and teacher educators, we have formulated what we call 'circuit-breaker' responses to these tensions, or rather, possible ways of attempting to deliberately interrupt some problematic constructions of 'health'. We do not want to suggest that this is a straightforward process of 'breaking circuits' of knowledge and practice. Socio-critical work is difficult to navigate, highly contextual and rare in practice (Wright, O'Flynn & Welch, 2018). We can hear the echoes of work from scholars like Lather (1998) who went so far as to state that 'implementing a critical pedagogy in the field of schooling is impossible' (p. 495). Yet, we take cues from Fitzpatrick and Russell (2015) and others who have highlighted how schools (and universities) are an important place to be different, think differently and make changes in the social reproduction or shaping of knowledge. We draw from and extend upon the rich body of scholarship in critical HPE as it continues to gain momentum and offer insight to innovate the field of health education (e.g. Fitzpatrick & Allen, 2019).

Over the past decades, there have been various attempts to focus greater attention on the social aspects of health at the centre of HPE (Leahy, Penney & Welch, 2017). Langer Primdahl, Reid and Simovska (2018) analysed the variety of forms of critical health education, highlighting the 'shades' of methodological and theoretical tools that are drawn on. We draw from these traditions, but also recognise that 'solutions' are far from straightforward, with critical work regarded as 'generative and incomplete' across different contexts and methods. In this spirit, we now outline the three 'tensions' and offer some examples of contexts and methods that have been used to act as 'circuit-breakers' by challenging normative and potentially damaging or counterproductive assumptions about health and the body in HPE.

Tension 1: (Mis)constructions of health in health and physical education

If we accept that school-based learning experiences are central to the development of children's social, emotional and cognitive skills (Solmon & Lee, 2008), as well as their sense of self in relation to health and the body (Burrows & Wright, 2004), then HPE is a consequential practice. This means that the kind of knowledge production that teachers support – in what they do and say – is a practice of micro-learning in children's health knowledge. This does not imply a disregard for other influences on children's learning through and beyond the school setting, but that the enactment of curriculum (formal, informal and hidden) is a project of significant responsibility. The teacher – and the knowledge they value, (mis)construct and share – is one of the most important factors in students' learning (Solmon & Lee, 2008). Indeed, teachers' biographies, and philosophies more broadly, are entangled in their knowledge, understanding and practice of the teaching process (Loughran, 2006; McEvoy et al., 2017).

In many cases, knowledge related to health is equated with certain forms of personal conduct, the absence of which opens the individual to moral censure (Crawford, 1980). Within the Australian context, and with a focus on HPE, Lupton (1999) has long since identified the dominance of particular health-related knowledge associated with neoliberal notions of citizenship and personal identity (e.g. the belief that an individual's ill health is a consequence of their own poor choices or risk taking rather than, for example, the complex array of social determinants of health). If such values and beliefs are not challenged – for example, through ITE or professional learning and continuing professional development – they are likely to continue to be embedded in both rhetoric and pedagogy and directly influence the HPE experiences of children in schools (Wright et al., 2018).

A study on HPE teachers' constructions of the body and health in Swedish and Australian schools, by Webb, Quennerstedt and Öhman (2008), evidenced discourses related to both a 'fit healthy body' and an 'at risk healthy body'. Health was viewed in the fitness discourse as having 'a preventive character with a focus on preventing risks, injuries and disease connected with poor aerobic capacity, poor muscular strength and a physically inactive lifestyle' (Webb et al., 2008, p. 360). As such, for the participating teachers, the link between physical activity and health was deemed as solely physiological. Webb and colleagues (2008) discussed the circulation of healthism[1] in this context, with health presented as a goal that individuals should strive for. This was evidenced in Swedish HPE, for example, through a focus on 'healthy bodies as individual, biological and instrumental and also in the way that the body is seen as machine, where risk is managed and based on facts from physiology and anatomy' (Webb et al., 2008, p. 368).

Focusing specifically on the Australian context, Welch and Wright (2011) surveyed and interviewed pre-service primary teachers and thereafter explored their meanings of health and the body. Their findings suggested that generalist pre-service primary teachers could be categorised into three positions – agreement, disagreement and negotiators – which informed their HPE teaching philosophies. Teachers adopting an 'agreement' position viewed health as related to weight, believing that above average weight was 'unhealthy' and the result of individual choices. Meanwhile, those adopting a 'disagreement' position held the belief that weight and body shape were not indicators of 'health'. Finally, teachers categorised as 'negotiators' discussed the different aspects of health and how weight could be part of this but acknowledged that the relationship is complex. More recent research, also emanating from Australia, suggests that pre-service HPE teachers often have a 'weak understanding of socially contextualised and constructed aspects of health' as well as a narrow pedagogical repertoire related to 'health' within HPE (Fane, Pill & Rankin, 2019, p. 297). As this research infers, this is concerning as both confidence and pedagogical competence are necessary for quality HPE to exist.

Circuit-breakers for misconstructions of health?

It is important to acknowledge that challenging HPE teachers' historically-rooted philosophies and practices related to health is complex and challenging work. As teacher Dan Russell shared in Fitzpatrick and Russell's study (2015, p. 168):

> Overall, the biggest difficulty for me is having the guts to openly resist and make change within the school environment. So often it is easier to consent and passively resist from a position of silent reproach than it is to publicly fight back.

Stretching our gaze to scholarship on public health (e.g. Sallis et al., 2006) and whole-school approaches to change (e.g. McMullen, Ní Chróinín, Tammelin,

Porgozelska & van der Mars, 2015), we know that for sustainable change to occur, intended shifts in teachers' philosophies, and therefore the knowledge/s they privilege in their practice, need to be supported across time (e.g. from ITE through career phases) and context (e.g. school, university, professional development, public pedagogies, etc.). We need to continue to work in these various spaces to cultivate small wins or 'micro-victories' (Burrows, Leahy & Wright, 2018) as part of our practices (e.g. developing and enacting a broad and balanced HPE programme that goes beyond a sport focus and not privileging or promoting particular bodies as 'desirable'). Such actions may ultimately lead to a reshaping and reconstruction of meanings in HPE.

Tension 2: The contested purpose of health and physical education

It is tricky business making claims as to the purpose of HPE. The inclusion of this unique learning area has often been justified on the basis of evidence alluding to children's declining physical skill and fitness levels, increased obesity rates and worsening states of mental health. The different purposes of HPE have at times fallen into what Tinning (2015, p. 711) refers to as two camps: 'instrumentalist' (where the purpose of HPE is promoting physical activity for public health) or 'educationalist' (where the purpose of HPE is educating about health from a socio-cultural perspective). In the UK context, teachers' philosophies have been found to position health promotion as the key function of PE, identifying sport as an important vehicle (Green, 2003). The trouble comes when there is little evidence to demonstrate that HPE in schools can positively influence the prevalence of these health-related issues in young people (Leahy et al., 2016). Despite this, a major focus has been on the need to provide children with information about the risks of non-participation in physical activity and unhealthy food consumption in the pursuit of 'healthy lifestyles'. This focus, as others have pointed out, is informed by medico-scientific knowledge that promotes intervention in children's health behaviours, to prevent and cure 'obesity' (Powell & Fitzpatrick, 2015). Characterised as 'regulative' and 'surveillant', the policies and practices that have emerged in schools are said to influence the ways children come to know themselves as 'fat'/'thin' or 'healthy'/'unhealthy' (Rich, 2010). Thus, children's sense of self and embodiment are tied up in prevailing messages about an ethic of duty to oneself, often enveloped in individualised responsibility for exercise and diet as a means to be 'healthy' or 'thin' (i.e. healthism). Gard (2011) notes how the rise of this public health agenda through health imperatives in schools has taken place particularly throughout the last decade(s). It is now well documented that there has been a normalised emphasis on schooling practices that promote physical activity and healthy eating with the aim of preventing childhood overweight and obesity (McDermott, 2012). The problem here lies with the disproportional emphasis placed on moralising heath and the corporeal body at the expense of other forms of health knowledge and skill development.

As we highlight this tension, we do not discredit the importance of physical activity and nutritional education for children via the development of skills and knowledge in schools. However, the ways in which these topics materialise are often contested and informed by competing and contradictory ideas (Pringle & Pringle, 2012). Too often these ideas are not given equal space in HPE. Language and public pedagogies of health also create tricky associations with HPE. Traditionally, the terms 'fitness' and 'health' have been confounded and, as such, some teachers have tended to use the term fitness when referring to health (Alfrey et al., 2012). It is suggested that the ideologies and core assumptions that seem to have infiltrated HPE teachers' philosophies have resulted in them having a relatively narrow focus on the 'product' or 'effects' of physical fitness (Alfrey et al., 2012) rather than focusing on the educative purposes of health and movement.

Circuit-breakers for the contested purpose of health and physical education?

There have been a multitude of responses to the persisting and narrow focus on HPE as a context within which young people should learn to 'make good choices' (e.g. choosing the 'right' foods and taking part in the 'right' amount of physical activity). With educative purpose, health literacy and critical inquiry in mind, a number of scholars have worked with HPE teachers to enact interventions that employ, for example, the 'Investigation Vision Action Change' (IVAC) model (Boberova, Paakkari, Ropovik and Liba, 2017) and the socio-ecological model (O'Connor & Alfrey, 2015) to support participatory, action-oriented teaching whereby children are supported to investigate different health challenges that affect them, imagine possible alternatives and act towards bringing about change. The HPE propositions outlined above offer the tools for critical and strengths-based approaches to pedagogy. These kinds of approaches go beyond traditional notions of HPE and encourage teachers and students to grapple with the purpose of HPE and the ways in which health is constructed, and engaged with, in this context.

ITE, as the start of the professional learning journey, is arguably a context within which we have the time to disturb common-held assumptions related to HPE. As teacher educators, we provide formal spaces for pre-service teachers to negotiate and co-construct diverse meanings of health drawing on the social determinants of health and the socio-cultural, political and historical landscape within which they live and work.. We also prompt pre-service teachers to reflect on their biographies and explore the ways in which their experiences have informed their philosophies and pedagogies related to HPE. This can be done via activities where they interview their families on what health means to them to explore a range of different social and generational perspectives to demonstrate how meanings of health vary and are linked to history, gender and social expectations and events. In addition, we cannot dismiss the more informal and unintended ways in which pre-service teachers challenge and disturb – in the best sense of the word –each other's constructions of 'health' in HPE. We suggest that mapping such activities to ITE assessment is an important feature of deliberate attempts to enhance pre-service teachers' engagement as well as their knowledge, skills and reflective capacities in challenging dominant discourses of fitness and health in HPE.

Tension 3: Privileged and marginalised bodies in and beyond health and physical education

It is important to consider what meanings of 'health' and 'fitness' are being privileged in and beyond HPE, especially as they intersect with gender, class and race. For example, Camacho-Miñano, MacIsaac and Rich (2019, p. 661) argue that 'Instagram can be a hugely persuasive public pedagogy, influential in shaping how young women learn about the body'. This points to the ways the wellness industry and its purposes shape what versions of health are socially valued. In HPE, then, we need to consider how knowledge is produced and by whom. Who are the dominant voices influencing what is being taught in the name of HPE? What bodies and skills are valued explicitly and implicitly? What topics are well resourced, and who is providing the resources?

Varea and Pang (2018) found that pre-service HPE teachers' perspectives on bodies were heavily influenced by both functionality and aesthetics discourses. They commented that the teachers' constructions of 'healthy bodies' were largely 'restricted to being attractive and related to white bodies' (p. 404). Meanwhile, Fullagar (2019) found that health and physical (in)activity have very different embodied (affective and material) meanings for women from working classes, people with disabilities and mental health issues and other marginalised groups. In exploring meanings of (in)activity, we need to consider diverse everyday material (e.g. safety of local transport and activity facilities) and different meanings of family 'togetherness' in leisure time. Drummond (2020) notes how the embodied challenges for boys and men are often tied to sports participation. Because sports participation goes unquestioned as a social norm and good, males can disguise their preoccupations with body consciousness for the 'sake of sport' or 'devotion to succeed in a chosen sport' (p. 6). Evidently, not all bodies in HPE are equal and this warrants consideration.

Circuit-breakers for privileged and marginalised bodies?

The conflation of health and body function and aesthetics is commonplace in HPE (Azzarito, 2009; Varea & Pang, 2018). However, equating only a seemingly fit and functional body with health is problematic in that it marginalises

many bodies within discussions and practices related to health. By challenging this conflation in our classrooms and gymnasiums, we can begin to shift
understandings around what it means to be and have a healthy body. For example, in Fitzpatrick and Russell (2015), Russell shares his reflections on being a
critical HPE teacher, and in so doing prompts students to question taken-for-
granted assumptions about the body, health and HPE. They reflect on when
'Dan turns up to teach his PE class wearing a bright pink tie with a vintage shirt
and roughly cut-off jeans. He has on thick black-rimmed glasses (with missing
lenses) and he carries an old leather briefcase' (Fitzpatrick & Russell, 2015,
p. 159). We know that HPE teachers' bodies, and what they wear, can do powerful work in this context (Webb et al., 2008) and this is one example of a context
and method that can be used to challenge students' and teachers' assumptions
around the kinds of bodies that belong, or not, in HPE. We 'must create environments that are less threatening and more size accepting, and that emphasise
health and wellness rather than a focus on efforts to attain a socially constructed
aesthetic appearance ideal to increase motivation for movement' (Alberga &
Russell-Mayhew, 2016, p. 155).

As teachers and teacher educators, it can be useful to look beyond the HPE
context in order to support us in critically reflecting upon the kinds of bodies that our philosophies and pedagogies privilege. Indeed, Burrows and
colleagues (2018) provide rich examples of deliberate interruptions to the philosophies and knowledge systems that perpetuate sometimes troubling practices
in HPE. Within health sciences scholarship, research findings from work by
Williams and Annandale (2020) on obesity-related stigma have been translated
into a comic entitled 'The Weight of Expectation' (http://www.actwithlove.
co.uk/woe.html). Whilst some of the language used in this comic means that it
is not necessarily suitable for school-aged children, it could be used as a thinking
tool for the kinds of activities we can do in the name of challenging assumptions
related to 'healthy bodies' and health more generally.

Conclusion

This chapter has highlighted the importance of understanding the ways in
which both specialist and generalist teachers understand and teach about
meanings of health and the body in HPE. The concept of 'philosophies'
has helped us identify the threads that tie the past (including traditions of
HPE and teachers' individual biographies), present (including current socio-
political context) and future (including the implications this might have
for student learning). By sharing a few of our pedagogical responses – or
'circuit-breakers' – to the tensions raised, our intention is to encourage HPE
teachers and teacher educators to also reflect on their own constructions of
health (e.g. their use of language, material practices and unconscious bias),
and also how those constructions influence their teaching practices and thus
student learning. We need to be creative in seeking resources from further
afield to broaden HPE pedagogies, especially when students are so likely to

be readily shaped by the hegemonic meanings of health and the body that come from beyond the school context.

Reflection points

- Which students are most likely to feel a sense of belonging and success in HPE?
- What teaching practices and pedagogies influence students' sense of belonging and success in HPE?
- To what extent do your own experiences of your body shape and function inform how you imagine and teach HPE?
- How can you create equitable experiences of movement participation and skill development for students in HPE?

Note

1 Healthism is both an ideological and a regulative discourse that manifests as a tendency to conceive health as a product of individual choice. Healthism represents a collection of taken-for-granted assumptions, positioned at the intersection of morality, blame and health, that can lead to a privileging of "healthy" and "productive" individuals.

References

Alberga, A. and Russell-Mayhew, S. (2016). Promoting physical activity for all shapes and sizes. In E. Cameron and C. Russell (Eds.), *The fat pedagogy reader: Challenging weight-based oppression through critical education*. pp. 151–159. New York, NY: Peter Lang.

Alfrey, L. and Brown, T.D. (2013). Health literacy and the Australian Curriculum for Health and Physical Education: A marriage of convenience or a process of empowerment? *Asia-Pacific Journal of Health, Sport and Physical Education*, 4(2), 159–173.

Alfrey, L., Cale, L. and Webb, L. (2012). Physical education teachers' continuing professional development in health-related exercise. *Physical Education and Sport Pedagogy*, 17(5), 477–491.

Azzarito, L. (2009). The panopticon of Physical Education: Pretty, active and ideally white. *Physical Education & Sport Pedagogy*, 14(1), 19–39.

Boberova, Z., Paakkari, L., Ropovik, I. and Liba, J. (2017). Democratic school health education in a post-communist country, *Health Education*, 117(5), 469–484.

Brown, T.D. (2013). 'In, through and about' movement: is there a place for the Arnoldian dimensions in the new Australian Curriculum for Health and Physical Education? *Asia-Pacific Journal of Health, Sport and Physical Education*, 4(2), 143–157.

Burrows, L. and Wright, J. (2004). The good life: New Zealand children's perspectives on health and self. *Sport, Education and Society*, 9(2), 193–205.

Burrows, L., Leahy, D. and Wright, J. (2018). Cruel optimism? Socially critical perspectives on the obesity assemblage. In R. Pringle, H. Larsson and G. Gerdin (Eds.), *Critical research in sport, physical and health education*. Routledge pp. 200–212.

Camacho-Miñano, M., MacIsaac, S. and Rich, E. (2019). Postfeminist biopedagogies of Instagram: Young women learning about bodies, health and fitness. *Sport, Education and Society*, 24(6), 651–664.

Charlton, A. (1981). Health education and the teacher's role. *International Journal of Health Education*, 24(2), 102–112.

Crawford, R. (1980). Healthism and the medicalization of everyday life. *International Journal of Health Services*, 10(3), 365–388.

DinanThompson, M. (2013). Claiming 'Educative Outcomes' in HPE: The potential for 'Pedagogic Action'. *Asia-Pacific Journal of Health, Sport and Physical Education*, 4(2), 127–142.

Dowling, F. (2006). Physical education teacher educators' professional identities, continuing professional development and the issue of gender equality. *Physical Education and Sport Pedagogy*, 11(3), 247–263.

Drummond, M. (2020). *Boys' bodies: Sport, health and physical activity.* London: Palgrave Macmillan.

Fane, J., Pill, S. and Rankin, J. (2019). How do pre-service physical education teachers understand health education and their role as health educators? *Business Information Review*, 78(3), 111–117.

Fitzpatrick, K. and Allen, J. M. (2019). What does critical health education in schools look like? Two ethnographic narratives of critical practice. *Health Education Journal*, 78(6), 647–661.

Fitzpatrick, K. and Russell, D. (2015). On being critical in health and physical education. *Physical Education and Sport Pedagogy*, 20(2), 159–173.

Fullagar, S. (2019). A physical cultural studies perspective on physical (in)activity and health inequalities: The biopolitics of body practices and embodied movement. *Revista Tempos E Espaços Em Educação*, 12(28), 63–76.

Gard, M. (2011). *The end of the obesity epidemic.* London: Routledge.

Green, K. (2003). *Physical education teachers on physical education: A sociological study of philosophies and ideologies.* Chester: Chester Academic Press.

Keay, J. (2005). *Influences on Professional Learning: A figurational analysis of the experiences of two female physical education teachers.* International Association of Physical Education and Sports for Girls and Women (APESGW) Congress, University of Alberta, Edmonton, Canada, 10–13 August 2005.

Kirk, D. (1988). Ideology and school-centred innovation: A case study and a critique. *Journal of Curriculum Studies*, 20(5), 449–464.

Langer Primdahl, N., Reid, A. and Simovska, V. (2018). Shades of criticality in health and wellbeing education. *Journal of Curriculum Studies*, 50(6), 733–753.

Lather, P. (1998). Critical pedagogy and its complicities: A praxis of stuck places. *Educational Theory*, 48(4), 487–498.

Leahy, D., O'Flynn, G. and Wright, J. (2013). A critical 'critical inquiry' proposition in health and physical education. *Asia-Pacific Journal of Health, Sport and Physical Education*, 4(2), 175–187.

Leahy, D., Penney, D. and Welch, R. (2017). Schooling health: The critical contribution of curriculum in the 1980s. *History of Education Review*, 46(2), 224–235.

Leahy, D., Burrows, L., McCuaig, L., Wright, J. and Penney, D. (2016). *School health education in changing times: Curriculum, pedagogies and partnerships.* London: Routledge.

Loughran, J. (2006). *Developing a pedagogy of teacher education: Understanding teaching and learning about teaching.* London: Routledge.

Lupton, D. (1999). *Risk and sociocultural theory: New directions and perspectives.* Cambridge: Cambridge University Press.

Lynch, T. (2015). Health and physical education (HPE): Implementation in primary schools. *International Journal of Educational Research*, 70, 88–100.

Lynch, T. (2017). How does a physical education teacher become a health and physical education teacher? *Sport Education and Society*, 22(3), 355–376.

Macdonald, D. (2013). The new Australian Health and Physical Education Curriculum: A case of/for gradualism in curriculum reform? *Asia-Pacific Journal of Health, Sport and Physical Education*, 4(2), 95–108.

McCuaig, L., Quennerstedt, M. and Macdonald, D. (2013). A salutogenic, strengths-based approach as a theory to guide HPE curriculum change. *Asia-Pacific Journal of Health, Sport and Physical Education*, 4(2), 109–125.

McDermott, L. (2012). 'Thrash yourself Thursday': The production of the 'healthy' child through a fitness-based PE practice. *Sport, Education and Society*, 17(3), 405–429.

McEvoy, E., Heikinaro-Johansson, P. and MacPhail, A. (2017). Physical education teacher educators' views regarding the purpose(s) of school physical education. *Sport, Education & Society*, 22(7), 812–824.

McMullen, J., Ní Chróinín, D., Tammelin, T., Pogorzelska, M. and van der Mars, H. (2015). International approaches to whole-of-school physical activity promotion. *Quest*, 67 (4), 384–399.

O'Connor, J. and Alfrey, L. (2015). Activating the curriculum: A socio-ecological action research frame for health and physical education. *Sport, Education and Society*, 20(6), 691–709.

Penney, D. (2020). Health education policy and curriculum: Bernsteinian perspectives and a whole new Ball game. In D. Leahy, K. Fitzpatrick and J. Wright (Eds.), *Social theory and health education* (pp. 114–125). London: Routledge.

Powell, D. and Fitzpatrick, K. (2015). 'Getting fit basically just means, like, non-fat': Children's lessons in fitness and fatness. *Sport, Education and Society*, 20(4), 463–484.

Pringle, R. and Pringle, D. (2012) Competing obesity discourses and critical challenges for health and physical educators. *Sport, Education and Society*, 17(2), 143–161.

Rich, E. (2010). Obesity assemblages and surveillance in schools. *International Journal of Qualitative Studies in Education*, 23(7), 803–821.

Sallis, J.F, Cervero, B., Ascher, W., Henderson, K., Kraft, K. and Kerr, J. (2006). An ecological approach to creating active living communities. *Annual Review of Public Health*, 27, 297–322.

Solmon, M. and Lee. A. (2008). Research on social issues in elementary school physical education. *The Elementary School Journal*, 108(3), 229–239.

Tinning, R. (2015). 'I don't read fiction': Academic discourse and the relationship between health and physical education. *Sport, Education and Society*, 20(6), 710–721.

Varea, V. and Pang, B. (2018). Using visual methodologies to understand pre-service Health and Physical Education teachers' subjectivities of bodies. *Sport, Education and Society*, 23(5), 394–406.

Webb, L.A., Quennerstedt, M. and Öhman, M. (2008). Healthy bodies: Construction of the body and health in physical education. *Sport, Education and Society*, 13(4), 353–372.

Welch, R. and Wright, J. (2011). Tracing discourses of health and the body: Exploring pre-service primary teachers' constructions of 'healthy' bodies. *Asia-Pacific Journal of Teacher Education*, 39(3), 199–210.

Williams, O. and Annandale E. (2020) Obesity, stigma and reflexive embodiment: Feeling the 'weight' of expectation. *Health*, 24(4), 421–441.

Wright, J., O'Flynn, G. and Welch, R. (2018). In search of the socially critical in health education: Exploring the views of health and physical education preservice teachers in Australia. *Health Education*, 118(2), 117–130.

SECTION III

Locating places of and spaces for health

INTRODUCTION

Amanda Mooney

Often coupled with reference to living in a knowledge society is an increased recognition of the significance of various places and spaces in which young people's learning occurs beyond formal schooling contexts such as the home, communities and online/digital spaces (Sefton-Green, 2019). In an era where information can be collected, synthesised and communicated more rapidly than at any other time in history, the nature of education and learning more broadly across these 'informal' contexts raises questions about the forms of learning that are enabled, controlled and constrained, particularly given these contexts are often beyond the regulatory reach of formal educational institutions. In 2020, the profound implications of the COVID-19 pandemic for education and learning beyond formal schooling have arguably been amplified. 'Remote learning' predominantly enabled through advances in digital technology has prompted a renewed focus on the places and spaces in which young people's learning occurs and the knowledge produced through these experiences. In the context of learning about the body, health and physical activity, common to each of the chapters in this section are calls for greater criticality and awareness of the shifts in normative boundaries around 'where' learning occurs, the modes through which messages about the body, health and physical activity are conveyed (the 'how') and, perhaps more importantly, the dominant discourses that are perpetuated and conveyed through these various message systems and the influences they have on the young people we teach (the 'what'). As Evans and Davies (2004) argued some time ago, any interrogation 'of "health" issues within and/or beyond schools … requires that we look afresh at how educational (including "health") knowledge is selected, organised, differently valued, transmitted and defined' (p. 5).

The three chapters within this section of the book work to make visible the various ways in which messages about the body, health and physical activity are constructed, controlled and conveyed to young people and collectively prompt us to consider how young people engage with these messages. With a theoretical coherence broadly located across the spectrum of poststructuralist inquiries, each of the three chapters 'attend carefully to questions of emergence, particularity, and historicity' (Koopman & Matza, 2013, p. 817) in their consideration of the influences of corporatisation, consumerism and biopedagogies, digital technologies and public pedagogies and the home as a pedagogised space or 'field' and the influence these have on young people's health and physical activity. As Wright (2004) explains, at the core of the theoretical basis of poststructuralist approaches is an acknowledgement that knowledge is socially constructed and the intent of researchers within this tradition is not to claim to capture truths per se, but rather, 'they are concerned with how individuals, groups, cultures and institutions construct realities and with what effects' (p. 23).

Each of the chapters provides a nuanced account of the ways in which young people experience and construct knowledge – at times in problematic ways – about the body, health and physical activity beyond the boundaries of the 'school gates'. Yet, it is important to note that the powerful influence of these 'learnings' about one's physical abilities constructed through dominant contextual and cultural conditions is not left at the school gate but rather becomes very much a part of the physical education (PE) experience within schools. Indeed, as myself and colleagues have argued elsewhere, 'critical pedagogical opportunities' are needed within PE for young people to make sense of their own 'physical culture, and their embodiment of it, critically' (Mooney, Casey & Smyth 2012, p. 34). Accordingly, each chapter in this section provides new insights into the ways in which the different aspects of contextual learning occur through *social spaces* (Lefebvre, 1991). A key provocation, therefore, is to understand and make sense of the ways in which knowledge is socially constructed by young people in these informal learning spaces and to consider the ways in which the spaces themselves enable certain processes that shape both learners' learning and their identities.

While perhaps a less common concept in the PE literature, 'spatial analysis' describes a particular theoretical approach common to cultural geographers which examines the meanings, knowledge, social practices, identities and relations that can be produced through interactions with, and within, various places and spaces. Lefebvre's (1991) conceptualisation of *social space* provides a framework to consider the ways in which social and cultural practices shape spaces and the experiences of those interacting in these spaces (van Ingen, 2003). In reading through the three chapters within this section, I was drawn to Lefebvre's (1991) concept of space as a social construct given its potential to help identify how knowledge produced in different spaces 'shapes our understanding of the world and is central in establishing, maintaining, and challenging power relations' (Jeanes et al., 2020, p. 3). Further, it provides a theoretical lens to make sense of the ways in which spaces (and the knowledge and identities produced within them) are produced, maintained and contested through discourses and practices that are inherently political and ideological – spaces are not simple abstract concepts or containers where social relations play out (Mooney & Hickey, 2019). Specifically, Lefebvre (1991) argues there are three 'moments' integral to the production of social space – spatial practices (perceived space), representations of space (conceived space) and spaces of representation (lived space). For Lefebvre (1991), spatial practices as perceived bring together both the physical environment (the material) and the actions that occur within it. As Jeanes and colleagues (2020) point out, spatial practices can be mapped, are able to be 'seen' (visually) and are site-specific. Perceived space draws attention to the everyday activities that occur in physical spaces and, importantly, spatial practices help us to understand which places are able to be accessed, by whom and under which circumstances and, perhaps more specifically, how perceptions about accessing these spaces are controlled – social spaces can be 'read' by their practices.

Chapter 8, by Powell and Piggin, enables us to 'read' the ways in which children's physical activity practices have become increasingly corporatised and to consider the impact that biopedagogies of consumption – described in marketing/advertising policies and practices – have in shaping children and young people into a certain type of healthy, active citizen-consumer. Drawing on case studies of two corporate organisations (McDonald's and Sanitarium), Powell and Piggin critically examine and make visible some of the disconcerting ways in which spatial practices govern and influence children and young people's notions of physical activity and being healthy. The chapter urges us to consider the 'social space' of public health and education amidst questionable and contradictory messaging and to contest the role of the food industry as 'health promoting'.

The following chapter, by MacIsaac and Hooper (Chapter 9), examines young people's health-related engagements with digital spaces and presents us with an opportunity to consider digital spaces as a representation of space or 'conceived space' (Lefebvre, 1991). Specifically, this form (or moment) of social space relates to how we think about a social space and is influenced by the workings of discourse (van Ingen, 2003). For van Ingen (2003), conceived space can be identified and understood through an analysis of the signs, codes of practice and regulation of these practices within a specific social space. She explains that these are the 'kinds of social spaces that we engage in through our thoughts, ideas, plans, codes and memories' (van Ingen, 2003, p. 203) and, as MacIsaac and Hooper point out, we have witnessed a significant increase in the range and types of digital spaces – which are themselves a social space – related to health, fitness and the body in recent years. The chapter provides rich examples of the work of various signs, codes of practice and practices that regulate and govern young people's engagement with digital spaces and highlights how these experiences shape the ways in which young people think about health, physical activity and themselves as a result of their interactions in digital spaces. MacIsaac and Hooper offer key insights into the ways in which (often) unwritten rules regulate or govern ways of engaging with digital 'social spaces' and the ways in which modes of digital surveillance shape young people's knowledge construction. Seeking to move beyond a binary view that digital spaces for health are inherently 'good' or 'bad' for young people, MacIsaac and Hooper consider the affordances of these conceived spaces for young people's self-presentation of physically active identities in online environments – something they are often powerless to control in the temporal and very visible 'moment' of the PE classroom.

In the final chapter of this section (Chapter 10), Pang's exploration of British Chinese youth's home environments and their influence on physical activity practices can be considered through Lefebvre's (1991) concept of spaces of representation or 'lived space'. As van Ingen (2003) explains, 'space was often understood as something concrete that could be mapped, analysed and explained … Lived space combines all spaces simultaneously and generates … local forms of knowing, that are geographically and historically contingent and the result of socially specific spatial practices' (p. 204). Therefore, lived space can be experienced passively but it can also be a site of active resistance. As Jeanes and colleagues (2020) explain, 'this is where spatial practices and imagined spaces converge. Lived space is both oppressive and enabling. It is not only the location for many regulating practices, but also offers the opportunity to develop counter spaces to resist and contest regulatory regimes' (p. 3). Pang's chapter examines specific examples of the 'lived' experiences of British Chinese youth in the 'in-between' space of hypervisibility and invisibility where they are often positioned as the 'model minority', academically successful but disinterested in sport. Through a Bourdieusian field analysis, Pang examines the home environment as a pedagogised space through which micro-level interactions become significant in shaping physical activity practices and dispositions, illustrating the ways in which 'lived space' is experienced through the intersections of gender, class, race, ethnicity and culture.

Each of the chapters in this section presents opportunities to consider social spaces beyond the boundaries of the school gate, in which children and young people's knowledge of the body, health and physical activity are shaped, experienced and regulated/governed. Lefebvre's (1991) concept of social space presents a framework to draw attention to the various ways in which social practices and messages become regulated, controlled and resisted by young people, but perhaps more significantly, compels educators to recognise the growing impact of knowledge construction around health and physical activity in spaces beyond the classroom. Evident in each of the chapters, and the reflective questions posed at the end of these, is a provocation to consider the role that teachers of PE might play in making more visible the sinister side of messages and knowledges conveyed in these social spaces beyond the school gates, and to consider strategies to support young people's critical engagement with, and agentic responses to, these messages. This must be a key aim of critical pedagogy if PE is to become more inclusive, fair and equitable (Kirk, 2019). Taking into account the three chapters presented in this section – and the ongoing implications the COVID-19 pandemic will have for ways of, and spaces for, learning – an important consideration within our pedagogical practice should be how we can support our learners beyond the boundaries of our classrooms. However, it must be noted that while the use of critical pedagogies can support this aim, as Kirk (2019) points out, their effectiveness in practice is reliant on the alignment of curriculum, teaching, learning and assessment and the message systems inherent in each.

References

Evans, J. and Davies, B. (2004), 'Pedagogy, symbolic control, identity and health', in J Evans, B Davies & J Wright (eds), *Body Knowledge and Control: Studies in the Sociology of Physical Education and Health*, Routledge, London, UK, pp. 3–18.

Jeanes, R., Spaaij, R., Farquharson, K., McGrath, G., Magee, J., Lusher, D. and Gorman, S. (2020), 'Gender Relations, Gender Equity, and Community Sports Spaces', *Journal of Sport and Social Issues*, https://doi.org/10.1177/0193723520962955.

Kirk, D. (2019), *Precarity, Critical Pedagogy and Physical Education*, Routledge, Milton Park, Abingdon, Oxon, UK.

Koopman, C. and Matza, T. (2013), 'Putting Foucault to Work: Analytic and Concept in Foucaultian Inquiry', *Critical Inquiry*, vol. 39, pp. 817–840.

Lefebvre, H. (1991), *The Production of Social Space* (D. Nicholson-Smith, Trans.), Blackwell, Malden, MA.

Mooney, A. and Hickey, C. (2019), 'The place of social space: Classed identities in a regional sporting club', in S Pinto, S Hannigan, B Walker-Gibbs & E Charlton (eds), *Interdisciplinary Unsettlings of Place and Space: Conversations, Investigations and Research*, Springer, Singapore, pp. 31–44.

Mooney, A., Casey, M. and Smyth, J. (2012), 'You're No-One If You're Not a Netball Girl: Rural and Regional Adolescent Girls' Negotiation of Physically Active Identities', *Annals of Leisure Research*, vol. 15, no. 1, pp. 19–37.

Sefton-Green, J. (2019), 'Introduction: Learning beyond the school – International perspectives on the schooled society', in J Sefton-Green & O Erstad (eds), *Learning Beyond the School: International Perspectives on the Schooled Society*, Routledge, Milton Park, Abingdon, Oxon, UK, pp. 1–15.

van Ingen, C. (2003), 'Geographies of Gender, Sexuality and Race', *International Review for the Sociology of Sport*, vol. 38, no. 2, pp. 201–216.

Wright, J. (2004), 'Post-structural methodologies: The body, schooling and health', in J Evans, B Davies & J Wright (eds), *Body Knowledge and Control: Studies in the Sociology of Physical Education and Health*, Routledge, London, UK, pp. 19–32.

8

CORPORATIONS IN PHYSICAL ACTIVITY SPACES

Teaching young people about health?

Darren Powell and Joe Piggin

Introduction

This chapter focuses on the connections between children's physical activity, health, education and consumption. Specifically, we explore how the corporate (and philanthropic) commercialisation of physical activity works to tie consumerism to notions of health, physical activity, identity and the body. We argue that physical activity has become a space that is increasingly commercialised and reveal how biopedagogies of consumption (i.e. marketing/advertising policies and practices) attempt to shape children into a certain type of healthy, active citizen-consumer; a child who understands and practices movement and health in ways that closely align with ideologies of neoliberalism, capitalism, individualism and consumerism.

Selling children's healthy lifestyles

In current times, the ideology of consumerism is 'one of the most dominant forces in society; we undoubtedly live in a consumer world, and we enact processes of consumption in almost every aspect of our lives' (Sandlin & McLaren, 2010a, p. 2). This is certainly also true for children and young people who are increasingly targeted by corporations and their advertisers inside and outside the school gates: a 'corporate assault' on children and childhood (see Boyles, 2008). Although there are many ways to define and theorise consumerism and consumption (see Sandlin & McLaren, 2010a), in this chapter, we view these concepts rather broadly, seeing consumption as a process – or a set of sociocultural practices – and consumerism as an ideology which supports capitalism by promising that 'consumption is the answer to all our problems' (Storey, 1996, p. 115). Indeed, corporations (and their partners) have helped to reimagine a variety of social, economic and political problems through the mantra of 'less state, more market'; neoliberalism and consumer capitalism are positioned as a secure means to redevelop all areas of, and fix all problems in, modern societies.

One 'problem' that corporations and a range of other institutions and actors are attempting to solve is that of children's (un)healthy bodies and lifestyles. For instance, organisations across multiple sectors in society are now encouraged to work together to be 'part of the solution' to childhood obesity, which has resulted in a vast array of anti-obesity/healthy lifestyle education programmes, resources, products, curricula, sponsorship and events in schools across the globe (Powell, 2020). These corporatised and commercialised spaces in schools represent reforms of both public health and public education that are aligned with neoliberal ideals of competition, freedom of choice, individual responsibility, enterprise and active consumption. They also represent, as we will demonstrate later in this chapter, how the notion of a 'social good' (e.g. ensuring children have access to physical activity) is now conflated with the 'private good' – how the private sector attempts to profit from concerns about children's bodies and behaviours.

Our chapter builds on the work of other critical researchers who have problematised the corporatisation and commercialisation of children and childhood. There is not the space here to summarise the large corpus of literature that relates to our research. However, it is important to note that a number of scholars have identified and critiqued the role that the private sector plays in shaping public health and public education (e.g. Gard & Pluim, 2014), including those who have illuminated the intersections between education, advertising and children (e.g. Kincheloe & Steinberg, 1997; Kenway & Bullen, 2001).

At the risk of overgeneralising, there is one significant and recurring point that critical scholars make about how consumer culture impacts on children's lives and well-being: corporations now use a variety of tactics to mobilise children to become uncritical consumers of corporate strategies, corporate products and the corporate brand image (see Spring, 2003; Sandlin & McLaren, 2010b). Importantly, these tactics – which we refer to as *biopedagogies of consumption* – attempt to shape children's identities and lifestyles, whereby 'the child-citizen is governed to become the child-consumer so that notions of individualism, self-responsibility, corporeality and consumerism reign supreme' (Powell, 2018, p. 381). This is also the case when corporations invade children's physical activity spaces; a practice that is often promoted as healthy, but is fundamentally problematic.

Governing children to be healthy, active consumers

We draw on the notion of biopedagogies of consumption to illuminate how children are attempted to be 'taught' by advertisers and marketers to be active, healthy and non-fat consumers of corporate products. The concept of biopedagogies encapsulates Foucault's ideas about biopower (see Foucault, 1984, 2003b), government and governmentality (see Foucault, 1991). Governmentality refers to the application of certain ways of thinking about government. This includes ration alities of government and technologies of government. The former refers to how particular problems and practices of government are rationalised by those with the 'will to improve' (Li, 2007a) children's health, bodies and behaviours, while the latter refers to the technical means by which children's conduct is conducted. Foucault (1991) argued that government was not necessarily an oppressive form of top-down power enacted by the state onto individuals but rather was 'under-taken by an "ensemble" of authorities, institutions and agents, using an array of technologies, tactics and bodies of knowledge, in an attempt to guide individu-als' conduct towards definite, albeit unpredictable ends' (Powell, 2019, p. 201). Government actors are, therefore, not restricted to formal state authorities (i.e. police, schools, public health agencies) but can also be from a range of for-profit institutions (e.g. multinational corporations) as well as not-for-profit institutions (e.g. charities) on a local, national or even global scale.

One key, and highly influential, for-profit institution is the food and drink industry. By conceptualising government 'as a productive network that runs through the whole social body, much more than as a negative instance whose function is repression' (Foucault, 2003a, p. 307), Foucault shifts our thinking about power away from modes of government viewed as primarily negative, oppres-sive or ponderous, and towards forms of power that are exercised, productive and omnipresent; a capillary or web-like structure that focuses on life – *biopower*.

Biopower was conceptualised by Foucault (1984) as a productive form of power, an evolution of the power over life, where the supervision of these life processes is made possible by regulations and interventions – a '*bio-politics of the population*' (Foucault, 1984, p. 139, emphasis in original). Biopolitics and biopower are enabled by the implementation of a variety of technologies that attempt to discipline individual bodies *and* regulate populations (Foucault, 1984), including corporatised physical activity, sport and health and physical education (HPE) programmes (see Powell, 2015).

The governmentality of childhood obesity and children's health is often achieved through *biopedagogies*. The term biopedagogies is an assemblage of the concept of pedagogy with Foucault's (1984) concept of biopower: the various strategies used by disciplinary institutions (e.g. schools, corporations, govern-ment agencies) to control individuals and populations – the 'power over life'. In this way, biopedagogies are not a simplistic process of passing knowledge about physical activity or health onto children but are complex 'practices that impart knowledge writ large, occurring at multiple levels across countless domains and sites' (Harwood, 2009, p. 21). It is these numerous spaces – homes, classrooms, sports clubs, shops and online fora where dominant discourses of health 'work' on children's thoughts, actions and identities. What follows is a critical exam-ination of biopedagogies of consumption – the diverse business strategies, or technologies of consumption (Miller & Rose, 1997) used in physical activity ini-tiatives sponsored by food companies to reimagine their companies, their prod-ucts and their child-consumers as 'healthy'.

The corporatisation of children's physical activity

Case study 1: McDonald's Fun Football

For many years, McDonald's has focused heavily on sponsoring youth football in countries around the world. However, the relationships formed between a large multinational food corporation and national sporting organisations are problematic. Tensions often arise in sponsorship agreements such as these through: the connection of fast food (often perceived as unhealthy) with sport (often claimed to promote health); the pervasiveness and predatory exploitation of the credulity of children (Vandevijvere & Swinburn, 2015); and the perceived invasion by corporations into learning spaces for children. These spaces, from formal education settings such as schools to public spaces such as sports fields and recreational centres, are all sites where children are expected to learn certain things about health delivered by legitimate authority figures.

Given these various tensions, how does McDonald's attempt to legitimate its involvement with children in these spaces? The company uses a wide array of tactics and techniques to not only adorn children in their branded sport clothing, but also surround them with bright signage, branded footballs and celebrity ambassadors draped in branded track suits – doing so with unapologetic eagerness and verve. Predictably, McDonald's – and the football organisations they form relationships with – publicly promotes their sponsorship initiatives in a positive light:

- McDonald's aims to provide 5 million hours of 'Fun Football' until 2022 (McDonald's, 2020a).
- In 2017, McDonald's celebrated 250,000 kit donations to children in the UK (McDonald's, 2017).
- An England football manager claimed, 'McDonald's has played a *pivotal* role in supporting grassroots football for seventeen years and 'Fun Football' is another *crucial* step in continuing to make football accessible for young children …' (McDonald's, 2019, emphasis added).
- A promotional video by New Zealand Football (2016), which celebrated McDonald's sponsorship, included the following extracts:

  FOOTBALL COACH: Without that support it would be a lot more difficult … trickier to coach the kids and help them develop.
  YOUNG PLAYER: The gear that McDonald's supplies is awesome *because if you didn't have it you couldn't play, so it's great.*
  YOUNG PLAYERS IN UNISON: It's a beautiful game … I'm loving it! [the McDonald's marketing slogan]

- A former chief executive of McDonald's claimed their input into grassroots football was 'crucial' (McDonald's, 2013).

Whether or not children can opt out of wearing the branded clothing, or whether parents or caregivers are asked for their consent, is unclear. Whatever the case, the children involved in these initiatives become potentially unwitting ambassadors for McDonald's by both internalising and emanating the brand.

Of course, many sport organisations have safeguarding policies, but it is not traditional for these policies to include the protection of children from exploitation by companies promoting ultra-processed food. Indeed, the use of both children's and coaches' voices in relation to the necessity of equipment and financial sponsorship from McDonald's is concrete manifestation of the power of corporate biopedagogies. By hearing (and being asked to espouse) that a corporation is essential or crucial in providing sporting opportunities, young people are led to connect the joyful, creative, playful and social experience of football games with the brand of a global corporation. However, messages about 'health' do not typically feature in such constructions. For example, in 2013, McDonald's commissioned a report by academics to assess what their Football Association partnerships had achieved over a 10-year period. Terms that were conspicuous by their absence from the final report were 'diet', 'nutrition' and even 'health'. However, much attention was given to participants who praised the equipment and financial support made available by McDonald's (McDonald's, 2013). And so, sponsorship is promoted through marketing material and yet some of the ostensibly useful educational outcomes, such as learning about a healthy diet, were either not measured or, if they were, not included in the final report. As such, the sponsorship arrangements between McDonald's and football organisations are, as Vandevijvere and Swinburn (2015) suggest, powerful, pervasive and predatory.

These rhetorical practices contribute to a positive narrative of the corporation, one that is at times subtle, such as framing sponsorship as crucial in press releases, and at times evocative and grand, such as football celebrities distributing football shirts to young people. This is a distinct and concerted effort by both sports associations (which have a duty of care to the young people they claim to educate) and the corporation to praise one another for their partnership, and to reposition McDonald's as a healthy, caring corporation.

Case study 2: Sanitarium Weet-Bix Kids TRYathlon

The Sanitarium *Weet-Bix Kids TRYathlon* is a triathlon event for children and young people (age 7–15) that has been running in New Zealand since 1992. The entry fee – which costs up to NZ$60 per child – enables children to participate in the race, as well as receiving a Weet-Bix Kids TRYathlon medal, an official Weet-Bix Kids TRYathlon t-shirt, a branded drawstring kit bag and swim cap, a 'free' Weet-Bix breakfast and the chance to win prizes and meet sports celebrities (https://tryathlon.co.nz/). Children and their families are also encouraged to visit an online shop to purchase a range of branded Weet-Bix products (see Sanitarium Weet-Bix Kids TRYathlon, 2020a). Schools are an important space to be targeted by Sanitarium, with discounted fees being offered to schools that join the event, as well as in-school support from TRYathlon 'coaches', and the chance to win a range of prizes. In 2018, 'over 800 schools created a School Group and participated in the Sanitarium Weet-Bix Kids TRYathlon' (Sanitarium Weet-Bix Kids TRYathlon, 2020b, para. 4) – approximately a quarter of all primary and secondary schools in New Zealand.

The event is funded and organised by the Sanitarium company, a breakfast cereal producer that holds a significant market share in New Zealand and consistently outsells multinational cereal corporations such as Kellogg's and Nestlé (Adams, 2012). Unlike its publicly listed competitors, Sanitarium is unique in that it is wholly owned by the Seventh-day Adventist Church. This means that, in New Zealand, Sanitarium 'is exempt from paying company tax on their earnings because their profits help fund the church's charitable and religious activities' (Adams, 2012, para. 5). Sanitarium, therefore, acts as a legal charity – New Zealand Health Association Limited – which reported a total income of NZ$232,721,376 in the 2019 financial year (New Zealand Government, 2020).

The TRYathlon is supported by a number of for-profit partners/sponsors, including companies such as Toyota, Haier, Bike Barn, St Pierre's Sushi, Asics, Garmin, Elastoplast, Anchor and Watties, as well as their 'sports development partner' Triathlon New Zealand[1]. Importantly, the event is 'sponsored' by Sanitarium's own Weet-Bix brand cereal (not to be confused with Weetabix in the UK) with the marketing and branding of this product saturating virtually every aspect of this sporting event (see https://tryathlon.co.nz/ for multiple examples).

'Teaching' the healthy, active child-consumer

Using the cases outlined above, we can examine how companies attempt to use their physical activity initiatives to govern children and others. To do this, we interrogate the governmentality (Foucault, 1991) of such programmes by looking at the rationalities and technologies of government. One way to analyse the specific *rationalities* of governmental interventions is to examine the multiple 'styles' of thinking about government. There are a number of significant dimensions that constitute political rationalities (Rose, 1999; Miller & Rose, 2008). For example, rationalities of government are based on 'regimes of truth', such as those who are authorised to speak truths and how truths are spoken (see Rose, 1999). They also represent a particular conception of people to be governed, such as the lazy, fat, unhealthy child. These rationalities are 'made thinkable' (Miller & Rose, 2008, p. 59) through idioms and rhetoric, such as those which describe children in terms of being 'obese' and needing to live 'healthy lifestyles'. For example, Sanitarium's official rationale for the Weet-Bix Kids TRYathlon is based on the 'holy trinity' of children's health in contemporary times: physical activity, healthy eating and not being fat. Two decades ago, Sanitarium published a media release outlining their aim 'to promote the importance of regular exercise, coupled with a nutritious balanced diet and match it with the indomitable spirit that embodies the Kiwi Kids 'have-a-go' philosophy' (Scoop, 2000, para. 18). They stated that not only did their event win the Guinness Book of Records title for the world's largest children's sporting event, but that it also:

> demonstrates the company's commitment to the health and well-being of New Zealanders. With increasing levels of child obesity and related low levels of activity, getting active and developing healthy eating habits at a young age is more critical now than ever before. Sanitarium's Weet-Bix Kids TRYathlon series are all about promoting a healthier lifestyle for Kiwi kids.
>
> *(Scoop, 2000, para. 33–35)*

The company continues to draw on dominant discourses, 'truths' and assumptions about childhood obesity, physical (in)activity and (un)healthy eating. By doing so, Sanitarium positions itself, its products, its partners' products and its sporting event as 'part of the solution' to obesity and children's unhealthy lifestyles (see also Powell, 2020):

> Helping our community to enjoy a better life is part of the Sanitarium mission. That's why statistics on childhood obesity and physical inactivity rates are something we had to respond to.
>
> We own and operate a national event that aims to get more people moving more often …
>
> … It isn't about being sporty or winning at all costs. It's all about getting out there andss giving it a go, having fun with family. Above all, it's about inclusiveness, building self-confidence and instilling a love of physical activity that will last a lifetime.
>
> *(Sanitarium, 2020a, para. 1–3)*

Foucault's notion of governmentality reminds us that the rationalities that underpin any problem of government are not merely represented in 'thought' alone; they must first be rendered thinkable (Miller & Rose, 2008) and then technical (Li, 2007b). Put simply, technologies of government are how rationalities are actualised – how they are 'done' (Inda, 2005). It is through the convergence and congealing of rationalities and technologies that those with the 'will to govern' (e.g. McDonald's, Sanitarium) attempt to achieve particular ends.

In the cases outlined above, there are multiple technologies of government that endeavour to shape children's (and others') 'bodies and souls, thoughts, conduct, and way of being' (Foucault, 1988, p. 18). For instance, one group of technologies that are evident in both physical activity programmes are *technologies of consumption* (Miller & Rose, 1997). These are evident in the various marketing, advertising and public relations tactics that attempt to extend the 'logic' of the market place into children's lives and foster children as a particular kind of 'healthy' consumer. In both the McDonald's Fun Football and Sanitarium Weet-Bix Kids TRYathlon initiatives, we can see multiple technologies assembled together that attempt to forge alignments between children (and adults), discourses of health and consumption, namely: product placement, free gifts, sponsorship, partnerships, philanthropy, charity and corporate social responsibility.

One technology, *product placement* (or embedded marketing), tries to connect Weet-Bix with children's understanding of health and self (see Powell, 2016, for other examples of product placement). Sanitarium does this by ensuring its Weet-Bix Kids TRYathlon events are saturated with images of Weet-Bix, the Weet-Bix logo and children eating Weet-Bix (see Sanitarium Weet-Bix Kids TRYathlon, 2020c). Furthermore, children are directed to the 'Nutrition' web page, where eating Weet-Bix is reinforced as both a means to help them train for the TRYathlon and to ensure they are 'strong and healthy':

> Healthy eating will help make sure that you have the energy you need to train.
>
> Eating wholegrains like Weet-Bix and lots of yummy fresh fruits, like PickMee apples [a gold sponsor of the TRYathlon], and vegetables will give your body the nutrients and energy it needs. They also have lots of vitamins and minerals that your body needs to be strong and healthy.
>
> Stay away from foods that are high in fat, salt and sugar; these foods usually don't have a lot of nutrients …
>
> … For some great breakfast ideas check out the Better Brekkie recipes on the Weet-Bix website at weetbix.co.nz.
>
> *(Sanitarium Weet-Bix Kids TRYathlon, 2020c, para. 1–5)*

In comparison, McDonald's appears to be far more cautious in explicitly promoting their products (e.g. Happy Meal) to children, presumably because a number of countries have adopted stricter (albeit mostly self-regulated) advertising codes that restrict a company's ability to promote food and drink that do not meet national nutrition guidelines. However, the internationally recognisable golden arches logo is frequently plastered over the various resources and equipment provided to football clubs and children. In New Zealand, for instance, McDonald's logos are attached to the educational material that coaches use to develop their sessions. Since the McDonald's logo is connected with various age categories, at times a large McDonald's logo appears up to four times on single pages in the resource (McDonald's, 2020b).

From a governmentality standpoint, there are many instances of an active 'management of possibilities' (Foucault, 2003c, p. 138) of the conduct of children. As well as the macro-politics that inspire such behaviour (such as sports clubs having insufficient funds to manage themselves), there are micro-politics at play. These include: to what extent are children compelled to use McDonald's branded equipment and clothing? To what extent can coaches of these children resist the imposition of fast-food company branding? The extent to which

young people involved in sponsored sport can question these practices is relatively unknown, but their co-option into wearing branded clothing and speaking positively about the corporation in promotional videos should certainly be
questioned.

Product placement is assembled with another technology of consumption –
free gifts. For instance, children who enter and attend the Sanitarium Weet-Bix
Kids TRYathlon are rewarded with prizes, medals and other Weet-Bix branded
paraphernalia, as well as a 'free' breakfast. Similarly, branded football clothing,
footballs and player of the day certificates (with food vouchers) have all been
prominent aspects of McDonald's sponsorship arrangements for more than a
decade.

Although these types of marketing tactics are fairly conspicuous, there are
a number of other stealthier strategies used by companies to ensure their governmental ambitions are realised, including partnerships, philanthropy, charity
and corporate social responsibility. For example, Sanitarium promotes its 'community projects' as part of its 'investment into the health and wellbeing of New
Zealand families' (Sanitarium, 2020b, para. 4). These include the KickStart
Breakfast programme – a collaboration between Sanitarium, Fonterra and the
New Zealand Government to provide free breakfasts to children in schools
in low socio-economic communities – as well as the aforementioned Weet-
Bix Kids TRYathlon. In a similar vein, McDonald's involvement in local and
national football programmes is officially based on concerns about children's
health and the need to work alongside other organisations. For instance, in 2013,
McDonald's stated that:

> There continues to be concern about obesity rates and related risks to
> human well-being among consumers, governments, NGOs, and health
> and nutrition experts … We know we cannot address this problem alone,
> but we are committed to being part of the solution.
>
> *(as cited in Powell, 2020, p. 56)*

Further, in the International Food and Beverage Alliance's 2008–2013 progress report, McDonald's used their football programme as evidence they
were meeting their commitment to 'promoting physical activity and healthy
lifestyles', stating that by 'collaborating with local cultural, civic and non-
profit organisations, McDonald's empowers local communities to grow
strong. McDonald's supports a range of initiatives around the world, focused
on children's well-being' (International Food and Beverage Alliance, 2014,
p. 60).

Food and drink companies use physical activity initiatives as a form of
'strategic philanthropy' reinventing themselves as healthy, socially responsible and community-oriented, and further enabling them to 'maximise the
impact of giving and to align contributions with the company's business goals
and brand characteristics' (King, 2006, p. 8). This type of philanthropy is also

a means to shape public policy, such as forestalling stricter regulatory controls on the marketing or production of food. For instance, in New Zealand, both McDonald's and Sanitarium were members of the *Healthy Kids Industry Pledge*, an alliance between food and drink industry representatives and the Ministry of Health, that made a commitment (albeit a non-binding, self-regulated commitment) to work together and 'fight' childhood obesity. On this, Sanitarium stated:

> At Sanitarium, our mission is to share with our community a message of health and hope for a better life. Our commitment to our mission along with the concerning rates of childhood obesity and physical inactivity in New Zealand is why we are backing the New Zealand Ministry of Health's Healthy Kids Industry Pledge.
>
> We take seriously the issues related to our role in the food industry and the health of children in New Zealand. Our vision to inspire and resource our community to experience happy, healthy lives has led us to create our own additional pledges.
>
> *(Sanitarium, 2020c, para. 1–2)*

In the case of McDonald's, in the UK, the corporation has used (and continues to use) their community football programme to demonstrate their 'health-promoting', socially responsible physical activity initiatives to policymakers. For example, McDonald's provided evidence to the UK Parliament's House of Commons (2004) Health Committee obesity inquiry, arguing not only that 'McDonald's believes that the issue of obesity can only be addressed through effective partnerships' (p. 228), but also that their 'championing of physical activity goes far beyond branding opportunities. [McDonald's] are committed to a long-term programme to advocate and support the development of healthier lifestyles' (p. 227).

These types of promises, pledges and commitments help companies *be seen* to be part of the solution to childhood obesity and unhealthy lifestyles. After all, 'for corporations to build a philanthropic image, their educational and healthy programmes must be seen *and* be profitable' (Powell, 2020, p. 48, emphasis in original). Technologies such as partnerships, philanthropy, charity and corporate social responsibility all combine together in ways that help promote the 'official' aims of companies (i.e. to promote children's physical activity and health), yet also work to hide their more self-serving, less altruistic goals. In the end, these forms of 'healthy' corporate philanthropy:

> help to re-assemble organisations and individuals to be seen as philanthropic and charitable, as well as healthy and educational. They work to mask private sector players less altruistic interests: branding, public relations strategies, avoidance of stricter regulations and legislation, and the desire

to profit. They transfer the responsibility of government for the health and education of children to industry groups, corporations and charities.

(Powell, 2019, p. 210)

In this way, the 'will to give' physical activity and sports programmes to children across the globe should not simply be understood as a change in business strategy but, as King (2006, p. 98) asserts, 'part of a struggle over how and by whom socio-economic management on a transnational scale should be undertaken'. They are also excellent examples of how modern government works; that although the state continues to act as a key player in the government of children (and their health), 'so too are the myriad of institutions, sites, social groups and interconnections at the local level, whose concerns and activities may support, but often conflict with, the imperatives of the state' (Lupton, 1995, p. 9). However, as we (and other researchers) continue to ask, are these new types of arrangements 'win-win' for everyone involved? And if not, how might children in particular 'lose'?

Conclusion

This chapter aimed to critically examine how corporatised physical activity initiatives may act as biopedagogies that 'have the power to teach, to engage "learners" in meaning making practices that they use to make sense of their world and their selves and thereby influence how they act upon themselves and others' (Wright, 2009, p. 7). Biopedagogies of consumption such as the sponsorship of physical activity initiatives and sports events, product placement (even of 'healthy' products) and the provision of free gifts such as food and sports equipment to children – often in the name of 'fighting obesity' or 'promoting health' – are far from benign or even healthy. They represent a calculated strategy by powerful players to market to children (and parents and policymakers) a 'particular brand of health' (Vander Schee, 2008, p. 5) that is tightly tied to neoliberal notions of self-responsibility, individualism and freedom of choice. The promotion of physical activity has become far more than a means to encourage children to move and play, but a tactic to achieve the goals of multinational corporations and numerous other for-profit and not-for-profit organisations. To these ends, the reinvention of the food industry as 'health promoting' is now inextricably interconnected with the reinvention of children as 'healthy', active consumers.

Reflection points

- Aside from food and beverage companies, what other organisations (including corporations, industry groups, charities, social enterprises, government agencies) are involved in the funding and/or implementation of physical activity initiatives in your own context?
- How might these different organisations benefit from being involved in these initiatives?

- How might children – especially certain groups of children– 'lose' (or even be harmed) from these arrangements?
- What are some of the political, economic, environment, historical, social and cultural factors that make commercialised physical activity initiatives possible?
- What can we do to challenge the corporatisation of children's physical activity spaces?

Note

1 Triathlon New Zealand is the national sporting organisation for triathlon and multisport in New Zealand.

References

Adams, C. (2012, June 30). *Lifting the lid on Sanitarium*. NZ Herald. https://www.nzherald.co.nz/business/news/article.cfm?c_id=3&objectid=10816412.

Boyles, D. R. (2008). *The corporate assault on youth: Commercialism, exploitation, and the end of innocence*. New York, NY: Peter Lang.

Foucault, M. (1984). *The history of sexuality, volume 1: An introduction*. London: Penguin.

Foucault, M. (1988). Technologies of the self. In L. H. Martin, H. Gutman & P. H. Hutton (Eds.), *Technologies of the self: A seminar with Michel Foucault* (pp. 16–49). Amherst, MA: University of Massachusetts Press.

Foucault, M. (1991). Governmentality. In G. Burchell, C. Gordon & P. Miller (Eds.), *The Foucault effect: Studies in governmentality* (pp. 87–104). Chicago, IL: Harvester Wheatsheaf.

Foucault, M. (2003a). Truth and power. In P. Rabinow & N. Rose (Eds.), *The essential Foucault: Selections from essential works of Foucault 1954–1984* (pp. 300–318). New York, NY: The New Press.

Foucault, M. (2003b). *Society must be defended: Lectures at the Collège de France 1975–1976*. New York, NY: Picador.

Foucault, M. (2003c). The subject and power. In P. Rabinow & N. Rose (Eds.), *The essential Foucault: Selections from essential works of Foucault 1954–1984* (pp. 126–144). New York, NY: The New Press.

Gard, M., and Pluim, C. (2014). *Schools and public health: Past, present, future*. Lanham, MD: Lexington.

Harwood, V. (2009). Theorizing biopedagogies. In J. Wright & V. Harwood (Eds.), *Biopolitics and the obesity epidemic: Governing bodies* (pp. 15–30). New York, NY: Routledge.

House of Commons. (2004). *House of Commons Health Committee – Obesity – Third report of session 2003–04, volume II*. London: The Stationary Office Limited.

Inda, J. X. (2005). Analytics of the modern: An introduction. In J. X. Inda (Ed.), *Anthropologies of modernity: Foucault, governmentality, and life politics* (pp. 1–19). Carlton, Victoria: Blackwell.

International Food and Beverage Alliance. (2014). *Five commitments in five years: Review of progress 2008–2013*. https://www.ifballiance.org/uploads/ifbaResource/report/59e4a7ab6572b_ifba-progress-report-2008-2013-final-11-sept-2014.pdf.

Kenway, J., and Bullen, E. (2001). *Consuming children: Education-entertainment-advertising*. Maidenhead: Open University Press.

Kincheloe, J. L., and Steinberg, S. R. (Eds.). (1997). *Kinderculture: The corporate construction of childhood.* Boulder, CO: WestviewPress.

King, S. (2006). *Pink Ribbons, Inc.: Breast cancer and the politics of philanthropy.* Minneapolis, MN: University of Minnesota Press.

Li, T. M. (2007a). *The will to improve: Governmentality, development, and the practice of politics.* Durham, NC: Duke University Press.

Li, T. M. (2007b). Governmentality. *Anthropologica, 49*(2), 275–281.

Lupton, D. (1995). *The imperative of health: Public health and the regulated body.* London: Sage.

McDonald's. (2013). *10 years of teamwork. McDonald's national grassroots football partnerships 2002–2012.* https://m.mcdonalds.co.uk/content/dam/UK01NewsAssets/Reports/Ten%20Years%20Of%20Teamwork%20grassroots%20report.pdf.

McDonald's. (2017). *McDonald's celebrate 250,000 kit donations.* https://www.youtube.com/watch?v=UU6D63jydhc.

McDonald's. (2019). *Gareth Southgate and Marvin Humes invite thousands of children to try football.* https://www.mcdonalds.com/gb/en-gb/newsroom/article/Football.gareth_southgate.html.

McDonald's (2020a). *Fun Football.* https://www.mcdonalds.com/gb/en-gb/football.html.

McDonald's. (2020b). *Junior framework, games and activities.* https://www.sporty.co.nz/asset/downloadasset?id=bd2f865d-956d-43b4-8f2e-6d67fea0aedd.

Miller, P., and Rose, N. (1997). Mobilizing the consumer: Assembling the subject of consumption. *Theory, Culture and Society, 14*(1), 1–36.

Miller, P., and Rose, N. (2008). *Governing the present.* Cambridge: Polity.

New Zealand Football. (2016). *McDonald's junior football at Western Springs.* Available from https://www.youtube.com/watch?v=i75SoKGt9JE&feature=emb_logo.

New Zealand Government. (2020, January 7). *Charity services.* https://www.register.charities.govt.nz/CharitiesRegister/ViewCharity?accountId=580fe12e-831c-dd11-99cd-0015c5f3da29&searchId=4419f060-590d-456c-a4d0-e140b4fcba94.

Powell, D. (2015). *"Part of the solution"?: Charities, corporate philanthropy and healthy lifestyles education in New Zealand primary schools.* (PhD Thesis, Charles Sturt University). https://researchoutput.csu.edu.au/.

Powell, D. (2016). Governing the (un)healthy child-consumer in the age of the childhood obesity crisis. *Sport, Education and Society, 23*(4), 297–310.

Powell, D. (2018). Culture jamming the 'corporate assault' on schools and children. *Global Studies of Childhood, 8*(4), 379–391.

Powell, D. (2019). The 'will to give': Corporations, philanthropy and schools. *Journal of Education Policy, 34*(2), 195–214.

Powell, D. (2020). *Schools, corporations, and the war on childhood obesity: How corporate philanthropy shapes public health and education.* Abingdon: Routledge.

Rose, N. (1999). *Powers of freedom: Reframing political thought.* Cambridge: Cambridge University Press.

Sandlin, J. A., and McLaren, P. (2010a). Introduction. In J. A. Sandlin & P. McLaren (Eds.), *Critical pedagogies of consumption: Living and learning in the shadow of the 'shopocalypse'* (pp. 1–20). New York, NY: Routledge.

Sandlin, J. A., and McLaren, P. (2010b). *Critical pedagogies of consumption: Living and learning in the shadow of the 'shopocalypse'.* New York, NY: Routledge.

Sanitarium. (2020a, January 7). *Promoting active, confident, healthy kids.* https://www.sanitarium.co.nz/social-purpose/fighting-lifestyle-diseases/events/sanitarium-promotes-active-healthy-kids.

Sanitarium. (2020b, January 7). *Profits for charitable services.* https://www.sanitarium. co.nz/about/sanitarium-story/profits-for-charitable-purposes.

Sanitarium. (2020c, January 7). *Healthy kids industry pledge.* https://www.sanitarium. co.nz/social-purpose/fighting-lifestyle-diseases/healthy-kids-industry-pledge.

Sanitarium Weet-Bix Kids TRYathlon. (2020a, January 7). *Shop.* https://tryathlon. co.nz/shop/.

Sanitarium Weet-Bix Kids TRYathlon. (2020b, January 7). *Schools.* https://tryathlon. co.nz/schools/.

Sanitarium Weet-Bix Kids TRYathlon. (2020c, January 7). *Nutrition.* https://tryathlon. co.nz/nutrition/.

Scoop. (2000, August 28). *Taupo to Stage Weet-Bix Kiwi Kids Tryathlon.* https://www. scoop.co.nz/stories/SP0008/S00008/taupo-to-stage-weet-bix-kiwi-kids-tryathlon. htm.

Spring, J. (2003). *Educating the consumer-citizen: A history of the marriage of schools, advertising, and media.* New York, NY: Routledge.

Storey, J. (1996). *Cultural studies and the study of popular culture.* Athens, GA: University of Georgia Press.

Vander Schee, C. (2008). Consuming health: Health curricula and the production of a healthy student. In D. Boyles (Ed.), *The corporate assault on youth: Commercialism, exploitation, and the end of innocence* (pp. 1–26). New York, NY: Peter Lang.

Vandevijvere, S., and Swinburn, B. (2015). Getting serious about protecting New Zealand children against unhealthy food marketing. *New Zealand Medical Association, 128*(1417), 36–40.

Wright, J. (2009). Biopower, biopedagogies and the obesity epidemic. In J. Wright & V. Harwood (Eds.), *Biopolitics and the obesity epidemic: Governing bodies* (pp. 1–14). New York, NY: Routledge.

9

YOUNG PEOPLE'S HEALTH-RELATED ENGAGEMENTS WITH/IN DIGITAL SPACES

Sarah MacIsaac and Oliver Hooper

Introduction

Schools are often considered key sites for teaching young people about health, with the subject of physical education (PE) regarded as especially important in this process (Cale, Harris & Hooper, 2020). However, as Rich and Miah (2014) explain, much learning around health and the body occurs through public pedagogies – through various forms, processes and sites of education beyond the boundaries of formal schooling. Public pedagogy previously occurred mostly within families or through mediums such as the traditional media. However, as digital spaces become ever more prominent within our societies, they are increasingly becoming influential avenues for learning (Lupton, 2015). Research suggests that young people engage frequently with such digital spaces, with 15–16-year-olds having improved access to technologies such as smartphones, laptops and tablets and spending increasing amounts of time online (Organisation for Economic Cooperation and Development [OECD], 2017). Concurrently, there has been a significant increase in the range and types of digital spaces related to health, fitness and the body such as: health- and lifestyle-related apps; wearable devices and self-tracking technologies; exergames; online podcasts, blogs and internet forums; and social media platforms.

Research suggests that young people value digital spaces for learning about health as they consider online information to be extensive and readily accessible (Radovic, McCarty, Katzman & Richardson, 2018). However, there are concerns about young people's engagements with digital spaces, including those around screen time and sedentary behaviours (Haycraft, Sherar, Griffiths, Biddle & Pearson, 2020), body dissatisfaction (Tiggeman & Slater, 2013) and cyberbullying (Smith et al., 2008). Goodyear, Armour and Wood (2019a) note that adults tend to focus on the risks posed by young people's engagements with digital spaces. However, as Lupton (2015) warns, we should not adopt a binary view that digital spaces for health are inherently good or bad for young people. Instead, we must explore critically how and why young people use and engage with these spaces and the resulting implications. Whilst we know that young people engage frequently with these digital spaces, we are much less clear about *how* this engagement influences their knowledge and behaviours (Goodyear et al., 2019a).

Within this chapter, we explore key digital spaces within which young people learn about health and their bodies, specifically wearable devices and self-tracking technologies and social media platforms. We consider how young people use these digital spaces, what they access and learn as they do so and the resulting implications of such use. Subsequently, we consider how young people's engagements with/in digital spaces may influence their experiences of, and engagements with, PE in schools. Finally, we explore how PE teachers might make constructive links between the health-related learning occurring within digital spaces and that within PE and how they might help young people engage positively with such digital spaces.

Wearable devices and self-tracking technologies

Wearable devices – such as smartwatches – and self-tracking technologies provide popular means by which people can monitor their health and their bodies. These technologies allow users to record and analyse, for example, their physical activity levels, bodily metrics, food consumption, menstrual cycles and mood state – with some versions of these technologies specifically marketed towards children and young people. These wearable devices and self-tracking technologies are often considered efficient means of public health promotion where generated data is marketed as serving a pedagogical function by increasing an individual's self-knowledge and self-awareness in order to support them in achieving an optimum state of health (Lupton, 2015). Such self-knowledge often comes in the form of numbers, charts and infographics, with the self essentially becoming 'quantified' (Williamson, 2015; Rich, 2018). Individuals draw upon the data generated about themselves – creating 'data doubles' – which they can use to conceptualise how 'healthy' they are and to analyse how they can 'improve' (Rich & Miah, 2017). Indeed, many such technologies encourage individuals to transform their bodies and their lifestyle choices, providing opportunities for people to monitor their success in doing so by way of progress reports, targets and comparisons with both norms and other users' data – a form of peer surveillance as it were (Rich, 2018).

A key claim by those advocating for wearable devices and self-tracking technologies is that they are motivational in relation to health behaviours. These technologies can be used to set targets for people to work towards, with many also employing 'nag technology' – for example, providing users with prompts as to when they should stand up, drink water or rest (Lupton, 2015). Further, the opportunity for individuals to compare and contrast their current 'performance' with their historic data, and the data of others, incorporates a competitive element that some may find encouraging. Research conducted with young people seems to indicate that they do consider such mechanisms motivating, at least, to an extent. For example, studies have identified that some young people enjoy having tangible goals to meet, having access to real-time data and feeling a sense of competition (Kerner & Goodyear, 2017; Goodyear, Kerner & Quennerstedt, 2019b). However, the same studies also show that young people's motivation can be fairly short-lived, perhaps only lasting a few weeks, until interest wanes. Young people in these studies felt under pressure to be more active when peers could see what they were doing and were motivated to engage with 'healthy' behaviours for extrinsic as opposed to intrinsic reasons (Goodyear et al., 2019b). Kerner and Goodyear (2017) also found that young people felt less competent in themselves when they did not meet goals or targets set for them within digital spaces or when they felt they were not doing as well as their peers and, consequently, they would disengage with the technology.

Technology encouraging users to focus on bodily and behavioural norms and ideals has the potential to bring about feelings of shame should individuals perceive that they are not meeting relevant 'standards' – especially within a culture where individuals are encouraged to declare publicly the choices they are making and to document their progress in line with these (Rich & Miah, 2017). Therefore, engagements with wearable devices and self-tracking technologies may exacerbate the dissatisfaction that many young people already feel around their bodies (Grogan, 2017). For example, adolescent girls in a study by Depper and Howe (2017) expressed how digital content can promote notions of an 'ideal' body, which is unrealistic for many girls and potentially damaging for their perceptions of self. Allied to this, focusing on norms and ideals can also be problematic in that it can encourage rather narrow and simplistic interpretations of what it means to be 'healthy'. As Goodyear and colleagues (2019b, p. 213) note, this can lead to young people conceptualising being healthy as a 'practice of being told, adopting and repeating easily described behaviours' – such as exercising for a particular amount of time per day, or consuming a particular number of calories.

It is important to consider such research when utilising wearable devices and self-tracking technologies in schools, particularly within the subject of PE – a context for which an array of health-related technologies have been developed or, in some cases, reappropriated. Teachers have opportunities to use technology creatively in order to engage young people and enhance their learning, making such learning relevant to that which takes place beyond the school context. For example, they might use apps that provide customisable fitness, dance or yoga routines, technology for recording and analysing sports performance or apps for tracking physical activity and monitoring bodily metrics such as heart rate. However, researchers have voiced concerns around the uncritical implementation of such technologies within PE, particularly with regard to ethical issues around surveillance (Lupton, 2015).

Lupton (2015) classifies five modes of digital surveillance: private (people voluntarily monitoring their own data), communal (people voluntarily sharing their data with others), pushed (people being encouraged to share their data), imposed (people being forced to share their data) and exploited (people's data being used solely for others' purposes). Lupton (2015) claims that digitised PE has the potential to include all five modes of digital surveillance. For example, the use of an app to monitor young people's physical activity levels could involve those who are interested engaging with the app to self-monitor their own efforts within lessons, trying to improve it each week (private surveillance). Class leader boards or group challenges may then enable young people to compare and contrast their data with others in the class (communal surveillance). Teachers may encourage young people to engage with this technology, perhaps with rewards for those improving on their personal bests (pushed surveillance). However, some young people may not want to track or share their data but will have little choice since that is the task that the teacher has set for them (imposed surveillance). Finally, young people may be unaware where their data goes or what it is used for – these apps and associated technologies provide key commercial opportunities for the companies which have developed and own them, especially through the sale of generated data (exploited surveillance). Interestingly, research suggests that young people do not necessarily consider wearable devices and self-tracking technologies to have educational value within PE, despite their increasing prevalence within this context (Goodyear et al., 2019b). Depper and Howe (2017) note that the young people within their study perceived the implementation of such technologies within the PE context as damaging to what they considered to be more enjoyable aspects of the subject – most notably, the social interactions within it. Accordingly, these young people expressed that they considered such technologies to be more appropriate for use in individualistic contexts such as when exercising alone.

Employing wearable devices and self-tracking technologies within PE is not necessarily straightforward. Whilst there may be benefits to their implementation, there can also be limitations and potentially unintended consequences. Teachers must be mindful of the ways in which these devices and technologies can negatively influence young people's knowledge and behaviours and seek to support them to engage appropriately with them – for example, by setting goals that are personalised and self-referenced, as opposed to making comparisons with norms and peers (Kerner & Goodyear, 2017). However, in addition to engaging with these devices and technologies, young people also interact with wider digital spaces – such as social media platforms – and so consideration must be given to the impact that these interactions might have on young people and, in particular, their identities.

Social media platforms

Social media platforms are key digital spaces where young people learn about, and form meanings around, health, physical activity and their bodies. These online social spaces such as Facebook, Instagram, Twitter and Snapchat allow people, groups and organisations to create their own profile pages visible to other users. Profiles are often self-orientated spaces where people share and reveal information about themselves through the presentation of text, photographs and videos. Individuals can also connect and interact with other users – both publicly and privately – and can communicate by sharing information of interest through comments, pictures or stories. 'Normal' individuals therefore become collaborative producers of media, as well as consumers, by creating and posting content, browsing content posted by others and reinforcing such content through 'liking', 'favouriting' and commenting (Sirna, 2014).

Social media platforms are now a ubiquitous part of young people's everyday lives, something which they access and engage with frequently (Goodyear & Quennerstedt, 2020). Young people have reported that using social media helps them to feel connected to friends, in some cases worrying that a lack of online presence carries the risk of being isolated or 'cut off' from social happenings (MacIsaac, 2016). Social media platforms may also be an important site for seeking affirmation, where there are opportunities to feel popular and accepted, despite associated social risks around ridicule and cyberbullying (Goodyear & Quennerstedt, 2020). Young people may also engage with social media as a form of entertainment, browsing online spaces to talk to and 'look at' other people, and to find out news and information (MacIsaac, 2016). As boyd (2014) suggests, whilst many characterise young people as being 'obsessed' with technology and seemingly 'hooked' on social media, in most cases it is socialising and a desire for connectedness to which young people are 'addicted'.

Social media platforms are a particularly significant site for identity construction amongst young people, especially within neoliberal societies where there is much focus on who people are, what they do, their successes and failures and their relationships with others (Griffin, 2014). As Chambers and Sandford (2019) note, adolescence is an intense and significant period for a person's identity development and engagements with social media can have a profound impact on their ways of knowing and being. As young people actively engage with social media platforms, they continually create an impression of themselves, both advertently and inadvertently, and potentially to large audiences – with many young people considering social media to be *the* place where they become most 'known' to others (MacIsaac, Kelly & Gray, 2018). Therefore, young people may be acutely aware that others are scrutinising their online content and so will think strategically about how they present themselves.

Young people may feel that their bodies and appearances are especially scrutinised online and associations have been found between social media use and body image concerns, especially when image-related activity accounts for much time online (Tiggeman & Slater, 2013; Meier & Gray, 2014). Social media platforms are highly visual and still images and replayable videos provide opportunity for deeper scrutiny than face-to-face interactions. Further, as many photos and videos are shared and exchanged within online social spaces, users can be exposed to a wealth of images of bodily 'perfection', which they may seek to emulate (Perloff, 2014). These can come in the form of advertisements, step-by-step guides for diet and exercise, motivational images and quotes, as well as straightforward images of others. Such content can also incite 'appearance conversations' as people comment and discuss, for example, how 'good' others look (Meier & Gray, 2014). Therefore, social media platforms bring together what have been identified as two key influences on bodily perceptions – image-driven media and peers (Mabe, Forney & Keel, 2014). Research has also examined cyberbullying on social media platforms and appearance-related bullying has been found to be commonplace (Berne, Frisen & Kling, 2014).

Such research is worrying because social media platforms can become spaces where young people construct their perceptions of themselves, especially as they compare and contrast themselves to others (Fardouly, Diedrichs, Vartanian & Halliwell, 2015). Individuals often make 'upward' social comparisons to those they perceive to be 'better' than them, potentially leading to feelings of inadequacy. Whilst traditional media has provided people with opportunities to compare themselves with 'unreachable' celebrities or athletes, social media provides opportunities to make comparisons with peers of similar social standing. As Perloff (2014) suggests, 'upward comparisons' are especially detrimental when made with reference to those we are in direct competition with and whom we perceive as having similar opportunities and resources to ourselves. MacIsaac and colleagues (2018) evidence how young people's comparisons with one another via social media can have a very powerful influence on how they feel about themselves and how they conduct themselves socially within the school context. However, when making such comparisons, many individuals overlook or under-estimate the fact that their peers are intentionally making visible or enhancing the 'good' and 'flattering' parts of their lives and bodies whilst hiding or neglecting to reveal the less savoury or mundane parts. Peer images can be just as 'unrealistic' as celebrity images, especially when 'normal' individuals make use of photoshopping apps, filters, lighting and angles to alter and edit their own images (Meier & Gray, 2014). Research by MacIsaac (2016) provides further evidence of this within the school context, with young people reporting their use of photoshopping apps and filters to alter images of themselves before posting them online, stating that they felt more comfortable having their bodies seen on social media where they had more control over their appearance.

Social media platforms are also used purposefully by young people to learn about their health and their bodies. For example, over half of young people in a study by Goodyear et al. (2019a) used social media to search for health-related information, particularly information around exercise workouts, diets and body transformations. Young people in their study also reported to have discovered such content inadvertently, for example, noticing content on their timelines that had been automatically sourced (based on their 'likes' or their followers' 'likes'), engaging with content which their peers had created or posted, and/or finding content which was partially related to terms that they had searched for

(Goodyear et al., 2019a). Often, this content is laden with 'fitspirational' rhetoric where images of 'fit', 'healthy' and 'strong' bodies are framed as virtuous and empowered alongside motivational messages to inspire others to also adopt idealised diet and exercise practices (Camacho-Miñano, MacIsaac & Rich, 2019).

Within a 'fitspirational' culture, individuals often post pictures of their own bodies and bodily practices online so that engagements with health and fitness become 'public facing, social experiences' (Rich & Miah, 2014, p. 301). Similar to when using wearable devices and self-tracking technologies, these individuals compliantly subject themselves to the gaze of others through disclosure whilst concurrently monitoring and scrutinising themselves. They may also share images of others whose bodies and bodily practices they admire, such as celebrities or athletes. Camacho-Miñano and colleagues (2019) evidence how young people use and value content posted by 'famous' individuals and social media 'influencers' as they construct knowledge around the body and physical activity. These young people used such content to assist them in 'bettering' their bodies – for example, learning specific workouts that could target certain body parts or 'problem' areas. They also spoke about deriving pleasure from the observable results of physical activity rather than from engaging in the practice of physical activity itself. However, they were critical of such culture around the body, aware that many of the 'fitspirational' images they were seeing were altered and filtered and that some of the associated diet and exercise practices were not necessarily healthy. Some also claimed that 'fitspirational' rhetoric was demotivating and made them feel body dissatisfaction as they compared themselves against unattainable ideals. Nonetheless, they still desired to be like those 'fitspirational' individuals (Camacho-Miñano et al., 2019).

It is important for PE teachers to be aware of what young people learn about health and the body on social media platforms, as well as how they learn about these, as young people's learning within PE will inevitably be influenced as a result. PE, in many ways, is a social space which shares several similarities with online social spaces. Both are high-stakes avenues for identity construction and for accumulating (or not) social capital – that is, networks generated through social processes, which facilitate relationships and foster belonging. Further, both are spaces where bodies are highly visible and under much scrutiny. Indeed, PE has long been a place where certain individuals have felt uncomfortable, judged, vulnerable and exposed (Sykes & McPhail, 2008). Engagements with social media can have a magnifying effect on these issues, particularly as the ways in which young people perceive and evaluate the body evolve. For example, MacIsaac (2016) highlights how engagements with social media can enable young people to become very skilled at scrutinising one another whilst being hyper-attuned to self-presentation processes. Through engagements with social media, participants in her study learnt exactly what details to look for in each other's bodies and were able to examine one another in meticulous fashion both online and offline. They were immersed in a culture where 'appearance conversations' were the norm and where it was accepted to talk openly about other people's bodily successes and failures. This meant that their perceptions of being under surveillance within offline spaces were heightened. They were self-conscious within PE, paying attention to very smallest of details in relation to their bodies – and believing that their peers were paying close attention too. As such, many of their actions were deliberately thought out and, for some young people, this distracted them from learning within PE (MacIsaac, 2016).

Young people can feel a lack of control over their bodily identities within PE, which sharply juxtaposes the intense control over self-presentation afforded to them online. They may feel at risk of becoming discredited since 'destructive' information – potentially inconsistent with the carefully crafted idealised image of themselves presented online – can easily come to the fore (Goffman, 1963). For example, whilst a young person can post a flattering 'selfie' of themselves on social media, perhaps digitally altered and filtered, within PE their perceived flaws cannot be hidden, and they can therefore feel very exposed. The simplest way to avoid a loss of reputation is to withdraw physically and emotionally from threatening situations – with the PE environment having been identified as a 'risky' social space for young people, where there is increased potential for body-related embarrassment and shaming (Sykes & McPhail, 2008). Further, the potential for identities to be spoiled is even greater within a culture where offline social happenings can instantaneously be shared widely online. Young people may be acutely aware that their peers can share things that have happened within lessons on social media platforms and may be concerned about others having access to smartphones with cameras and video-recording capacities in PE (MacIsaac, 2016).

Social media – like wearable devices and self-tracking technologies – presents challenges within PE that must be carefully navigated. Teachers must be cognisant of the potential impacts of social media on young people's (developing) identities and should seek to support them by fostering critical engagement with/in such digital spaces.

Critical engagements with/in digital spaces

Many young people consider digital spaces to be 'go to' sources for learning about health and the body and, in some cases, claim to value knowledge constructed online more than that constructed within the school or PE environment (MacIsaac, 2016). There are many merits to learning about health and the body across a range of contexts and digital spaces do have potential to be both powerful and positive contributors to young people's learning in this regard. Therefore, teachers should ensure that they are not so distracted by the perceived risks of digital spaces that they become blind to the possible benefits. Instead, they should seek to support young people to engage judiciously with such spaces and with the wealth of (often unregulated) material that they may be exposed to online (Goodyear et al., 2019a). This could involve encouraging them to articulate why they engage with certain digital spaces and how this engagement might help them meet desired outcomes, supporting them to decipher how trustworthy any information they engage with is and helping them to understand the structure of the internet, the levels and types of surveillance they are under, and where their data goes and what it is used for (Chambers & Sandford, 2019).

Research consistently evidences that young people have much capacity to engage critically with/in digital spaces in relation to health-related learning but that it can be difficult to resist narrow and superficial engagements (Depper & Howe, 2017; Camacho-Miñano et al., 2019; Goodyear & Quennerstedt, 2020). PE has much potential to be an educative space in this regard, where a capacity for critical engagement with/in digital spaces can be nurtured. As Camacho-Miñano and colleagues (2019) suggest, having opportunities within the curriculum where young people are encouraged to critically reflect upon digital spaces and their engagements with/in these is important. Critical inquiry within PE around issues relating to health and the body has previously been facilitated through activities such as journaling, photography, storytelling and group discussion (Oliver & Lalik, 2004; Pringle, 2008; Azzarito, 2012). We propose that teachers could usefully adapt such ideas within the PE environment to engage young people in critical debates around the health- and body-related messages they interact with online.

Digital spaces such as social media platforms can open up powerful means of resistance to hierarchical power relations and dominant norms and can enable people to challenge taken-for-granted ways of thinking and being. They may be more egalitarian sites for knowledge production than, for example, the traditional media since users simultaneously construct knowledge as well as consume it and are therefore exposed to a range of viewpoints from diverse sources (Sirna, 2014). The interactive element of social media provides new dimensions to how bodily norms and values are internalised by young people. For example, when a young person sees someone post a selfie and, accordingly, an abundance of people 'liking' it and commenting with phrases such as 'wow, your abs are AMAZING!', they perceive that developing visible abdominals is desirable (Meier & Gray, 2014). They also begin to perceive that this is not just how celebrities or athletes look but how they, and people like them, could and should look. Supporting young people to recognise and appreciate their role in (re)producing some of the narratives around health and the body – that we are encouraging them to be critical of – may be one way forward and may help them to understand that they too can have a voice in changing these (Sirna, 2014).

Critical inquiry is much more effective when it is action-based and ongoing (Fitzpatrick & Russell, 2015). When there is a disproportionate focus on critiquing the taken-for-granted, it can actually close down the potential for young people to think positively and creatively about how things could be different (Gray, MacIsaac & Harvey, 2018). As Macdonald (2002) explains, a critical approach should foster a commitment in young people to 'do something' and help them to respond to their critical thoughts and feelings with critical action. Young people should therefore be supported to develop ideas of actions that they could take to respond to their critiques of dominant physical culture. As part of this, it may be useful to encourage young people to consider and reimagine how they use wearable devices or self-tracking technologies and/or how they engage with social media platforms. Although it can be difficult to refute or resist dominant ways of thinking and acting individually, collectively action can be more easily facilitated, for example, through whole-class activities (Sirna, 2014).

It is important to note that critical inquiry about physical experience should not become detached from physical experience itself. Young people can engage in critical inquiry across the school curriculum; however, it is through a more embodied approach to critical inquiry that PE – and other movement-based subjects such as dance and drama – can make special and unique contributions (Fitzpatrick & Russell, 2015). Being critically aware is not always enough to empower young people to perceive or use their bodies in alternative ways but combining critical inquiry with positive bodily experience can be transformative (Liimakka, 2011). As Camacho-Miñano and colleagues (2019) suggest, it is important to help young people develop self-compassion, awe and respect for their own bodies as they experience movement. PE can play an important role in this regard, by supporting young people to become more aware of their bodies intrinsically, particularly when many digital technologies encourage them to quantify the self and view their bodies in terms of data as opposed to listening to bodily feelings and sensations. Leder (1990) suggests that individuals often do not notice their bodies when they are functioning effectively. However, they pay attention to their bodies during times of 'dysfunction' – for example, when experiencing pain or when feeling embarrassed during social interaction. Therefore, individuals become more aware of the limits, constraints and deficiencies of their bodies as opposed to being aware of their inherent possibilities. When young people learn to move their bodies in new ways, for example, by learning new skills, PE teachers can encourage them to think about: what parts of their bodies helped them to do that skill; how the various parts of their bodies worked together; and how doing that skill made them *feel*. Teachers can therefore shift young people's attentions away from the surface of their bodies and instead encourage them to focus on their internal feelings (Satina & Hultgren, 2001). As a young person develops their kinaesthetic awareness, they may begin to perceive their body as being part of themselves and deserving of respect (Liimakka, 2011). Consequently, rather than relying upon external sources such as their peers, the media and the internet, young people can learn to value their bodies by referencing how they feel and by acknowledging the opportunities their bodies afford them.

Conclusion

Within this chapter, we have explored key digital spaces within which young people learn about health and the body – focusing in particular on wearable devices and self-tracking technologies and social media platforms. We have outlined the diverse ways in which young people engage with these digital spaces and highlighted the potential implications of such engagements. These spaces present both opportunities and challenges in relation to health-related learning, which young people have to navigate on a daily basis. Young people's engagements with/in digital spaces undoubtedly influence their health-related learning within PE and as such warrant consideration by PE teachers. We argue that the subject of PE is well placed to support young people's learning in this regard and that constructive links can be made between the learning that occurs within the subject and that which occurs more informally through digital spaces. Young people must be supported to engage judiciously with digital spaces and critical inquiry represents one such means of doing so. However, it is important to note that critical inquiry about physical experience must not become detached from physical experience itself. Indeed, it is on account of such embodied approaches to critical inquiry that PE is so well placed to support young people's critical engagements with/in digital spaces.

Reflection points

- How might young people's engagements with/in digital spaces influence their health-related learning?
- What opportunities might the PE curriculum present for making links between young people's health-related learning within the subject and that which occurs within digital spaces?
- How can teachers support young people's positive engagement with/in digital spaces?

References

Azzarito, L. (2012). Photography as a pedagogical tool for shedding light on 'bodies-at-risk' in physical culture. *Visual Studies*, 27 (3), 295–309.

Berne, S., Frisen, A. and Kling, J. (2014). Appearance-related cyberbullying: A qualitative investigation of characteristics, content, reasons and effects. *Body Image*, 11 (4), 527–533.

boyd, d. (2014). *It's complicated: The social lives of networked teens.* Yale: Yale University Press.

Cale, L., Harris, J. and Hooper, O. (2020). Debating health knowledge and health pedagogies in physical education. In S. Capel and R. Blair (Eds.), *Debates in physical education.* London: Routledge.

Camacho-Miñano, M. J., MacIsaac, S. and Rich, E. (2019). Postfeminist biopedagogies of Instagram: Young women learning about bodies, health and fitness. *Sport, Education and Society*, 24 (6), 651–664.

Chambers, F. and Sandford, R. (2019). Learning to be human in a digital world: A model of values fluency education for physical education. *Sport, Education and Society*, 24 (9), 925–938.

Depper, A. and Howe, P. D. (2017). Are we fit yet? English adolescent girls' experiences of health and fitness apps. *Health Sociology Review*, 26 (1), 98–112.

Fardouly, J., Diedrichs, P. C., Vartanian, L. R. and Halliwell, E. (2015). Social comparisons on social media: The impact of Facebook on young women's body concerns and mood. *Body Image*, 13 (1), 38–45.

Fitzpatrick, K. and Russell, D. (2015). On being critical in health and physical education. *Physical Education and Sport Pedagogy*, 20 (2), 159–173.

Goffman, E. (1963). *Stigma: Notes on the management of spoiled identity*. London: Penguin Books.

Goodyear, V. A. and Quennerstedt, M. (2020). #Gymlad – Young boys learning processes and health-related social media. *Qualitative Research in Sport, Exercise and Health*, 12 (1), 18–33.

Goodyear, V. A., Armour, K. M., and Wood, H. (2019a). Young people and their engagement with health-related social media: New perspectives. *Sport, Education and Society*, 24 (7), 673–688.

Goodyear, V. A., Kerner, C., and Quennerstedt, M. (2019b). Young people's uses of wearable healthy lifestyle technologies; surveillance, self-surveillance and resistance. *Sport, Education and Society*, 24 (3), 212–225.

Gray, S., MacIsaac, S. and Harvey, W. (2018). A comparative study of Canadian and Scottish students' perspectives on health, the body and the physical education curriculum: The challenge of 'doing' critical. *Curriculum Studies in Health and Physical Education*, 9 (1), 22–42.

Griffin, C. (2014). What time is now? Researching youth and culture beyond the 'Birmingham school'. In D. Buckingham, S. Bragg and M. J. Kehily (Eds.), *Youth cultures in the age of global media*. Basingstoke: Palgrave Macmillan.

Grogan, S. (2017). *Body image: Understanding body dissatisfaction in men, women and children*. London: Routledge.

Haycraft, E., Sherar, L. B., Griffiths, P., Biddle, S. J. H. and Pearson, N. (2020). Screen-time during the after-school period: A contextual perspective. *Preventative Medicine Reports*, 19 (September), 101116.

Kerner, C., and Goodyear, V. A. (2017). The motivational impact of wearable healthy lifestyle technologies: A self-determination perspective on Fitbits with adolescents. *American Journal of Health Education*, 48 (5), 287–297.

Leder, D. (1990). *The absent body*. Chicago, IL: University of Chicago Press.

Liimakka, S. (2011). I am my body: Objectification, empowering embodiment, and physical activity in women's studies students' accounts. *Sociology of Sport Journal*, 28 (4), 441–460.

Lupton, D. (2015). Data assemblages, sentient schools and digitised health and physical education (response to Gard). *Sport, Education and Society*, 20 (1), 122–132.

Mabe, A. G., Forney, K. J. and Keel, P. K. (2014). Do you 'like' my photo? Facebook use maintains eating disorder risk. *International Journal of Eating Disorders*, 47 (5), 516–523.

Macdonald, D. (2002). Critical pedagogy: What does it look like and why does it matter? In A. Laker (Ed.), *The sociology of sport and physical education*. London: Routledge.

MacIsaac, S. (2016). *'We are the selfie generation!': An ethnographic study of contemporary bodily culture within a Scottish school and physical education context*. Doctoral Thesis. University of Edinburgh.

MacIsaac, S., Kelly, J. and Gray, S. (2018). 'She has like 4000 followers!': The celebrification of self within school social networks. *Journal of Youth Studies*, 21 (6), 816–835.

Meier, E. P. and Gray, J. (2014). Facebook photo activity associated with body image disturbance in adolescent girls. *Cyberpsychology, Behavior, and Social Networking*, 17 (4), 199–206.

Oliver, K. L. and Lalik, R. (2004). Critical inquiry on the body in girls' physical education classes: A critical poststructural perspective. *Journal of Teaching in Physical Education*, 23 (2), 162–195.

Organisation for Economic Cooperation and Development [OECD]. (2017). *PISA 2015 results (volume III): Students' well-being.* Paris: OECD Publishing.

Perloff, R. M. (2014). Social media effects on young women's body image concerns: Theoretical perspectives and an agenda for research. *Sex Roles*, 71 (11), 363–377.

Pringle, R. (2008). 'No rugby-no fear': Collective stories, masculinities and transformative possibilities in schools. *Sport, Education and Society*, 13 (2), 215–237.

Radovic, A., McCarty, A. C., Katzman, K., and Richardson, P. L. (2018). Adolescents' perspectives on using technology for health: Qualitative study. *Pediatrics and Parenting*, 1 (1), e2.

Rich, E. (2018). Gender, health and physical activity in the digital age: Between postfeminism and pedagogical possibilities. *Sport, Education and Society*, 23 (8), 736–747.

Rich, E. and Miah, A. (2014). Understanding digital health as public pedagogy: A critical framework. *Societies*, 4, 296–315.

Rich, E. and Miah, A. (2017). Mobile, wearable and ingestible health technologies: Towards a critical research agenda. *Health Sociology Review*, 26 (1), 84–97.

Satina, B. and Hultgren, F. (2001). The absent body of girls made visible: Embodiment as the focus in education. *Studies in Philosophy and Education*, 20 (6), 521–534.

Sirna, K. (2014). Social media: Virtual environments for constructing knowledge on health and bodies? In K. Fitzpatrick and R. Tinning (Eds.), *Health education: Critical perspectives.* London: Routledge.

Smith, P. K., Mahdavi, J., Carvalho, M., Fisher, S., Russell, S. and Tippett, N. (2008). Cyberbullying: Its nature and impact in secondary school pupils. *Journal of Child Psychology and Psychiatry*, 49 (4), 376–385.

Sykes, H. and McPhail, D. (2008). Unbearable lessons: Contesting fat phobia in physical education. *Sociology of Sport Journal*, 25 (1), 66–96.

Tiggeman, M. and Slater, A. (2013). NetGirls: The Internet, Facebook, and body image concern in adolescent girls. *International Journal of Eating Disorders*, 46 (6), 630–633.

Williamson, B. (2015). Algorithmic skin: Health-tracking technologies, personal analytics and the biopedagogies of digitized health and physical education. *Sport, Education and Society*, 20 (1), 133–151.

10

BRITISH CHINESE YOUTHS' PHYSICAL ACTIVITY PRACTICES AND THE INFLUENCE OF HOME ENVIRONMENTS

Bonnie Pang

Introduction

This chapter examines the relationship between British Chinese youths' physical activity practices and their home environments. Bourdieu acknowledges that cultural reproduction is constructed and transformed through social space. Therefore, by situating British Chinese youths' physical activity within Bourdieu's field analysis, this chapter seeks to explore how these young people construct their 'tastes' (Bourdieu, 1984) in physical activity and how these are (re)produced and transformed through interactions within their home environments. Bourdieu's analysis of cultural production is situated within and constituted in relation to others. As such, the relational concept of cultural production is useful for exploring how British Chinese youths inhabit the myriad social spaces in their everyday lives which may or may not align with their cultural dispositions regarding physical activity at home (Bourdieu & Passeron, 1990).

British Chinese youths' lived experiences of physical activity

It is well documented that British Chinese communities live simultaneously in an in-between state of hypervisibility and invisibility in the UK (Pang, 2021). The positioning of British Chinese communities within the UK is the result of a range of historical, relational, situational, discursive and academic influences across time. Existing research has highlighted how 'Chinese' invisibility is entwined with broader contemporary health and physical activity concerns, for example, about Asians' lack of physical activity in academic discourses and everyday representations of 'Chineseness' in the UK and Australia (e.g. Pang, 2018; Pang & Hill, 2018). Indeed, British Chinese young people are often positioned as the 'model minority' who are academically successful but fragile, reserved and disinterested in sport (Archer & Francis, 2005).

Critical studies on young people's health report that minority ethnic youths are either underrepresented in public health messages or are represented as 'bodies at risk' because they do not conform to the Western parameters of physical activity and health regimes (Gard & Wright, 2001; Azzarito, 2009). Such notions are reflected in statistics that tend to report narrowly on minority ethnic groups living in Western contexts, often categorising them as 'inactive' and discussing them as a collective – with 'Chinese' typically being discussed alongside other minority ethnic groups in population surveys on physical activity. For example, the Active Lives Survey (Sport England, 2019) reported that Chinese (and 'other') who are aged 16 and above are more likely to be physically inactive compared to those from white British groups. Furthermore, females from Chinese and other and black backgrounds are reported to be less likely to participate in sport compared with those from white British backgrounds (Sport England, 2017).

Studies such as that by Wang, Blake and Chattopadhyay (2019) are equally problematic in that they frame 'ethnic Chinese' globally as a monolithic category and compare their physical activity levels to global recommendations by the World Health Organisation. This 'groupism' effect (Brubaker, 2003) – that is, defining ethnic groups by discrete and sharply differentiated boundaries – continues to reify and racialise physical activity practices. Taken together, pervasive healthism discourses (Crawford, 1980) and those related to groupism within and beyond the interrelated and everchanging fields mean that some young people and their experiences can be 'othered' or silenced when manifest in physical activity and education settings. As such, there is a need to capture the gamut of experiences, taking into account the ambivalences, agencies, generational differences and broader socio-cultural factors that construct individuals' practices as they are assembled within specific geographic and local contexts.

As China becomes a world superpower, at least partly due to its global economic influence, Chinese diasporic[1] individuals/communities are being (re)positioned in different fields. In this sense, the Chinese diaspora, which is based on economic and political power, is attributed to diasporic capitalism that attends to the social spaces of migrations and citizenship (Mu & Pang, 2019). When macro-level forces are translated into micro-level practices, 'Chineseness' has symbolic capital, as it encompasses a sense of positive identification, belongingness and solidarity among people of a common cultural heritage and ancestral root (Ang, 2003). This study extends the Chinese diasporic understanding of youth physical cultures by examining the microcosms of British Chinese youths' lived experiences and how their habitus and cultural investments at home contribute to their physical activity practices.

British Chinese youths' physical activity practices and Bourdieu's field analysis

This chapter positions British Chinese youths' homes as a 'field' and aims to provide an in-depth analysis of their micro-level interactions with their parents in constructing their physical activity practices. As Bourdieu and Wacquant (1992, p. 97) noted:

A field may be defined as a network, or a configuration, of objective relations between positions. These positions are objectively defined, in their existence and in the determinations they impose upon their occupants, agents, or institutions, by their present and potential situations *(situs)* in the structure of the distribution of species of power (or capital) whose possession commands access to the specific profits that are at stake in the field, as well as their objective relation to other positions (domination, subordination, homology, etc.)

Family upbringing can enculturate Chinese children into a system of embodied dispositions based on capital investments. Capital does not exist and cannot function except in relation to a field (Bourdieu & Wacquant, 1992). In other words, capital only has meaning and value within a specific field. Bourdieu (1986) suggested that there are four main types of capital: social, economic, symbolic and cultural. Social capital refers to networks and relationships generated through social processes (such as social connections and social groups), while economic capital refers to income, assets and other material possessions. Symbolic capital relates to legitimation and power (such as recognition and fame) while cultural capital takes three different forms: the embodied state (such as modes of thinking and bodily appearance); the objectified state (such as possession of sport equipment); and the institutionalised state (such as attainment of qualifications) (Bourdieu, 1986). Drawing on Bourdieu's corporeal sociology, Shilling (2004) further suggested the notion of physical capital, which is included in the embodied state of cultural capital. Physical capital refers to the everyday use of the body including various modes of movement, posture and appearance (Light & Quay, 2003) and the 'value placed upon the size, shape and appearance of the flesh' (Shilling, 2004, p. 474).

In seeking to understand social reality, Bourdieu and Wacquant (1992) highlighted the 'three necessary and internally connected moments' of field analysis (p. 104). The first moment analyses the position of the field with regard to power relations, the second identifies the unequal distribution and the (mis)recognition of capital among agents in the field and the third examines the habitus within the field under consideration (Bourdieu & Wacquant, 1992). Bourdieu (1977, p. 72) defines habitus as:

> Systems of durable, transposable dispositions, structured structures predisposed to function as structuring structures, that is, as principles of the generation and structuring of practices and representations which can be objectively regulated and regular without in any way being the product of obedience to rules, objectively adapted to their goals without presupposing a conscious aiming at ends or an express mastery of the operations necessary in order to attain them and, being all this, collectively orchestrated without being the product of the orchestrating action of a conductor.

For Chinese diaspora youth, their body, gender, socio-economic status and culture, among many other habitual states, are subjective structures in constant response to the objective structures of the field, such as their home environments. Pang, Macdonald and Hay (2015) provide evidence to this effect in their examination of the influence of the home environment on Australian Chinese youths' physical activity practices. They found that traditional Chinese family power relations limited the choices these young people had regarding physical activity which was complicated by the cultural and social fluidity of their lived experiences. The young people's pursuit of cultural capital within their lifestyle choices was also partly related to their family values which included notions of excelling, hyper-investment in academic success and, especially for the girls, skin colour and safety.

Rethinking health experiences and active lifestyles for (British) Chinese youth

The Rethinking Health Experiences and Active Lifestyles – Chinese Students (REHEAL-C) project was an ethnographic study undertaken during 2019–2020 in the UK. The project examined the physical activity and health-related experiences of 12 British Chinese youths (11–15-year-olds) at two Chinese supplementary schools[2] in Leeds and Manchester. The following discussion draws on data from individual and focus group interviews conducted with five of the young people. The young people's characteristics varied in terms of their home locations (Halifax, Leeds, Manchester), their birthplace (England, Mainland China), language-use patterns at home (English only to a mixture of English, Malaysian, Mandarin, Cantonese), parents' birthplace (Malaysia, Hong Kong Special Administrative Region [HKSAR], Mainland China) and day school attendance (state, academy, grammar, independent, faith). The young people were all born in England – with both parents having a Chinese ancestral background – apart from Wendy, who was born in Mainland China and moved to England at the age of five (and whose father is white British), and Keith, who was also born in Mainland China and moved to England when he was 1-year-old. Data analysis employed Bourdieu's concepts to exemplify the various forms of capital possessed by the participants and to explore how these were constructed through their physical activity experiences at home. It further sought to identify the discourses present within their talk, thus drawing attention to specific words and phrases that informed participants' thoughts about their habitus and diverse physical activity practices.

Juxtaposing the voices of British Chinese youths and their mothers

Within this section, I seek to juxtapose the voices of the five young people and their mothers in their talk about physical activity to highlight how their experiences are grounded in their particular home environments and influenced by factors such as gender and social class. Bourdieu's conceptual tools – field, capital and habitus – are utilised to consider the implications for the reimagining of this social space, which constructed these young people's orientations towards themselves and their physical activity practices.

What did the young person say?	What did their mother say?
Eleven-year-old Wendy was born in Mainland China to a Chinese mother and a white British father before she moved to England at the age of five. Wendy engages in a range of activities within and beyond school including tap dance, chamber choir, drama, ukulele, violin, oboe and mathematical Olympiads. Wendy has a younger brother and she enjoys playing games with him.	Wendy's mother Dianna teaches at a Chinese school on weekends and spends much time taking care of the children as a housewife. She encourages her children to participate in various activities for self-cultivation (Xiu-yang, 修養)[3] alongside 'pushing' them to study for a brighter future.
Twelve-year-old Karen was born in England but she then moved to another county because her parents were locum doctors seeking permanent work while she was growing up. She learned to swim in early childhood and continues to swim on a weekly basis. At home, Karen practices several hobbies such as guitar, boxing, baking and cooking. She thinks that her mother is overprotective as she does not allow her to walk the dogs alone and feels she is overconcerned about her sleeping over at friends and being with other families. Karen has an older brother.	Karen's mother Linda financially supports her sport and leisure activities and thinks that swimming is an important life-saving skill. However, Linda admits that she never attends Karen's sport activities except when collecting her from them, though the family do attend Karen's yearly sports day to support her. Linda encourages Karen to participate in sport and physical activity because she regrets not having these opportunities when she was growing up.
Eleven-year-old Ann was born in England to Chinese parents who own a Chinese takeaway. Ann's parents work long hours, and the family live above the takeaway that they own. Ann's weekly schedule is full of activities including Chinese school, Latin dance, Chinese dance, violin, piano and English tutoring. Ann has an older brother and a younger sister.	Ann's mother Sandy grew up in a lower class family in Hong Kong and therefore did not have the opportunity to take up any structured leisure or cultural activities associated with self-improvement. Sandy is conscious of the highly structured and strategic investment of her time and money in her three children's activities as she pushes them to participate in a range of sporting and musical activities, which she said is a way to fulfil her childhood dreams.
Twelve-year-old James was born in England. James is an only child, and his father works as a manager in a renowned Chinese restaurant in the city centre. He describes his mother as a housewife. James spends a lot of time at home playing the piano, reading and watching anime and K-pop on YouTube. His mother sometimes encourages him to go to the leisure centre or shopping malls to get out of the house. He believes he is 'balanced in the entertainment and learning spectrum' within his life.	James's mother Beth spends much time communicating with her son and is aware of his strengths and interests. Beth is sometimes concerned about James's physical growth and encourages him to play more basketball, as he is one of the shortest in his class. Beth is pleased that James was involved in the interviews in this project, as this experience has enabled him to feel more confident.

(Continued)

What did the young person say?	What did their mother say?
Twelve-year-old Keith was born in Mainland China and moved to England at the age of one. His parents manage a takeaway, and his Dad spends many hours working there. He admits that he spends most of his time on his mobile phone playing random games. Keith hopes to join a football club and become a professional footballer, but his mother seems to be discouraging this aspiration. Keith has two younger sisters.	Keith's mother Gloria thinks that children in England have too much freedom with too little responsibility and homework. Her perception is that English parents are not strict enough when compared to Chinese parents. Gloria expects Keith to be independent, and he travels by himself to extracurricular activities. Gloria admitted she has higher expectations of Keith than her two younger daughters, as he should be the role model for his two sisters and will have to be the 'breadwinner' for his own family in the future.

The contrasting perspectives of these British Chinese youths and their mothers with regard to physical activity participation are particularly interesting. The structure of each young person's family was different, from where they lived, to their parents' occupations and even whether they had siblings (or not) – with these varying factors impacting on their habitus formation. As their parents communicated their hopes and expectations to them, the young people learned to identify, negotiate and/or resist the familial practices. These narratives demonstrated that the more legitimate these families made certain (physical) activities, the greater the necessity for young people to invest their capital to become more competent in them – with the home essentially becoming a 'pedagogised' space.

Home as a 'pedagogised' space

The home space provided a pedagogical structure for young people to develop and to adopt dispositions related to physicality and physical activity. The home seemed to be a contested space where these young people would 'test the waters' with their parents, occupying their own space to demonstrate their agency and establish personal meanings in relation to lifestyle and physical activity. However, at times, traditional Chinese values were reinforced through hierarchical relationships and respect for one's parents (as 'superiors'). For example, Karen liked her home and being in her bedroom, but she found her parents intrusive with regard to her private space:

> My two favourite rooms are the entrance hall and my bedroom because, of course, my bedroom is my own space, but then my parents are just like, 'We own the whole house, so we can just barge in whenever we want'.

Of the five young people, Karen seemed to have the most space at home and to be the most active, as she engaged in stretching, yoga, boxing, trampolining, riding on her exercise bike and playing with her dogs. Ann similarly disliked her father's paternalistic parenting style and his way of talking at her. She could only seek refuge by staying in her room upstairs above their Chinese takeaway. Ann felt shame when her father focused on school performance and neglected her other needs:

> Honestly, my dad, anytime we're doing something other than study, he says, 'You need to study', and then he gives us a lecture, and I'm like, 'Get out', and I have to end up pushing him out of my room. 'Daniel in your class, he's so smart. You should be like him', and I'm like, 'Stop comparing me to everyone'.

Although James's father worked as a manager at a renowned Chinese restaurant and spent little time at home with him, he still found time to talk to his mother and father about football, and they sometimes watched it together as a family. Different from his English peers, James sometimes felt quite lonely during holidays, as the Chinese restaurant that his father worked in was even busier during these times. That said, James spent most of his time studying or playing video games with friends online and catching up with his older brother, who had moved out of the family home. For Ann, she mostly had family time on Mondays, as this was the only day her parents were able to take time off from working at the Chinese takeaway. They would usually chat together rather than going out shopping and spending extra money which they could not afford. Despite the planned family time on Mondays, Ann's parents would find her 'disappearing', as she liked to spend time on her own at home playing on her mobile phone and doing homework upstairs.

The configuration of the home space evidently impacted on how these five young people engaged in different physical activities and their lifestyles, with those growing up in a takeaway, such as Ann, often spending time alone occupying themselves. As these students embodied the 'pedagogised' family structure (Dagkas & Quarmby, 2012) through everyday communication and practices, they developed dispositions related to whether they could make themselves seen and heard within the confined spaces at home.

Legitimised capital and habitus

The young people's relative positions in their social spaces – in relation to their legitimised capital – facilitate a deeper understanding of the types of physical activity they could take up. With consideration of cultural capital, not all forms are equal, and not all parents valued their child's capital similarly. Thus, certain young people were more privileged than others with regard to the accumulation of physical capital in sport and physical activity. Wendy, Karen, Ann and James seemed better equipped to navigate the structures that facilitated engagement in sport and physical activity because they could better understand the 'rules of the game' (i.e. where they could access sport clubs and classes). Contrastingly, Keith lacked understanding with regard to how he might join a football club and thereby was unable to accumulate the social and cultural capital required for his sporting development. Concurrently, mothers had different perceptions of the benefits that investment in sport and physical activity might bring to their children based on their social class. This is exemplified by Dianna, who wanted her child (Wendy) to engage in a range of activities for self-cultivation and also as a means of securing a brighter future that could bring social mobility.

What is striking is that Ann's mother (Sandy) and Karen's mother (Linda) both emphasised their regrets regarding the lack of opportunities in their respective childhoods to take part in sporting activities and/or learn music, which influenced their compelling need to 'push' their children to take up the opportunities they constructed. Linda, now of a higher social class, believed her childhood regret was one of the reasons she promoted Karen's participation in sport and physical activity especially with recognising the importance of swimming as a life-saving skill. Linda believed that Karen had a lot of talent in swimming, but because Linda worked full time, she could not afford to be a 'Tiger Mum'[4] and push Karen further in committing to swimming training and competitions. Linda implied that perhaps Karen's 'talent' was also the product of an investment of time and cultural capital, suggesting their privileged middle-class family habitus had promoted the 'renaissance child' (Vincent & Ball, 2007, p. 1071). Karen's habitus highlighted her middle-class status – from her having been cared for by diverse au pairs throughout her childhood, to attending independent schools – she had been able to access a wide cultural repertoire. This repertoire, in turn, provided further possibilities for developing different physical activity practices constructed between Chinese and British cultures – such as boxing, an activity that she routinely participated in.

On the contrary, Ann's physical activities were shaped by her mother's wishes for her to excel in them, by gaining prizes and accruing the symbolic capital required to continue with the activity, as the cost of failure might bring shame not only to Ann but also to her family. This resonated with Pang et al.'s (2015) study of Australian Chinese youths and their families' hyper-investment in both music and academic studies in the pursuit of excellence. Although sharing similar experiences of regret, Sandy differed from Linda when it came to providing physical activity opportunities for her children. Coming from a lower social class, she often struggled to fulfil all three of her children's wishes to participate in all of the sports and physical activities available to them through school and the community. Sandy was also conscious that her investment in activities for her children should be strategic, ensuring that it would yield the most profit in the future (e.g. getting a well-paid job).

Gloria, who was also from a lower social class, paid the least attention to her child's needs in sport and placed considerably more emphasis on Keith's academic studies. She had a much higher expectation of him than his sisters because, as a boy, he would have to lead a family in the future. Gloria did not seem to perceive her daughters as capital-accumulating subjects. Rather, she perceived women as capital-bearing objects whose value accrued depending on the dominant group to which they belonged, such as their husband and their family (Skeggs, 2004). This also resonated with a traditional 'Chineseness' that favours a particular set of discourses based on gender, social class and hierarchical practices which have constructed a lifestyle for Keith but which did not match the ever-changing structures in his life. The expectations that the mothers projected onto their children exemplified Bourdieu's (1986) discussion of how agents strive for a legitimate form of capital, in this case prowess in swimming, cultural activities such as dance and music and academic studies – as well as hetero-masculinity in boys – which could produce more 'profit' to enable these children to occupy better social positions.

It seemed that parents' inability to mourn their own losses in childhood contributed to the reproduction of an 'ideal lifestyle' for their children, which sometimes disregarded their children's individual dispositions and agency. Despite the different social classes among these five youths, their mothers, more so than their fathers, all seemed to have a strong affective investment (Reay, 2000, 2004) in their children. This enabled them to develop close bonds – or emotional capital (Zembylas, 2007) – within their families, which seemed to be the foundation that facilitated the young people's physical activity practices throughout the week.

The data demonstrated a gendered disposition composed of the valued masculine habitus that enabled the two boys (James and Keith) to be more active outdoors without close parental supervision. Beth's hope that James could grow taller through basketball conveys the perceived importance of the accumulation of the masculine form of physical capital, which appeared to be referenced against the ideological norms of hegemonic masculinity which values a mesomorphic physique (Flintoff & Scraton, 2001; Brown, 2010). While it is not necessarily problematic for males to possess such physiques, they remain physically and symbolically associated with the ideology of hegemonic masculinity, contributing to judgements on the legitimate son and their agency in physical activity. These results are similar to those of the study conducted by Pang et al. (2015) in Australia, which found that compared with girls, Chinese boys were given more freedom and encouragement by their parents to spend time outdoors, echoing wider research on the interrelationships between gender, identity, space and place with regard to young people and physical activity (Lee & Abbott, 2009; Stride, 2016).

Karen often said 'my mum always makes me do this' in the interviews. Sometimes she was aware of her habitus, and she engaged in 'habitus realisation' (Mu, Luke & Dooley, 2018) whereby she continued to develop new facets of herself by acknowledging her hidden dispositions. In this process, instead of challenging the doxa (i.e. the dominant familial structure) or being unconscious or leaving the practice of the home field, she was triggered by a new and ongoing environment which promoted reflexivity. For example, after being inspired by a movie about a woman boxer, she took up boxing at home. This inward turn helped her to develop new dispositions and to occupy a new social position in the field. Arguably, this realisation is a form of resistance and can be read as engaging in non-traditional 'Chineseness' that moved beyond filial piety[5]. However, as Bourdieu and Wacquant (1992, p. 113) note, '[P]ractices often hailed as "resistant" may have an impact only on the relatively "superficial effective" relations of a field rather than its deeper structural relations'. Therefore, rather than being completely freed from the regime of her 'mother's choice', Karen was reimagining traditional habitus and practices in

new ways alongside reproducing them to meet the demands at home. This ongoing ambivalent relationship shaped Karen's lived experiences as she navigated her
opportunities and responsibilities arising within and beyond the home.

Conclusion

This chapter has provided a diverse account of British Chinese youths' physical
activity practices and the influence of the home environment. The discussion
expands research into youths' physical activity and that related to ethnicity and
'Chineseness' by bringing issues of social class and gender to the fore. Bourdieu's
field analysis has been critical in shaping such knowledge and enables an interpretation of the specific social and cultural practices that produce certain 'tastes'
in physical activity. The young people's narratives demonstrate some 'room' at
home for 'habitus in the making' with some of them taking up new sports mobi-
lised by the broader cultural influences in their environments. Yet, there are
youths such as Keith and Ann, whose opportunities are hindered by the structural conditions of the family where there is more than one child and where
scarce resources and capital have to be shared. A key implication resulting from
this research is that, in seeking to promote British Chinese youths' physical activity practices, their ethnicity, gender, social class, intergenerational differences
and the possible lack of fathers' involvement ought not to be overlooked as critical factors influencing their capacity to contest, obfuscate and extend traditional
cultural norms through physical activity at home.

Reflection points

- How might the home environment influence young people's engagements
  in physical activity?
- What cultural factors might influence young people's engagement in physical activity?
- How might a young person's involvement in physical activity be mediated
  by factors such as gender or social class?

Notes

1 The term 'diaspora' originally referred to the exile of Jews from their historical homeland, Israel, and their involuntary mass dispersion to other parts of the world (Safran,
  1991). It was then extended to describe categories of people living outside their
  homeland, be they temporary sojourners, transnational migrants, first-generation
  emigrants, or their descendants (Gamlen, 2008). The diasporic Chinese community
  have long been known for their disposition of migration and are becoming increasingly visible in multicultural societies (Mu & Pang, 2019).
2 Chinese supplementary schools are attended by students with Chinese ethnic backgrounds at weekends. The students have the opportunity to learn about Chinese language and take part in Chinese cultural activity classes such as Chinese dance, drama
  and singing.
3 Xiu-yang 修養 (or self-cultivation practices) can be understood as a cultural tradition
  of Chinese philosophies. It has implications of pursuing the relational self, the authentic self and the nonself through nurturing one's character (Hwang & Chang, 2009).

4 The evocation of the 'Tiger Mum' (Chua, 2011) within the popular international media has generated comment on the difference between the Chinese way and the Western way of bringing up children. Chinese families are often portrayed as driven by a desire to prosper in a competitive world and have high expectations for their children to succeed in school. The 'Tiger Mum' represents disciplined, performance-oriented parenting that produces high-achieving children (Watkins, Ho & Butler, 2017).

5 Filial piety denotes respect for one's elders. The notion of filial piety has been regarded as an important value in Chinese culture influencing the way in which the elderly are treated in the family as well as in wider society (Slote, 1998).

References

Ang, I. (2003). Together-in-difference: Beyond diaspora, into hybridity. *Asian Studies Review, 27*(2), 141–154.

Archer, L., and Francis, B. (2005). 'They never go off the rails like other ethnic groups': Teachers' constructions of British Chinese pupils' gender identities and approaches to learning. *British Journal of Sociology of Education, 26*(2), 165–182.

Azzarito, L. (2009). The rise of corporate curriculum: Fatness, fitness, and whiteness. In J. Wright & V. Harwood (Eds.), *Biopolitics and the "obesity epidemic": Governing bodies* (pp. 183–196). London: Routledge.

Bourdieu, P. (1977). *Outline of a theory of practice.* Cambridge: Cambridge University Press.

Bourdieu, P. (1984). *Distinction: A social critique of the judgement of taste.* Translated by Nice, R. Cambridge: Harvard University Press.

Bourdieu, P. (1986). The forms of capital. In J. G. Richardson (Ed.), *Handbook of theory and research for the sociology of education* (pp. 241–258). New York, NY: Greenwood Press.

Bourdieu, P., and Passeron, J. C. (1990). *Reproduction in education, society and culture.* London: Sage.

Bourdieu, P., and Wacquant, L. J. (1992). *An invitation to reflexive sociology.* Oxford: University of Chicago Press.

Brown, S. (2010). What Makes Men Talk About Health. *Journal of Gender Studies, 10*(2), 187–195.

Brubaker, R. (2003). Neither individualism nor 'groupism' a reply to Craig Calhoun. *Ethnicities, 3*(4), 553–557.

Chua, A. (2011). *The battle hymn of the tiger mum.* London: Penguin Group.

Crawford, R. (1980). Healthism and the medicalization of everyday life. *International Journal of Health Services, 10*, 365–388.

Dagkas, S., and Quarmby, T. (2012). Children's embodiment of health and physical capital: The role of the "pedagogised" family. *Sociology of Sport Journal, 29*(2), 210–226.

Dika, S., and Singh, K. (2002). Applications of social capital in educational literature: A critical synthesis. *Review of Educational Research, 72*(1), 31–60.

Flintoff, A., and Scraton, S. (2001). Stepping into active leisure? Young women's perceptions of active lifestyles and their experiences of school physical education. *Sport, Education and Society, 6*(1), 5–21.

Gamlen, A. (2008). Why engage diasporas? Oxford: Centre on Migration, Policy and Society.

Gard, M., and Wright, J. (2001). Managing uncertainty: Obesity discourses and physical education in a risk society. *Studies in Philosophy and Education, 20*, 535–549.

Hwang, K. K., and Chang, J. (2009). Self-cultivation: Culturally sensitive psychotherapies in Confucian societies. *The Counselling Psychologist, 37*(7), 1010–1032.

Lee, J., and Abbott, R. (2009). Physical activity and rural young people's sense of place. *Children's Geographies, 7*(2), 191–208.

Light, R., and Quay, J. (2003). Identity, physical capital and young men's experiences of soccer in school and in community-based clubs, Melbourne Studies in Education. *Melbourne Studies in Education, 44*(2), 89–106.

Mu, G. M., and Pang, B. (2019). *Interpreting the Chinese diaspora: Identity, socialisation, and resilience according to Pierre Bourdieu.* London and New York: Routledge.

Mu, G. M., Luke, A., and Dooley, K. (2018). Re: Appropriating Bourdieu for a sociology of Chinese education. *Bourdieu and Chinese Education: Inequality, Competition, and Change.* London: Routledge.

Pang, B. (2018). Conducting research with young Chinese-Australian students in health and physical education and physical activity: Epistemology, positionality and methodologies. *Sport, Education and Society, 23*(6), 607–618.

Pang, B. (2021). Problematising the (in)visibility of racialized and gendered British Chineseness in youth health and physical cultures. *Sport, Education and Society, 26*(3), 228–238.

Pang, B., and Hill, J. (2018). Representations of Chinese gendered and racialised bodies in contemporary media sites. *Sport, Education and Society, 23*(8), 773–785.

Pang, B., Macdonald, D., and Hay, P. (2015). 'Do I have a choice?' The influences of family values and investments on Chinese migrant young people's lifestyles and physical activity participation in Australia. *Sport, Education and Society, 20*(8), 1048–1064.

Reay, D. (2000). A useful extension of Bourdieu's conceptual framework?: Emotional capital as a way of understanding mothers' involvement in their children's education?. *The Sociological Review, 48*(4), 568–585.

Reay, D. (2004). Gendering Bourdieu's concepts of capitals? Emotional capital, women and social class. *The Sociological Review, 52*(Suppl. 2), 57–74.

Safran, W. (1991). Diasporas in modern societies: Myths of homeland and return. *Diaspora: A Journal of Transnational Studies, 1*(1), 83–99.

Shilling, C. (2004). Physical capital and situated action: A new direction for corporeal sociology. *British Journal of Sociology of Education, 25*(4), 473–487.

Skeggs, B. (2004). Context and background: Pierre Bourdieu's analysis of class, gender and sexuality. In L. Adkins and B. Skeggs (Eds.), *Feminism after Bourdieu* (pp. 19–34). Oxford: Blackwell.

Slote, W. H. (1998). Psychocultural dynamics within the Confucian family. In W. H. Slote and G. A. DeVos (Eds.), *Confucianism and the family* (pp. 163–186). Albany, NY: State University of New York Press.

Sport England. (2017). *Active lives survey 2015–2016.* London: Sport England.

Sport England. (2019). *Active lives children and young people survey—Attitudes towards sport and physical activity 2017–2018.* London: Sport England.

Stride, A. (2016). Centralising space: The physical education and physical activity experiences of South Asian, Muslim girls. *Sport, Education and Society, 21*(5), 677–697.

Vincent, C., and Ball, S. J. (2007). 'Making up' the middle-class child: Families, activities and class dispositions. *Sociology, 41*(6), 1061–1077.

Wang, H., Blake, H., and Chattopadhyay, K. (2019). Barriers and facilitators to physical activity among ethnic Chinese children: A systematic review protocol. *JBI Database of Systematic Reviews and Implementation Reports, 17*(7), 1290–1296.

Watkins, M., Ho, C., and Butler, R. (2017). Asian migration and education cultures in the Anglo-sphere. *Journal of Ethnic and Migration Studies, 43*(14), 2283–2299.

Zembylas, M. (2007). Emotional ecology: The intersection of emotional knowledge and pedagogical content knowledge in teaching. *Teaching and Teacher Education, 23*(4), 355–367.

SECTION IV

Engaging with progressive pedagogies in health and physical education

INTRODUCTION

Rachel Sandford

Though examining different concepts and exploring various contexts, the four chapters included within this section all centre on the notion of developing progressive pedagogies in the areas of physical education (PE), physical activity and health. They each outline how educational systems, processes and practices are shaped by broader social and cultural factors, which become embedded over time in ways that reflect wider power relations and, ultimately, serve to privilege some and marginalise others. Moreover, they consider how the reproduction of dominant ideas (and ideals) over time can perpetuate inequalities in pedagogical practices and call on practitioners to both recognise and reflect on their own role within this process; encouraging them to consider if and how they might shape more equitable practice. As such, in their own way, each chapter articulates a social justice agenda and recognises the need for critical pedagogies that can challenge inequalities within practice.

In Chapter 11, Williams, Wiltshire and Gibson explore the relationship between health inequalities and PE in the UK through an equity lens. Recognising that physical activity is often considered a 'best buy' in public health discussions and that PE is an 'intuitively appealing' educational context in which interventions can be implemented, the authors consider key issues involved in shaping equitable and inclusive practice. Drawing on a case study of the National Child Measurement Programme (NCMP), they remind us that despite there being 'robust' evidence for social determinants of health, there is still a notable focus on lifestyle factors that seek to initiate individual behaviour change. Williams and colleagues argue that this reflects the process of 'lifestyle drift' (Hunter, Popay, Tannahill & Whitehead, 2010) that is evident in many government policies, which sees broad intentions of addressing wider social processes shift to embrace the rhetoric of individual choice and personal responsibility. However, in taking a critical approach to examining these issues within the chapter, the authors contest whether achieving a healthy lifestyle is indeed as 'logical, simple, and achievable' as political rhetoric would suggest. Moreover, they call on practitioners to ensure that their own practice does not reproduce such views.

Williams and colleagues explore both the causes and 'the causes of the causes' of poor health, noting that while people across all levels of society are affected by various health issues, those lower down the socio-economic spectrum are disproportionately disadvantaged – as the authors put it, 'less wealth translates into poorer health' (p. 171). Importantly, the authors also acknowledge the significance of considering the sustained nature of disadvantage, noting that 'the effects of social deprivation are far more likely to disadvantage people over time' (p. 172). While lifestyle interventions might therefore have some positive outcomes – and this is an important point to note – it is also possible that they might contribute to the perpetuation of inequalities. In looking to address this, Williams and colleagues make the case for social factors to be taken into account when designing interventions and call for consideration to be given as to whether targeted interventions might result in more equitable outcomes than universal approaches. By doing so, they argue that PE can become a context which facilitates more equitable experiences and, as they note, practitioners have a central role in this process.

In Chapter 12, Luguetti and McDonald continue the focus on practitioners and discuss the transformative potential of a pedagogy of love, suggesting that this offers a valuable means of rethinking pedagogical practices in the area of health and PE (HPE). Drawing on the work of Freire (1987), Noddings (1984) and hooks (2001), among others, the authors look to provide a rationale for a pedagogy of love and consider how it may best be enacted in practice, sharing learning from a field example in Brazil. In the early sections of the chapter, Luguetti and McDonald highlight how student teachers within the HPE field often articulate more humanistic ideas about equality that are underpinned by 'a common-sense perspective of individual ethics' (p. 184). Such views of equality, they argue, are problematic, as they fail to recognise subtle oppressions within the field – such as those related to racism, sexism or ableism – and suggest a rather narrow understanding of inequities. As such, the authors propose that there is a need for practitioners to engage in reflection to enable them to consider if/how they might work more effectively within a social justice framework. A pedagogy of love, it is suggested, can support this transformative agenda.

Luguetti and McDonald argue that a pedagogy of love starts with the process of reflection. It involves creating a space in which practitioners can begin to understand inclusive and exclusive experiences in their own lives and to consider the relevance of these experiences for understanding the lives of others. As part of this process, practitioners must be willing to step out of their comfort zone, position themselves as continuous learners and challenge their own perceptions and ideas. The authors argue that this reflective process has transformative potential which can support more honest, open and respectful relationships with students. Central to such an approach is the notion of student voice, and there is much focus on the need for practitioners to create democratic spaces in which they can engage in conversations with their students. Moreover, there is a recognition that these conversations should be transformative for both practitioner and student, empowering students to share their experiences and shape, collectively, more meaningful and authentic practices. Through supporting creativity and imagination, it is argued, a pedagogy of love can facilitate the identification of alternative possibilities and foster a social justice agenda within HPE contexts.

In Chapter 13, Wrench and Garrett similarly emphasise the need for collaborative conversations between practitioners and students. They argue that such collaboration can support culturally responsive pedagogy (CRP) and facilitate more equitable experiences for students within HPE, particularly for those who might be considered marginalised. Wrench and Garrett note that as classrooms become increasingly diverse, it is often particular ethnic minority students who disproportionately experience educational disadvantage. Moreover, they highlight that practitioners often report a lack confidence in working with marginalised students and that concerns have been raised about the preparedness of the teaching workforce to meet the needs of diverse students. Drawing on their work with pre-service teachers undertaking a final year HPE course within a Bachelor of Education degree programme in Australia, Wrench and Garrett reflect on such issues and explore the implications for practice with particular reference to working with Indigenous youth.

The authors note that CRP is framed by socio-cultural understandings of learning and underpinned by the notion that all curricula and pedagogies should be culturally based. CRP is therefore not a 'one-size-fits-all' approach but, rather, needs to be tailored to reflect the context and culture of the individuals within it to enhance both engagement and inclusion. A key point to note is the recognition of students (and more broadly their families/communities) as a valuable resource within this process, facilitating the creation of learning experiences that are culturally mediated (e.g. through the incorporation of culturally relevant games, language or values). The authors emphasise the strengths-based nature of this approach, but caution that while support for it is strong in theory, the practical enactment of CRP requires further attention. Within the chapter, Wrench and Garrett outline the significance of relational processes and identify three layers of relatedness that they argue represent a useful framework for shaping practice: ways of knowing, ways of being and ways of doing (after Martin & Mirraboopa, 2003). They argue that the implementation of these processes can enhance the confidence and capacity of pre-service teachers to engage with and enact CRP and also represent a means of moving past tokenistic efforts at incorporating cultural content into the curriculum.

Finally, in Chapter 14, Sperka, Stirrup and Hooper consider the place of outsourcing within (H)PE. Outsourcing has been of much interest in (H)PE in recent years, with some concerns expressed about its increasing prevalence – and pervasiveness – within the subject. Significantly, Sperka and colleagues emphasise that outsourcing is not inherently 'bad' but can perhaps result in inequitable experiences as a result of its application in practice. Moreover, they assert the need to focus on the context in which outsourcing is implemented, as there are often differences in the ways that outsourcing is enacted between countries, which typically reflect broader political agendas. Accordingly, drawing on recent work in this area, and examples of outsourcing implementation within the Australian and English contexts, the authors seek to offer research-informed proposals for 'best practice'.

Sperka and colleagues highlight a number of issues that are significant in shaping outsourcing practice. Within the Australian context, for example, it is noted that the recent standardisation of the curriculum has created a context in which tailored approaches have given way to more generalised delivery – something perceived to facilitate more extensive use of outsourcing. Meanwhile, in the English context, the relevance of and reliance on outsourcing is perceived to be linked to the short-term nature of funding initiatives (e.g. Physical Education, School Sport and Club Links [PESSCL], Physical Education and School Sport for Young People [PESSYP]) and the lack of specialist physical educators within primary settings. Acknowledging that outsourcing is 'here to stay', however, the authors seek to identify and consider important questions for the field, namely, who should identify outsourcing needs, how are roles/responsibilities distributed and what monitoring and evaluation is required? In addressing these questions, the authors highlight, among other things, the importance of recognising teachers' pedagogical knowledge/expertise, the relevance of listening and responding to student voice and the need for collaborative conversations between key stakeholders. They also emphasise the need to move away from deficit approaches to outsourcing and to consider the opportunities it can afford when shaped with educative intent. In this respect, they highlight the evolving role of practitioners as knowledge-brokers and boundary-spanners (Sperka, Enright & McCuaig, 2018) and point to the need for further attention to be paid to mapping this complicated landscape.

In considering these chapters together, it is evident that there are a number of shared ideas running through them. Firstly, each chapter highlights the complex landscape of educational practice and recognises the impact of historical, social and cultural factors in shaping lasting inequalities in student experience. Moreover, they all identify the need to check and challenge on account of this, encouraging practitioners to recognise, understand and reflect on issues of marginalisation – including their own (potential) role in this. As noted by Luguetti and McDonald (Chapter 12) and Wrench and Garrett (Chapter 13) in particular, this can be an unnerving process, requiring practitioners to step out of their comfort zone and be willing to embrace new and different ideas. Secondly, all of the chapters align with, albeit in various ways, the notion of relational pedagogy, highlighting the need for conversation and collaboration between key stakeholders. Importantly, this is underpinned by notions of youth voice, with the recognition that practitioners have much to gain from engaging with and learning from students' diverse interests and cultures. This will clearly be a key feature in shaping more tailored, context-specific and culturally responsive practices.

Finally, each of the chapters, notably, supports a strengths-based approach to challenging issues of inequity within PE, physical activity and health contexts. They note the need to recognise the complexities of practice and to avoid viewing issues narrowly through a deficit lens. Further, they highlight the importance of ongoing research in this area, noting that 'snapshot approaches' to challenging inequity may simply serve to perpetuate marginalisation. There are, therefore, some important questions evident within these chapters for those seeking to work with young people in PE, physical activity and health contexts. These include – though are certainly not limited to – how we can recognise/understand inequities in our own practice, how we can ensure we move from theoretical understandings of progressive pedagogies to practical enactment and how we can best facilitate the voices of our students in shaping learning experiences. By endeavouring to address these important questions within our own contexts, we can perhaps work towards ensuring that our pedagogies truly are progressive.

References

Freire, P. (1987). *Pedagogia do Oprimido [Pedagogy of the oppressed]* (17th ed.). Sao Paulo: Paz e Terra.

hooks, b. (2001). *All about love: New visions.* New York, NY: William Morrow.

Hunter, D. J., Popay, J., Tannahill, C. and Whitehead, M. (2010). Getting to grips with health inequalities at last? Marmot review calls for renewed action to create a fairer society. *BMJ*, 340, 323–324.

Martin, K. and Mirraboopa, B. (2003). Ways of knowing, being and doing: A theoretical framework and methods for indigenous and indigenist re-search. Journal of Australian Studies, 27(76), 203–214.

Noddings, N. (1984). *Caring, a feminine approach to ethics & moral education.* Berkeley, CA: University of California Press.

Sperka, L., Enright, E., and McCuaig, L. (2018). Brokering and bridging knowledge in health and physical education: A critical discourse analysis of one external provider's curriculum. *Physical Education and Sport Pedagogy, 23*(3), 328–343.

11

HEALTH INEQUALITIES

How and why physical education can help and hinder the equity agenda

Oli Williams, Gareth Wiltshire and Kass Gibson

Introduction

Research consistently demonstrates that social inequalities and health inequalities are closely aligned. Developing critical pedagogies in physical education (PE) relies upon understanding the relevance and influence of social inequalities within this context. Despite strong evidence for the social determinants of health, health policy and promotion often focus on individual lifestyle factors (e.g. physical activity and diet) with the aim of mass-scale behaviour change. Moreover, children and young people are routinely targeted for physical activity promotion and schools are positioned as important sites for health interventions, including initiatives that are part of a wider 'war on obesity'. For example, in the UK, children are weighed during class-time for the *National Child Measurement Programme* (NCMP) and revenue generated from the so-called sugar tax has been granted to schools to support PE, after-school activities and healthy eating initiatives. This chapter critically examines the relationships between health inequalities and PE through an equity lens to illustrate how and why PE offers possibilities for reducing – *and* exacerbating – health inequalities.

The social determinants of health and childhood obesity: The causes and the 'causes of the causes'

Despite long-standing and robust evidence demonstrating how health is influenced by social factors, including employment, housing, education and environment (e.g. Dorling, 2013; Smith, Bambra & Hill, 2016), the focus in much health policy and promotion is individual behaviour change (Kriznik, Kinmonth, Ling & Kelly, 2018). Allied to this, children in the UK are taught about health in a way that largely frames it as the outcome of choices made by individuals

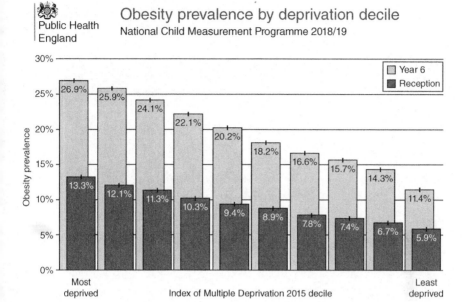

FIGURE 11.1   Obesity prevalence by deprivation decile (National Child Measurement
Programme 2018/19)

(see Chapters 5 and 6, this volume). Therefore, behaviour is commonly framed
as both the cause and the cure of issues such as obesity. However, Public Health
England's NCMP clearly illustrates a 'social gradient' in the incidence of childhood obesity[1] (see Figure 11.1).

Social gradients, also known as wealth-health gradients, describe a consistent
and enduring epidemiological phenomenon whereby lower socio-economic status tends to translate into worse health outcomes (e.g. higher incidence of disease
and reduced life expectancy). Significantly, compliance with advice regarding
what are known as 'health behaviours' (e.g. being regularly physically active, eating five or more fruits and vegetables a day, limiting alcohol consumption and not
smoking) also follows these social gradients (Nandi, Glymour & Subramanian,
2014). Overall, what social gradients demonstrate is that people throughout
society are affected by particular health issues but those lower down the socio-
economic spectrum are *disproportionately* disadvantaged by them. While there are
exceptions at an individual level, at a population level, the general rule is that less
wealth translates into poorer health.

The 'stepped' shape of the bars in Figure 11.1 illustrates a social gradient and
demonstrates an undeniable link between social inequality and the incidence of
children categorised with obesity. Comparing children within the same deprivation grouping (i.e. most or least deprived) demonstrates a big difference in
cumulative effects of social circumstances as children grow older. Not only is
the prevalence of childhood obesity in the least deprived grouping much lower

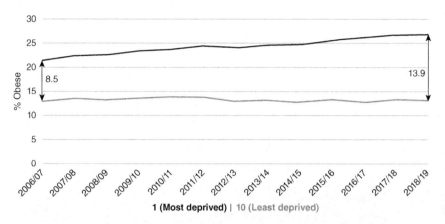

FIGURE 11.2 The gap between obesity prevalence for Year 6 children attending schools in the most and least deprived areas (National Child Measurement Programme 2018/19)

than the most deprived in absolute terms, but also the increase in prevalence from Reception to Year 6 is also much lower (5.5% increase compared to 13.6% increase). This demonstrates that the effects of social deprivation are far more likely to disadvantage people over time. Additionally, recent longitudinal data shows that the prevalence gap between the most and least deprived children is growing over time (National Child Measurement Programme, 2019; see Figure 11.2).

In health policy, when it comes to obesity there are broadly two main concerns: (i) treatment, for those already living with obesity and (ii) prevention, acting on social factors that have largely determined the significant rise in people being categorised with obesity over the past 50 years. Given that prevention is generally more effective the earlier intervention occurs, children are considered a target population. PE has become an intuitively appealing point of intervention for policymakers and initiatives are often welcomed by practitioners.

The UK government's *Change4Life* campaign (Department of Health, 2009) exemplifies a common problem in public health: despite clear awareness of the complexity and influence of social factors and inequalities, interventions do little to address them. *Change4Life* is a social marketing campaign driven by 'nudging' principles designed to facilitate individual behaviour change, rather than addressing the social factors and inequalities that have driven trends in obesity incidence (Mulderrig, 2017). Furthermore, the simplistic *Change4Life* slogan – 'eat well, move more, live longer' – implies adopting a 'healthy lifestyle' is logical, simple and achievable for all. In so doing, it emphasises individual behaviour change as a public health priority without accounting for social gradients or the complex social processes through which individual behaviour manifests and which differ significantly between social groups (Blue, Shove, Carmona & Kelly,

FIGURE 11.3   *Change4Life* image (left) contrasted with a critique by Ergert Saliasi in collaboration with AWL[2] (right)

2016). A visual critique of *Change4Life* can be seen above in Figure 11.3, along-side an official image from the *Change4Life* campaign.

Change4Life encapsulates the rhetoric of choice that characterises the predominant public health approach to obesity prevention. As re-emphasised recently, in a speech by the Conservative MP and Secretary of Health and Social Care, Matt Hancock: 'Prevention is also about ensuring that people take greater responsibility for managing their own health. It's about people choosing to look after themselves better, staying active and stopping smoking. Making better choices by limiting alcohol, sugar, salt and fat' (Campbell, 2018, para. 4). To appreciate the significance of this focus on 'making better choices', it is useful to contrast it with alternative political decisions that could address the social determinants of health – for example, by redistributing resources through taxation. Indeed, the 'moral repertoire' of 'shoulds' (Fullagar, 2002, p. 78) in political and popular culture is predicated on the notion that failing to 'eat well' and 'move more' represents a lack of willpower and/or a failure to act responsibly. As Rich (2011, p. 16) argued, discourses of moral responsibility and lifestyle modification dominant within the obesity debate 'not only position individuals as blameworthy but moralize and decontextualize health inequalities by glossing over the social and structural contexts'. The visual critique pictured above views *Change4Life* through a sociological lens, emphasising that the choices people make are influenced by their social circumstances. Social factors – such as socio-economic status, gender, race and ethnicity – can and do inhibit people, in various ways, from complying with health advice that otherwise appears to be in their best interests.

People of lower socio-economic status face the 'double burden' of being individually marginalised for experiencing predictable and enduring outcomes of social disadvantage (Elliott, Popay & Williams, 2016). That is, health inequalities, especially understood through a model of individual behaviour change, are often blamed on the 'lifestyle choices' of those lower down the socio-economic spectrum. Although there is significant evidence demonstrating that so-called lifestyle behaviours are causes of ill health, analysis must also address the 'causes of the causes' (Marmot, 2005). Such analysis entails asking not what ill health is caused by, but what causes people to behave in ways that cause ill health?

Health inequalities generally stem from avoidable social inequalities. On this, Baum and Fisher (2014, p. 214) argue that 'behavioural forms of health promotion are an inadequate strategy for addressing social inequities in health and are unlikely to resolve social differences in risky health behaviour' because:

> ... when people behave in ways that are not good for their health it is generally not because they are unaware of the risk but rather that the constraints of their life and accumulated dispositions over the life-course means they are unable or unwilling to change their behaviour. (p. 216)

Understanding health inequalities as largely socially determined should not be considered controversial or revolutionary but, sadly, in the current political climate, it often is. For instance, in England, the Chief Medical Officer's report – *Time to Solve Childhood Obesity* (Davies, Mytton & Pawson, 2019) – referred to the clear, severe and growing inequalities in the incidence of childhood obesity between socio-economic groups. However, the same report concluded that 'it is less clear why there are divergent trends' (p. 8), which resulted in recommendations to the UK government that failed to directly address social inequality as a contributory factor. Without meaningfully addressing the social determinants of health (i.e. reducing social inequality), individual behaviour change interventions are, at a population level, not only largely ineffective but also actually stand to increase health inequalities (Williams & Gibson, 2018). The key to understanding why this is the case is appreciating the distinction between inequality and inequity.

Health inequalities, the equity agenda and behavioural justice

As outlined above, health inequalities often feature in political rhetoric. However, it is common over time for government policies to go through a process of 'lifestyle drift' whereby 'governments start with a commitment to dealing with the wider social determinants of health but end up instigating narrow lifestyle interventions on individual behaviours, even where action at a governmental level may offer the greater chance of success' (Hunter, Popay, Tannahill & Whitehead, 2010, p. 23). This often occurs through investment in unsophisticated information, education and communication (IEC) projects (Nutbeam, 2008) – such as *Change4Life*. The IEC approach assumes non-compliance with health advice is due to the 'deaf ears phenomenon' (Warin, Turner, Moore & Davies, 2008,

p. 99), which implies the 'solutions' lie primarily in education. This blinkered view supports long-standing and popular arguments for physical activity representing the 'best buy in public health' rather than acting on social factors that play a far greater role in determining health outcomes, *including* compliance with recommended health behaviours (Fullagar, 2002).

While it is not an either/or scenario, the fact that it is common for lifestyle interventions to unintentionally exacerbate existing inequalities highlights the need for greater appreciation of the influence of social factors. When a new policy or intervention provides free opportunities 'for all' to be physically active, unless it accounts for social inequalities, it is liable to reproduce the 'inequality paradox' (Williams & Gibson, 2018). As explained by Frohlich and Potvin (2008, p. 219):

> ... vulnerable populations are the least able to positively respond to population-approach interventions ... those with the most resources at hand to adapt to new situations will be the first to derive maximum benefits from population-approach interventions.

Interventions may be successful at a population level by increasing average levels of physical activity. However, this increase is predominately achieved among already privileged groups. As such, by failing to support disadvantaged groups, interventions exacerbate existing inequalities. Ultimately, unless behavioural interventions account for the influence of social inequalities, it is highly likely they will reproduce the inequality paradox. This highlights the need to distinguish between inequalities and inequities.

Health inequalities are matters of *outcome*. They describe differences in health and illness experienced between different social groups (e.g. socio-economic, gender, ethnic). Inequities, by contrast, are matters of *process*. They are 'social factors that create, perpetuate and exacerbate inequalities' that would otherwise be 'avoidable through adequate attention being paid – in policy and intervention design – to the social determinants of health' (Williams, Coen & Gibson, 2019, p. 638). Promoting health equity is to recognise that treating everybody equally will exclude some people and fail to reduce inequalities. The relative effects of social disadvantage must be accounted for in intervention design with relative needs addressed appropriately. In short, because of existing inequalities, treating everybody the same is unfair. For example, if we want PE to realise its ambition of being an inclusive opportunity to promote health and well-being for all, then we must consider the appropriateness – or indeed necessity – of not treating all schools and all pupils the same.

The need to pursue an equity agenda is a long-standing sociological concern (see Box 11.1). Applying an 'equity lens' highlights that reproducing the inequality paradox is inevitable only if relevant social factors are ignored. As a case in point, while lifestyle drift detracts from efforts to act on the social determinants of

---

BOX 11.1 HEALTH EQUITY: NEW TERMINOLOGY, LONG-STANDING SOCIOLOGICAL CONSIDERATION

Being grounded in notions of fairness and justice, the rhetoric and debate regarding equity is primarily presented and understood as a political project and aim. Underpinning this is the need to understand fundamental socio-logical processes of social organisation, social change and individual action. Equity encapsulates addressing the gap between goals that are valued and therefore promoted in society (e.g. 'healthy' living) and the means that soci-ety provides people to achieve them. Although health organisations pursuing an 'equity agenda' is a relatively modern articulation, over 80 years ago, the work of sociologist Robert K. Merton was centrally concerned with this polit-ical challenge and sociological process – albeit using different terminology. Using the example of the American Dream and wealth, Merton (1938, p. 679) noted, in language prescient for contemporary equity advocates, 'of those located in the lower reaches of the social structure, the culture makes incom-patible demands. On the one hand they are asked to orient their conduct toward the prospect of large wealth … on the other, they are denied effective opportunities to do so institutionally'. Merton (1938) went on to explain that when people are encouraged to meet the goals of their society (e.g. 'healthy weight') but not given the support of their society to achieve those goals, the apparently deviant behaviour of individuals should not be considered the product of individual choices but rather social production. Therefore, devel-oping both our understanding and enactment of equity still requires asking the same question posed by Merton (1957): what are the consequences of living in a society that emphasises everyone will be successful if they apply their time, effort and ability, but within which equal emphasis is not placed on providing necessary social support structures to ensure making this applica-tion of time, effort and ability is actually possible for everyone to achieve? Or in this case, what happens when the cultural expectation is that everyone can and should live a healthy lifestyle, but social inequalities make this a far more demanding (and even unachievable) task for some relative to others?

---

health, lifestyle interventions need not exacerbate health inequalities. Targeting interventions exclusively for socially disadvantaged population groups – for instance, by working with 'underserved communities' (Choitz et al., 2010) – to address inequities and meet their needs has potential for supporting the promotion of health behaviours such as physical activity *and* therefore reducing health inequalities. Recognising that the social determinants of health should be prioritised in government policy, there are now calls for 'behavioural justice'. Those aligned with this movement argue that awareness of the protective effect of 'healthy' living is now ubiquitous and, with the culture of moral individualism so dominant, having the opportunity to live a 'healthy lifestyle' is a matter of social justice (Adler & Stewart, 2009).

Indeed, once policy has drifted into the terrain of lifestyle, the pressing concern becomes avoiding 'inequity drift' and 'citizen shift'. 'Inequity drift' describes interventions becoming less equitable over time and commonly occurs as a result of interventions having finite resources and ill-conceived sustainability plans (Williams, 2017). While physical activity interventions delivered in areas of deprivation may initially be designed to reduce 'barriers to participation' – such as a lack of local opportunities or unaffordable participation fees – these barriers tend to be resurrected once funding becomes scarce. For example, Williams (2017) observed local parents losing access to cheap, public provision of hourly childcare that facilitated leisure centre attendance when, in a cost-saving exercise, it was transformed into a private crèche. In a related process, Williams and Fullagar (2019, p. 33) describe 'citizen shift' as a 'necessary extension to understand the complex process of lifestyle drift'. It is the process whereby behavioural interventions further shift responsibility for overcoming the social determinants of health away from governments and onto the people disproportionately affected by them. For instance, this can occur when people living in deprived neighbourhoods get blamed for not 'taking advantage' of physical activity interventions. This is an example of 'triple disadvantage' where residents of deprived neighbourhoods (who already face a 'double burden') are further disadvantaged by the very interventions that have purportedly been designed to support them (Williams, 2017). Such interventions offer an avenue through which to frame non-compliance with health promotion as recalcitrance or personal failure rather than highlighting the inhibitory realities of their social circumstances.

This is where PE potentially offers a way of answering calls for behavioural justice. Schools offer an opportunity for targeted, equitable intervention because education is a foundational element of social inequality (Evans & Bairner, 2013). A person's socio-economic status and the school they attend can and does influence: (i) their capacity to achieve academic success and (ii) the potential to achieve success beyond/in spite of educational attainment (Brown, 2013). The most deprived areas tend to have schools with the lowest levels of educational attainment, which, in turn, promotes generational disadvantage (Education Research Group, 2009). This means a policy of providing targeted support for children and parents through schools located in deprived areas (including offering support to be physically active) has the potential for equitable lifestyle intervention. Therefore, PE represents a potentially important opportunity for delivering behavioural justice.

Physical education: Inequalities, inequities and interventions

PE and school sport have been recruited to fight the 'war on obesity' (see Chapter 1, this volume). Consequently, a pressing concern for critical scholars studying PE and school sport has been the insidious nature of health education at the intersection of physical activity and obesity policies and how this relates to the growing prevalence of body disaffection and disordered eating among young people (Evans, Rich, Davies & Allwood, 2008; Cale & Harris, 2013). While structural, socio-economic and geographical determinants of obesity are likely to explain much of the inequalities evident in the incidence of childhood obesity, there are processes within PE and school sport that contribute. Viewing PE through the lens of health equity helps to illustrate how and why: (i) inequalities in the education system lead to inequalities in PE provision; (ii) particular school-based initiatives intended to improve healthy behaviours can and do reproduce the inequality paradox; and (iii) the so-called sugar tax is unlikely to support PE to significantly reduce childhood obesity. This creates a need to critically appraise childhood obesity prevention strategies that bring PE to the fore.

Structural inequalities greatly influence PE provision. Under David Cameron's Conservative government, primary PE was protected from budget cuts through ring-fenced *Physical Education and Sport Premium* funding. The devolving of this funding means that each school has the freedom to decide how to spend their budget (between £17,000 and £21,000 depending on pupil numbers), which has led to significant inequalities in provision. Meir and Fletcher (2020) found that 'the move towards making schools more autonomous actually led to widening inequality' (p. 247) and ultimately 'reinforced a postcode lottery, whereby the school you attend determines your experience' (p. 251). Reducing inequalities requires initial inequities to be accounted for when distributing funds. Given that schools do not start on a level playing field, evenly distributing funds merely reinforces existing inequalities. Indeed, playing fields themselves offer an illustration of this (see Box 11.2).

Similarly, PE and school sport are at risk of reproducing the inequality paradox. A recent study by Wiltshire, Lee and Williams (2019) drew on theoretical concepts from Bourdieu to demonstrate that dispositions informed by social class influence the uptake of extracurricular opportunities. Activities more readily offered in school contexts (e.g. organised sports and fitness activities) disproportionately appealed to children of higher socio-economic status. Pupils who were largely disengaged by/from PE, and from more disadvantaged backgrounds, tended to feel that the opportunities available were not 'for the likes of us'. The activities they did outside of school (e.g. scootering and free running) were not provided in school. Even if they had been, the pupils expressed a reluctance to do them in the more sanitised school environment, as removing the more anarchic elements to which they were drawn would mean that 'it wouldn't be the same'. However, if interventions target and meet the needs of those disproportionately disadvantaged by social inequalities, they have the potential to enrich the lives of individuals by providing opportunities they are otherwise structurally excluded from.

The 'Golden Ticket' intervention pilot delivered by *Dundee Academy of Sport* and *Active Schools Dundee*[3] provides an interesting example. A total of 44% of children in Dundee live in the most deprived areas in Scotland and almost a third

---

BOX 11.2 THATCHERISM *STILL* STOPPING PLAY

PE was disproportionately inhibited by so-called Regulation 909 introduced in 1981 by Margaret Thatcher's Conservative government. This regulation gave schools the right to sell school land deemed surplus to requirements. However, rather than being 'surplus to requirements', prior to being sold schools were typically using this land as playing fields. Thousands of playing fields have been sold in subsequent decades, with a GMB Union (2019) report finding that between 2010 and 2019 over 200 were sold, stating that 'the Government has cut education funding to such an extent schools are being forced to flog their playing fields to make ends meet'. Regulation 909 was primed for exacerbating inequalities as there was/is significant variation in: how much land each school had/has to sell; geographical disparities in the worth of land; and the relative need to sell due to financial (in)stability.

(31%) of all children in the city live in poverty (Dundee City Council, 2019). Although unfortunately named[4], the Golden Ticket intervention recognised that children living in deprived areas were disproportionately reliant on their school for physical activity provision and that school holidays may therefore widen inequalities in activity. This potential widening was exacerbated by the costs associated with summer holiday activity programmes. As such, the aim of the Golden Ticket programme was supporting families most in need to access sport and activity camps during the summer holidays by removing the barrier of participation fees. Partnerships were made with local social services and schools in order to distribute the tickets and to support families to sign up to the activities.

There were limitations with the intervention. Distribution through schools was not limited to those children most in need and this compromised the targeted nature of the intervention, which in turn limited post-intervention claims about having supported those most in need. Additionally, social workers of looked-after children highlighted that participation fees are but one barrier, with others including: a lack of activities delivered in deprived areas creating travel and transport barriers; day-long activities requiring the need for packed lunches presenting financial barriers; and holiday activities presenting opportunities for self-consciousness and bullying related to (non-)ownership of functional and fashionable sportswear (see also, Sandford, Quarmby, Hooper & Duncombe, 2021).

It is certainly the case that the Golden Ticket intervention could have been designed and delivered differently and that doing so would have improved its impact on local inequalities. This example helps to illustrate how important intervention design is in terms of ensuring target populations are the exclusive beneficiaries in order to avoid reproducing the inequality paradox. It also demonstrates how even interventions designed to address inequities are liable to have a limited impact due to the multiple and intersecting social factors that inhibit physical activity. An alternative approach that would address the social determinants of health is redistributing resources through taxation (e.g. the 'sugar tax').

The *Soft Drinks Industry Levy*, colloquially known in England as the 'sugar tax', is an example of system-level intervention to drive behavioural change. The government predicted that the levy would raise £1 billion for schools. Significantly, for those in PE, revenue raised from the levy was initially used to double *Physical Education and Sport Premium* funding. While many celebrated the increased funding, paradoxically, a successful outcome for PE represents a failed outcome of the levy as it only generates revenue if manufacturers do not comply with government targets to reduce sugar in drinks. Therefore, announcing increased funding to support PE, after-school activities and healthy eating initiatives represents, ironically, an attempt to sugar-coat this reality.

Significantly, in terms of inequality, whereas traditional ideas of wealth redistribution via taxation align with the Robin Hood principle – that is, to take from those with more to give to those with less – the revenue generated through the levy was promised to a policy that has been demonstrated to widen existing inequalities (Meir & Fletcher, 2020). Therefore, even if the levy increases physical activity levels through PE, it is liable to increase inequalities to, although such exacerbation will now be avoided as this equity issue was short-lived. Demonstrating how fickle political commitments can be, it has subsequently been announced that previous commitments to ringfence taxes raised by the levy to support schools to address childhood obesity have been dropped. Existing inequalities will mean that schools with the least funding in the first instance will be hit hardest by this controversial U-turn, especially if their planned PE provision was reliant on the previously promised funds.

Conclusion

While the priority for those concerned with addressing health inequalities is rightly focused on preventing the policy-trend of lifestyle drift, the need to do so should neither negate the potential for so-called lifestyle behaviours to enrich the lives of people of lower socio-economic status nor ignore the fact that social disadvantage inhibits enacting these culturally valorised ways of being. Those working in fields directly related to the promotion and provision of these behaviours have a responsibility to ensure their practice is equitable in order to avoid exacerbating existing inequalities. This chapter has suggested that PE represents a potentially important site for advancing the equity agenda and delivering behavioural justice.

Realising this potential requires practitioners to avoid reproducing – purposefully or otherwise – discourses and behaviours that accentuate individual responsibility and/or ignore structural enablers and constraints. As such, both research and practice must remain sensitive to equal emphasis on goals – be they content knowledge-, performance-, or health-related – *as well as* opportunities and support to achieve them. PE researchers are increasingly attending to issues of diversity and PE teachers are often well versed in the challenges of increasing opportunities for students to participate in lessons. As such, in many ways, addressing health inequalities as relayed in this chapter mirrors the pedagogical concerns of the field, but at a social and policy level. Expressed differently, best practice of inclusive curricula and differentiated teaching are analogous to addressing health inequalities. However, this knowledge is not conveyed merely by osmosis. Rather, there are powerful forces promoting counter-discourses which act to preserve the privilege of the privileged at the expense of others. Explicit consideration, thoughtful planning and deliberate action are required to address inequalities. Therefore, in teaching generally, but especially in, through and about health promotion, equity really is the answer.

Reflection points

• What happens when the cultural expectation is that everyone can and should live a healthy lifestyle, but social inequalities make this a far more demanding (and even unachievable) task for some people relative to others?

• Simply informing people that inactivity causes ill health has proven relatively ineffective in promoting behaviour change. If the focus was instead on addressing the 'causes of the causes' of ill health (e.g. social factors inhibiting people from being more active), what could PE do to support students and parents to be more active?

• If the aim is to promote lifelong physical activity, why is it that many funded interventions only offer short-term solutions? Do the barriers they removed simply go away?

• What might be the effects of resurrecting barriers that interventions had previously removed?

Notes

1 Body mass index (BMI) and body weight are crude and often inaccurate measures of 'health' which are used to determine obesity. Contrary to popular wisdom, they are not entirely within an individual's control. Rather they are influenced by a complex web of biological, psychological and social factors. We draw on this example to highlight the social drivers and inequalities which are often neglected in childhood obesity interventions.

2 Ergert Saliasi is an independent artist and AWL is an art collective, the work of which focuses on challenging inequalities and injustices (see: http://www.actwithlove. co.uk/).

3 The first author evaluated the pilot of this intervention in 2015.

4 Taking its name from the story of Roald Dahl's *Charlie and the Chocolate Factory* – where a child living in poverty is afforded an opportunity by a rich, eccentric business owner – is perhaps at best an uncritical celebration of charity insensitive to the seriousness of the effects of social deprivation.

References

Adler, N, E. and Stewart, J. (2009). Reducing obesity: Motivating action while not blaming the victim. *The Milbank Quarterly*, 87(1), 49–70.

Baum, F. and Fisher, M. (2014). Why behavioural health promotion endures despite its failure to reduce health inequalities. *Sociology of Health and Illness*, 36(2), 213–225.

Blue, S., Shove, E., Carmona, C. and Kelly, M. P. (2016). Theories of practice and public health: Understanding (un)healthy practices. *Critical Public Health*, 26(1), 36–50.

Brown, P. (2013). Education, opportunity and the prospects for social mobility. *British Journal of Sociology of Education*, 34(5–6), 678–700.

Cale, L. and Harris, J. (2013). 'Every child (of every size) matters' in physical education! Physical education's role in childhood obesity. *Sport, Education and Society*, 18(4), 433–452.

Campbell, D. (2018). People must take responsibility for own health, says Matt Hancock. *The Guardian*, 5 November. Available at: https://www.theguardian.com/society/2018/nov/05/people-must-take-responsibility-for-own-health-says-matt-hancock (Accessed: 27 October 2019).

Choitz, P., Johnson, M. P., Berhane, Z., Lefever, G., Anderson, J. K. and Eiser, A. R. (2010). Urban fitness centres: Removing barriers to promote exercise in underserved communities. *Journal of Health Care for the Poor and Underserved*, 21(1), 221–228.

Davies, S., Mytton, O. and Pawson, E. (2019). Time to solve childhood obesity: An independent report by the Chief Medical Officer, 2019 Professor Dame Sally Davies.

Department of Health. (2009). *Change4life marketing strategy: In support of healthy weight, healthy lives*. London: Crown.

Dorling, D. (2013). *Unequal health: The scandal of our times*. Bristol: Policy Press.

Dundee City Council. (2019). Dundee city – Poverty profile. Available at: https://www.dundeecity.gov.uk/sites/default/files/publications/poverty_profile_2019_fairness_0.pdf (Accessed: 27 October 2019).

Education Research Group. (2009). *Attainment gaps between the most deprived and advantaged schools*. London: Sutton Trust. Available online at: http://eprints.lse.ac.uk/23921/1/Attainment_gaps_between_the_most_deprived_and_advantaged_schools_%28summary%29.pdf (Accessed: 9 October 2019).

Elliott, E., Popay, J. and Williams, G. (2016). Knowledge of the everyday: Confronting the causes of health inequalities. In K. E. Smith, C. Bambra and S. E. Hill (Eds.), *Health inequalities: Critical perspectives*. Oxford University Press, Oxford, pp. 222–237.

Evans, J. and Bairner, A. (2013). Physical education and social class. In G. Stidder and S. Hayes (Eds.), *Equity and inclusion in physical education and sport*. London: Routledge, pp. 141–158.

Evans, J., Rich, E., Davies, B. and Allwood, R. (2008). *Education, disordered eating and obesity discourse: Fat fabrications*. Abingdon, Oxon: Routledge.

Frohlich, K, L. and Potvin, L. (2008). Transcending the known in public health practice: The inequality paradox: The population approach and vulnerable populations. *American Journal of Public Health*, 98(2), 216–221.

Fullagar, S. (2002). Governing the healthy body: Discourses of leisure and lifestyle within Australian health policy. *Health: An Interdisciplinary Journal for the Social Study of Health, Illness and Medicine*, 6(1), 69–84.

GMB Union. (2019). More than 200 school playing fields sold off since 2010. Available at: https://www.gmb.org.uk/news/more-200-school-playing-fields-sold-2010 (Accessed: 27 October 2019).

Hunter, D. J., Popay, J., Tannahill, C. and Whitehead, M. (2010). Getting to grips with health inequalities at last? Marmot review calls for renewed action to create a fairer society. *BMJ*, 340, 323–324.

Kriznik, N. M., Kinmonth, A. L., Ling, T. and Kelly, M. P. (2018). Moving beyond individual choice in policies to reduce health inequalities: The integration of dynamic with individual explanations. *Journal of Public Health*, 40(4), 764–775.

Marmot, M. (2005). Social determinants of health inequalities. *The Lancet*, 365(9464), 1099–1104.

Meir, D. and Fletcher, T. (2020). The physical education and sport premium: Social justice, autonomy and school sport policy in England. *International Journal of Sport Policy and Politics*, 12(2), 237–253.

Merton, R. K. (1938). Social structure and anomie. *American Sociology Review*, 3(5), 672–682.

Merton, R. K. (1957). *Social theory and social structure*. New York, NY: The Free Press.

Mulderrig, J. (2017). Reframing obesity: A critical discourse analysis of the UK's first social marketing campaign. *Critical Policy Studies*, 11(4), 455–476.

Nandi, A., Glymour, M. M. and Subramanian, S. V. (2014). Association among socioeconomic status, health behaviors, and all-cause mortality in the United States. *Epidemiology*, 25(2), 170–177.

National Child Measurement Programme. (2019). NHS digital online publication Available at: https://digital.nhs.uk/data-and-information/publications/statistical/national-child-measurement-programme/2018-19-school-year/deprivation#deprivation-gap-for-obesity-year-6 (Accessed: 14 April 2020).

Nutbeam, D. (2008). What would the Ottawa Charter look like if it were written today? *Critical Public Health*, 18, 435–441.

Rich, E. (2011). 'I see her being obesed!': Public pedagogy, reality media and the obesity crisis. *Health: An Interdisciplinary Journal for the Social Study of Health, Illness and Medicine*, 15(1), 3–21.

Sandford, R., Quarmby, T., Hooper, O. and Duncombe, R. (2021). Navigating complex social landscapes: Examining care experienced young people's engagements with sport and physical activity. *Sport, Education and Society*, 26(1), 15–28.

Smith, K. E., Bambra, C. and Hill, S. E. (Eds.). (2016). *Health inequalities: Critical perspectives*. Oxford: Oxford University Press.

Warin, M., Turner, K., Moore, V. and Davies, M. (2008). Bodies, mothers and identities: Rethinking obesity and the BMI. *Sociology of Health and Illness*, 30(1), 97–111.

Williams, O. (2017). Identifying adverse effects of area-based health policy: An ethnographic study of a deprived neighbourhood in England. *Health & Place*, 45, 85–91.

Williams, O. and Fullagar, S. (2019). Lifestyle drift and the phenomenon of 'citizen shift' in contemporary UK health policy. *Sociology of Health & Illness*, 41(1), 20–35.

Williams, O. and Gibson, K. (2018). Exercise as a poisoned elixir: Inactivity, inequality and intervention. *Qualitative Research in Sport, Exercise and Health*, 10(4), 412–428.

Williams, O., Coen, S. E. and Gibson, K. (2019). Comment on: "Equity in physical activity: A misguided goal". *Sports Medicine*, 49(4), 637–639.

Wiltshire, G., Lee, J. and Williams, O. (2019). Understanding the reproduction of health inequalities: Physical activity, social class and Bourdieu's habitus. *Sport, Education and Society*, 24(3), 226–240.

12

'TRANSFORMING OURSELVES'

Towards a pedagogy of love in health and physical education

Carla Luguetti and Brent McDonald

Introduction

> When I started this project, I thought that as a teacher we know everything. This project changed my life ... I understood the importance of listening to students ... When I learned to really listen to them and understand their needs ... What I changed is that I [now] have a very strong connection with the kids and with their parents. I changed as a teacher, and the way I'm going to teach from now on is the way I learned here.
>
> *(Janaina, student teacher)*

Decades of teaching student teachers in health and physical education (HPE) indicates that one of their major goals is to treat all students equally regardless of their race/ethnicity, gender, sexuality, social class or ability (Philpot, 2016; Ovens et al., 2018). Research suggests that this belief in 'equality' is not driven by a desire for social justice, rather it comes from a common-sense perspective of individual ethics (e.g. Philpot, 2016; Ovens et al., 2018; Walton-Fisette & Sutherland, 2018; Schenker et al., 2019). This notion of equality in HPE is highly problematic, failing to recognise subtle forms of oppression in our classrooms such as racism, sexism, homophobia, classism and ableism. Most frequently, student teachers and in-service teachers articulate a humanistic approach, whereby there is an acceptance of diversity and difference; less prevalent are those teachers who understand inequities and the importance of teaching for democracy and empowerment within their classrooms.

Social justice perspectives provide student teachers and in-service teachers with a means of recognising inequalities within their pedagogical practice. Through a reflexive process, they begin to understand the impossibilities of treating students equally and perhaps even acknowledge their own privileges, transforming themselves. In line with a social justice perspective, we argue that love is an essential element of practice within HPE. For us, love is intrinsically linked with social justice where we cultivate a democratic classroom through dialogue, hope and imagination. Within the field of HPE, most researchers refer to an ethic of care instead of love. However, we believe that there are important differences and that to care does not necessarily mean to love.

The aim of this chapter is to discuss a pedagogy of love in HPE, to rethink pedagogical practices and to challenge teachers' assumptions that perpetuate domination and social injustice in HPE classes. This pedagogy creates a space for teachers to understand their own privileges and transform themselves. We begin this chapter by defining the concept of love, drawing specifically on the work of Paulo Freire (Freire, 1987, 2005; Darder, 2017). We argue that a pedagogy of love offers a platform to develop teachers' reflexivity and to help them to reflect on experiences of inclusion and exclusion in their own lives, which will support them to become more competent in accommodating linguistically, ethnically and culturally diverse students. Following this, we provide an illustration of a pedagogy of love based on work emanating from Brazil. We conclude the chapter by outlining points for reflection and critical challenges for future research in this area.

Care within health and physical education

Since the mid-1980s, researchers have focused on care as a moral basis for social justice in HPE (Rovegno & Kirk, 1995; Devís-Devís, 2006). These researchers have shown how existing social justice orientations might be broadened, enhanced and enriched, by giving equal weight to an ethic of care and responsibility, in addition to an ethic of justice and emancipation. Consequently, 'caring' has become a central concept for HPE educators and researchers who wish to challenge the status quo in their efforts to build a socially just society (Hellison, 1978; Ennis, 1999; Clark, 2019).

Don Hellison was a pioneering scholar who used physical activity and sport to design affective approaches to work with youth from socially vulnerable backgrounds. Within his early work, *Beyond Balls and Bats* (Hellison, 1978), he presented a humanistic approach based on his practical experience of teaching in low-income neighbourhoods in the US. He argued that HPE needed to move beyond skill development, or what he called a 'balls and bats' orientation, to make the gym a comfortable space, where youth feel free to explore their connections to their bodies, and to experiment with physical activities. Additionally, he stated that teachers should be able to freely interact with students – so that they might demonstrate their care for them, sharing their own identities and encouraging their students to do the same (Hellison, 1978).

Whilst care is recognised in HPE, researchers often use Nel Noddings' concept of an ethic of care (Noddings, 1984) as a foundation for their work (Owens & Ennis, 2005; Clark, 2019; Moen et al., 2020). Noddings (1984) explained that the notion of caring evolves from the natural sympathy that human beings innately feel for one another. Thus, relating to others, caring and being cared for are a basic reality of human existence. Caring can be accomplished when teachers demonstrate and nurture the notion of an ethic of care through activities that include modelling, dialogue, practice and confirmation (Owens & Ennis, 2005). Furthermore, Noddings (1984) suggests that caring requires continuity, and that caring relationships are facilitated when the caregiver is embedded in the community or culture.

Building on research about an ethic of care in HPE, we argue that care is an ingredient or dimension of love, 'but simply giving care does not mean that we are loving' (hooks, 2001, p. 22). We propose that love can constitute an important pedagogical intervention in struggles against unjust and unequal social and educational structures within our classrooms. We suggest that love is both an intention and an action, which means that what constitutes a loving act depends on the other and the context (Lanas & Zembylas, 2015). We argue for a love that has a social justice-informed theory focused on collective actions towards transformation. Here, we seek to contribute to the HPE field, building on the work of education scholars that have investigated love in social justice (hooks, 2001; Freire, 2005; Chabot, 2008; Lanas & Zembylas, 2015; Zembylas, 2017).

'Decolonising love'

> We must dare in full sense of the world, to speak of love without the fear of being called ridiculous, mawkish, or unscientific, if not antiscientific. We must dare in order to say scientifically, and not as mere blah-blah-blah, that we study, we learn, we teach, we know with our entire body. We do all these things with feeling, with emotions, with wishes, with fear, with doubts, with passion, and also with critical reasoning.
>
> *(Freire, 2005, p. 5)*

> When I talked of love with my generation, I found it made everyone nervous or scared, especially when I spoke about not feeling loved enough ... most folks were just frightened of what might be revealed in any exploration of the meaning of love in our lives.
>
> *(hooks, 2001, p. xix)*

Paulo Freire and bell hooks share the belief that it is complicated to speak of love in our society, including within education. Within her book, *All About Love: New Visions*, hooks (2001) argues that we receive messages on a daily basis telling us that love is about mystery and fantasy: love is something that cannot be known. Furthermore, she suggests that the expression 'to fall in love' reflects this mystery; since it is so difficult to choose love, it is better to fall in love – meaning we are not responsible for our actions. This way of seeing love reflects a mixture of fascination, confusion and fear. We also live in a world that values material possessions and money more than love. As hooks (2001) describes, the search for immediate satisfaction seems to be more important than love, which requires an investment of time, effort and commitment. Additionally, some consider love to be a soft emotion or feeling, confined to the privacy of romantic relationships and family contexts.

We believe in a 'decolonising love' whereby love is conceptualised as a practice that is both politically and socially constructed and which holds promise of being a compelling political force that has transformative potential in struggles against social injustice (Zembylas, 2017). According to hooks (2001), in contrast to commonly accepted assumptions of patriarchal culture, love cannot be present in a situation where one group or individual dominates another. Domination and love cannot coexist, because without justice there can be no love (hooks, 2001; Freire, 2005). Instead, decolonising love means that love is not interpreted in essentialist terms but rather manifests differently in different spaces and places (Zembylas, 2017). It constitutes a form of love that imagines a world in which ethical relationships are built beyond coloniality, without ignoring the long history of colonisation and oppression (Lanas & Zembylas, 2015). Decolonising love is a form of love that breaks the 'I' and provides a site for collective becoming, where teachers might admit they want to become different. It is a love based on *dialogue, solidarity* and *hope*.

Dialogue, solidarity and hope

Love requires a commitment to dialogue and the capacity to take risks for the benefit of our students and ourselves (Freire, 2005). One of the risks we must take as teachers is to relinquish oppressive practices in the classroom, such as the banking system of education, in which students are treated like empty receptacles to be filled with information (Freire, 1987). Love demands that we utilise dialogue as a means of subverting dominant positionalities, since love 'cannot exist in a relation of domination' (Freire, 1987, p. 89). Thus, love has a political and radicalised form that is never about absolute consensus, unconditional acceptance, unceasing words of sweetness, or endless streams of hugs and kisses. Through dialogue, HPE teachers can co-create programmes and curricula *with* students. Together, they build relationships and understand the barriers and facilitators students face in seeking to be physically active. Given what they learn, it is possible to create spaces for change or activism (praxis[1]).

Love requires solidarity – a commitment to others and to the cause of liberation (Freire, 1987, 2005; Darder, 2017). It is a commitment to the voices and perspectives of marginalised and non-dominant positionalities, which allows us to recast power differences in our classrooms, providing tools for dialogue, action and hope (Ty-ron & Ngangta, 2015). Education is inherently political (Freire, 2005), and the choices we make as educators to move towards socially aware and activist stances have an important place in our classrooms and curricula, and for the children with whom we work. Love includes a strong and deep commitment to caring for, protecting and empowering students in the face of everyday social barriers and oppressions and inspires a political passion to engage and support marginalised youth (Daniels, 2012). Solidarity is found only in the abundance of love (Freire, 1987). Solidarity emerges in HPE classes when teachers and students are committed to social inclusion and democracy (Freire, 1987). For example, when teachers create democratic spaces in HPE classes where they are willing to listen and learn from students' diverse cultures and backgrounds.

Love is connected to hope – necessary to persevere despite barriers – which Freire (1987) asserts is central to the transformative experience of education. Freire (2005, p. 2) continues to argue that 'hope is an ontological need' because otherwise our activism dies when we can imagine nothing better than what we see before us. To enact transformation, hope is a necessary ingredient, while its opposite, despair, leaves no room for activism or movement because of the over-whelming power from obstacles that hinder educators (Greene, 1995; Daniels, 2012). Hope creates room for movement, for possibilities to create different outcomes, whereas despair simply shuts them down. Within a pedagogy of love, teachers stimulate creativity and imagination in their students, as well as the capacity to critique their surroundings and thus challenge inequity and injustice. It is important that transformation occurs at the micro level – taking small steps towards changing oppressive practices to make a difference over time (Cook-Sather, 2002). For example, having recognised the barriers students might face in seeking to be physically active, teachers and students might collectively 'brain-storm' how to make change – which requires both imagination and hope.

Challenges of becoming a teacher who enacts social justice

> The persons responsible for education should be entirely wet by the cultural waters of the moment, of the space … After recognising that education is a consequence of our uncompletedness, about which we are conscious we can try an exercise of critical reflection.
>
> *(Freire, Freire & de Oliveira, 2014, p. 14)*

According to Freire et al. (2014), becoming a teacher requires recognition that education is a consequence of our incompleteness. Student teachers are challenged to imagine a world that is less dehumanising, more just, less discriminatory and more substantively democratic (Ladson-Billings, 2000; Freire, 2004). The process should be viewed as an educational philosophy where teachers with questions of justice, democracy and ethics create spaces for social change (Giroux, 2011; Hill et al., 2018; O'Sullivan, 2018). Indeed, becoming a teacher requires us to understand and negotiate power relations (Muhammad et al., 2015).

There are a number of challenges that teachers might face when enacting social justice. First, they may be uncomfortable with the necessary change in power relations that results from the adoption of a more democratic pedagogical process (Bovill, Cook-Sather & Felten, 2011; Enright, Coll, Ní Chróinín & Fitzpatrick, 2017; Luguetti & Oliver, 2020). Such change challenges conventional conceptions of learners as subordinate to the expert teacher (Bovill et al., 2011). Teachers need to break down power differentials so that students may experience the freedom to become critical thinkers and critical beings in the world (Freire, 2005). According to Nygreen (2006), divisions of race, gender, class and age are reproduced within collaborative groups, no matter how sincere the attempt to equalise power between teachers and students. In that sense, teachers need to be aware of and understand mechanisms of power relationship reproduction (Mcintyre, 2006; Nygreen, 2006). Sharing power is particularly challenging in HPE given that most of the teachers have a sporting background where they have usually learned that the coach/teacher is predominantly in charge of decision-making (Luguetti & Oliver, 2020). In the HPE field, we have a body of research that argues that teachers need to learn that listening to and hearing students' voices are valuable and important skills; a learning process that happens in action (Oliver et al., 2015; Luguetti & Oliver, 2020).

Second, teachers must be prepared to engage in what can be a very personal struggle with their assumptions about, and their relationships to, the people they are working with (Mcintyre, 2006; Oliver et al., 2015). For example, according to Mcintyre (2006), teachers working in socially vulnerable areas believe that hard work and merit lead to success regardless of the social and cultural contexts. This 'us' and 'them' dichotomy forms a binary position, for example, where white teachers (us) believe that they need to 'help' people from diverse backgrounds (them), which reifies the myth that teachers are 'white knights' whose mission is to 'save' the racialised poor and the downtrodden (Ladson-Billings, 2000; Mcintyre, 2006). Such a dichotomy is particularly problematic in the field of HPE, where the majority of studies conducted have been with teachers and student teachers who are predominantly white and middle class (Clark, 2019; Luguetti & McDonald, 2020). We believe there is much potential for including the voices of diverse teachers who share lived experience with students. We might be better able to validate the cultural knowledge that they bring and to translate this knowledge into more culturally responsive pedagogies (see Chapter 13, this volume).

A field illustration of a pedagogy of love

The following example illustrates the application of a pedagogy of love in Brazil (see Luguetti, Kirk & Oliver, 2019 for further discussion). We describe the experiences of the lead author when working with four student teachers and 110 youths from socially vulnerable backgrounds (age 7–13) in a co-created sport programme at a university in Brazil. Our intent was to create empowering possibilities by supporting youth in learning to name, critique and negotiate barriers to engagement in sport contexts. Youth and student teachers were involved in identifying barriers to sporting opportunities in their community. The youth, student teachers and researchers imagined alternative possibilities to the barriers identified and worked collaboratively to create realistic opportunities for the youth to begin to negotiate some of these barriers.

We implemented an activist sport approach, which made it possible for love to emerge as a form of teaching for social justice. The approach unfolded over an extended period (20 months) and youth participated in sports for 1 hour, twice a week (112 classes in total). The first part of the process for co-constructing the sport programme involved the youth and student teachers identifying barriers to learning opportunities through sport within their communities. We started by inquiring into what the youth liked/disliked broadly, their perceptions of school and family, their opinions about the training sessions and the barriers they encountered in relation to sport participation (Luguetti, Oliver, Dantas & Kirk, 2017). Based on the barriers the youth identified, we worked collaboratively with them in order to challenge these and make the sport, the context and the opportunities better. This approach is based on the notion that merely showing the inequality of 'what is' – while necessary – is insufficient. We assert that we must act in some way with our participants, by imagining and exploring that which might be.

The findings exemplify the three features of a pedagogy of love: (a) willingness to repeatedly challenge inequities through dialogue; (b) valuing solidarity; and (c) fostering hope and imagination. The first feature that emerged was the willingness to repeatedly challenge inequities. For example, the implementation of the activist sport approach helped us to identify gender inequity (e.g. lack of opportunities for girls' participation in team sports, particularly soccer), but we (youth, teachers and researchers) needed to be committed to challenging such inequities. We had to be patient and remain committed to naming, critiquing and negotiating the gender issues that arose in our context as well, particularly since they had the potential to reproduce these inequities at the beginning of the project. The second feature that emerged was the development of solidarity, cultivating a learning community between the participants. Solidarity emerged when the student teachers understood and shared the youths' struggles of trying to escape various forms of oppression. The student teachers came from the same low socio-economic communities as most of the young people and in order to develop solidarity, the student teachers had to be able to share the youth's life situations and understand their emotional needs. The solidarity between the participants, built through trust and empathy, created a space that resulted in a family-like group that cared for one another and their community. The third feature to emerge was a desire to foster participants' hope and imagination. The activist sport approach allowed all participants to nurture hope and imagination across the programme, with one youth speculating, 'we could push the houses back to have more space to play'. The possibility to imagine first emerged in the youths' conversations. They could metaphorically imagine alternatives to the barriers their community faced that adults could not, or would not, see.

The student teachers understood that love was represented beyond safety concerns. For them, love came to mean: (a) to create democratic spaces for students to care for each other and their community; (b) to understand and trust the students and to dream possible futures with them; (c) to be the best teacher in order to facilitate students' learning; and (d) to make sure all students are included. The reflexive experience that resulted from the activist approach was essential to move the student teachers from holding deficit views of the youth, to adopting critical approaches that deconstructed oppressive practices. At the beginning of the programme, most of the student teachers did not value the young people's voices, nor did they recognise the importance of love. The weekly collaborative meetings created a space where, over time, the student teachers could discuss their perceptions about love. Through these meetings, they reflected on their actions and they moved from a conception of love as 'don't get hurt' to a broader definition, aligned with the idea of social justice and equity. The reflexive process allowed the student teachers to understand that love means creating democratic spaces for students to care for each other and their community (Freire, 1987). The student teachers started to understand and trust the students and imagine possible futures with them. They understood the importance of facilitating students' learning and making sure that all are included.

Conclusion

The aim of this chapter was to discuss a pedagogy of love in HPE as a way of rethinking pedagogical practices to challenge teachers' assumptions that perpetuate domination and social injustice. According to Freire (1987), those who authentically commit themselves to the people – such as educators – must re-examine themselves constantly, which requires a profound rebirth and results in a process of transformation. It is a process of opening our own eyes as teachers and seeing the world through different eyes, coupled with a desire to open others' eyes (Cahill, Rios-Moore & Threatts, 2008). As Freire (1987, pp. 60–61) notes:

> The man or woman who proclaims devotion to the cause of liberation yet is unable to enter into *communion* with the people, whom he or she continues to regard as totally ignorant, is grievously self-deceived. The convert who approaches the people but feels alarm at each step they take, each doubt they express, and each suggestion they offer, and attempts to impose his "status," remains nostalgic towards his origins. Conversion to the people requires a profound rebirth. Those who undergo it must take on a new form of existence; they can no longer remain as they were.

One of the most important aspects of a pedagogy of love is considering the teacher as a continuous learner who is not afraid to reveal their own vulnerabilities. As described by Freire (1987), the teacher needs to be an educator with genuine humility, who is not afraid of acknowledging their ignorance. It is necessary to understand that we, as teachers, are the 'unfinishedness' of the human person described by Freire et al. (2014). According to Freire (1987), the person teaching is being formed or re-formed through this process, while the person who is being taught forms. Thus, being a teacher is not about transferring knowledge or content, it is about creating possibilities for the construction and production of knowledge (Freire, 1987). There is in fact no teaching without learning – it is a continuous process of becoming a subject (Freire, 1998). This continuous process creates a capacity for learning, not only to adapt to the world but especially to intervene, to re-create and to transform it (Freire, 1998).

We identified that a pedagogy of love worked with youth and student teachers from socially vulnerable communities, creating spaces for developing dialogue, solidarity and hope. However, we believe that a pedagogy of love can be translated into other contexts. It is a pedagogy that aims to create spaces for empowerment by naming, critiquing and challenging/negotiating different forms of oppression. In that sense, this pedagogy could be applied in other contexts where teachers aim to challenge inequities through micro-transformation – taking small steps towards changing oppressive practices. Future studies could explore this pedagogy in other contexts, creating spaces for youth and teachers to challenge the racism, sexism, homophobia, classism and ableism in their communities. We also believe that intersectionality should be considered in order to understand the complex forms of combined oppression that permeate different levels of HPE (Felis-Anaya, Martos-Garcia & Devís-Devís, 2018).

We suggest that teachers do not have to come from a disempowered position to be able to deliver this kind of pedagogy. To actually achieve the goal of 'treating everyone equally', teachers need to develop the attitudes, knowledge, skills and dispositions necessary to become competent in supporting linguistically, ethnically and culturally diverse students. Furthermore, they need to examine their own values and assumptions about working with youth who are different from them, and to recognise their own privileges. This process requires reflexivity in order to develop awareness of micro-oppressions that lead to micro-transformations.

Reflection points

- What might be the benefits of focusing on social justice within HPE?
- How might teachers seek to better understand their diverse students' needs and attend to these within HPE?
- How might a pedagogy of love be adopted in practice?

Note

1 Freire (1987) defined praxis as reflection and action directed at the structures to be transformed. According to Freire, through the processes of reflection and action, oppressed people can acquire a critical awareness or conscientisation of their own condition, struggling for liberation (Freire, 1987).

References

Bovill, C., Cook-Sather, A., and Felten, P. (2011). Students as co-creators of teaching approaches, course design and curricula: Implications for academic developers. *International Journal for Academic Development, 16*(2), 133–145.

Cahill, C., Rios-Moore, I., and Threatts, T. (2008). Different eyes/open eyes: Community-based participatory action research. In J. Cammarota & M. Fine (Eds.), *Revolutionizing education: Youth participatory action research in motion* (pp. 89–124). New York, NY: Routledge.

Chabot, S. (2008). Love and revolution. *Critical Sociology, 34*(6), 803–828.

Clark, L. (2019). The way they care: An ethnography of social justice physical education teacher. *Teacher Educator, 54*(2), 145–170.

Cook-Sather, A. (2002). Authorizing students' perspectives : Toward trust, dialogue, and change in education. *Educational Researcher, 31*(4), 3–14.

Daniels, E. A. (2012). *Fighting, loving, teaching: An exploration of hope, armed love and critical urban pedagogies*. Rotterdam: Sense Publishers.

Darder, A. (2017). *Reinventing Paulo Freire: A pedagogy of love*. New York, NY: Routledge.

Devís-Devís, J. (2006). Socially critical research perspectives in physical education. In D. Kirk, D. MacDonald & M. O'Sullivan (Eds.), *The handbook of physical education* (Vol. 9, pp. 37–58). London: Sage Publication.

Ennis, C. D. (1999). Creating a culturally relevant curriculum for disengaged girls. *Sport, Education, and Society, 4*(1), 31–49.

Enright, E., Coll, L., Ní Chróinín, D., and Fitzpatrick, M. (2017). Student voice as risky praxis: Democratising physical education teacher education. *Physical Education and Sport Pedagogy, 22*(5), 459–472.

Felis-Anaya, M., Martos-Garcia, D., and Devís-Devís, J. (2018). Socio-critical research on teaching physical education and physical education teacher education: A systematic review. *European Physical Education Review, 24*(3), 314–329.

Freire, P. (1987). *Pedagogia do Oprimido [Pedagogy of the oppressed]* (17th ed.). Sao Paulo: Paz e Terra.

Freire, P. (1998). *Pedagogy of freedom: Ethics, democracy, and civic courage*. Lanham, MD: Rowman & Littlefield Publishers.

Freire, P. (2004). *Pedagogy of indignation*. Boulder, CO: Paradigm Publisher.

Freire, P. (2005). *Teachers as cultural workers: Letters to those who dare teach*. Boulder, CO: Westview Press.

Freire, P., Freire, A. M. A., and de Oliveira, W. F. (2014). *Pedagogy of solidarity*. Abingdon: Routledge.

Giroux, H. A. (2011). *On critical pedagogy*. London: Bloomsbury Academic.

Greene, M. (1995). *Releasing the imagination: Essays on education, the arts, and social change*. Hoboken, NJ: Jossey-Bass.

Hellison. (1978). *Beyond balls and bats*. Washington, DC: American Alliance for Health Physical.

Hill, J., Philpot, R., Walton-Fisette, J. L., Sutherland, S., Flemons, M., Ovens, A., Phillips, S., and Flory, S. B. (2018). Conceptualising social justice and sociocultural issues within physical education teacher education: International perspectives. *Physical Education and Sport Pedagogy, 23*(5), 469–483.

hooks, b. (2001). *All about love: New visions*. New York, NY: William Morrow.

Ladson-Billings, G. (2000). Preparing teachers to teach African American students. *Journal of Teacher Education, 51*(3), 206–214.

Lanas, M., and Zembylas, M. (2015). Towards a transformational political concept of love in critical education. *Studies in Philosophy and Education, 34*(1), 31–44.

Luguetti, C. and McDonald, B. (2020). I always live in a quebrada [favela] and today I am here. So, you can be also here one day': Exploring pre-service teachers' perceptions of love for youth from socially vulnerable backgrounds. *European Physical Education Review.* 26(4), 1006–1022.

Luguetti, C., and Oliver, K. L. (2020). 'I became a teacher that respects the kids' voices': Challenges and facilitators pre-service teachers faced in learning an activist approach. *Sport, Education and Society,* 25(4), 423–435.

Luguetti, C., Kirk, D., and Oliver, K. L. (2019). Towards a pedagogy of love: Exploring pre-service teachers' and youth's experiences of an activist sport pedagogical model. *Physical Education and Sport Pedagogy,* 24(6), 629–646.

Luguetti, C., Oliver, K. L., Dantas, L. E. P. B. T., and Kirk, D. (2017). 'The life of crime does not pay; stop and think!': The process of co-constructing a prototype pedagogical model of sport for working with youth from socially vulnerable backgrounds. *Physical Education and Sport Pedagogy,* 22(4), 329–348.

Mcintyre, A. (2006). Activist research and student agency in universities and urban communities. *Urban Education,* 41(6), 628–647.

Moen, K. M., Westlie, K., Gerdin, G., Smith, W., Linner, S., Philpot, R., Schenker, K., and Larsson, L. (2020). Caring teaching and the complexity of building good relationships as pedagogies for social justice in health and physical education. *Sport, Education and Society,* 25(9), 1015–1028.

Muhammad, M., Wallerstein, N., Sussman, A. L., Avila, M., Belone, L., and Duran, B. (2015). Reflections on researcher identity and power: The impact of positionality on community based participatory research (CBPR) processes and outcomes. *Critical Sociology,* 41(7–8), 1045–1063.

Noddings, N. (1984). *Caring, a feminine approach to ethics & moral education.* Berkeley, CA: University of California Press.

Nygreen, K. (2006). Reproducing or challenging power in the questions we ask and the methods we use: A framework for activist research in urban education. *Urban Review,* 38(1), 1–26.

Oliver, K. L., Oesterreich, H. A., Aranda, R., Archeleta, J., Blazera, C., Crux, K., Martinez, D., McConnell, J., Osta, M., Parks, L., and Robinson, R. (2015). 'The sweetness of struggle': Innovation in physical education teacher education through student-centered inquiry as curriculum in a physical education methods course. *Physical Education and Sport Pedagogy,* 20(1), 97–115.

O'Sullivan, M. (2018). PETE academics as public intellectuals and activists in a global teacher education context. *Physical Education and Sport Pedagogy,* 23(5), 536–543.

Ovens, A., Flory, S. B., Sutherland, S., Philpot, R., Walton-Fisette, J. L., Hill, J., Phillips, S., and Flemons, M. (2018). How PETE comes to matter in the performance of social justice education. *Physical Education and Sport Pedagogy,* 23(5), 484–496.

Owens, L. M., and Ennis, C. D. (2005). The ethic of care in teaching: An overview of supportive literature. *Quest,* 57(4), 392–425.

Philpot, R. (2016). Physical education initial teacher educators' expressions of critical pedagogy(ies). *European Physical Education Review,* 22(2), 260–275.

Rovegno, I., and Kirk, D. (1995). Articulations and silences in socially critical work on physical education: Toward a broader agenda. *Quest,* 47(4), 447–474.

Schenker, K., Linnér, S., Smith, W., Gerdin, G., Mordal Moen, K., Philpot, R., Larsson, L., Legge, M., and Westlie, K. (2019). Conceptualising social justice –What constitutes pedagogies for social justice in HPE across different contexts? *Curriculum Studies in Health and Physical Education,* 10(2), 126–140.

Ty-ron, M., and Ngangta, C. W. (2015). Living the work: Promoting social justice and equity work in schools around the world. *Advances in Educational Administration*, *23*, 59–85.

Walton-Fisette, J. L., and Sutherland, S. (2018). Moving forward with social justice education in physical education teacher education. *Physical Education and Sport Pedagogy*, *23*(5), 461–468.

Zembylas, M. (2017). Love as ethico-political practice: Inventing reparative pedagogies of aimance in "disjointed" times. *Journal of Curriculum and Pedagogy*, *14*(1), 23–38.

13

CULTURALLY RESPONSIVE PEDAGOGY IN HEALTH AND PHYSICAL EDUCATION

Alison Wrench and Robyne Garrett

Introduction

Increased student diversity is a feature of schools across the globe (Santoro, 2013). In Australia, approximately 26% of students are from culturally and linguistically diverse backgrounds. It is, however, the 6% of Indigenous[1] students – together with those from particular ethnic minorities – who disproportionately experience the burden of educational disadvantage (Vass, 2017).

The racism of Australia's colonial and settler past is a presence that continues to frame the nation's Anglo-European-centric schooling systems, whereby educational practices default to white norms and ways of knowing (Rahman, 2013; Morrison, Rigney, Hattam & Diplock, 2019). In denial of the destructive impact of colonisation and Aboriginal sovereignty, Australia's colonial-settler past continues to 'haunt' contemporary policies and practices. When curricula and pedagogical practices, including those within health and physical education (HPE), fail to recognise or value the resources that students from Indigenous and diverse cultural backgrounds bring to their schooling, educational marginalisation and disadvantage are perpetuated (Santoro, 2013; Vass, 2017). This, in turn, counters any claims of 'closing the gap'[2], or that pedagogy today actually *is* responsive to diversity.

Education policies communicate narratives and understandings about race, culture and whiteness. Most recently, two Australian policy directives attempt to address the void in cultural responsiveness and indicate that this is now a pressing issue (Moodie & Patrick, 2017). The Australian Curriculum (AC) asks teachers to embed Aboriginal and Torres Strait Islander histories and cultures into their curricula as a 'cross curricular priority'. Additionally, the Australian Professional Standards for Teachers include standards which address teaching practices to meet the needs of Indigenous, ethnically and linguistically diverse students as well as reconciliation (Australian Institute for Teaching and School Leadership, 2020)[3].

Embedding Indigenous histories, cultures and knowledges has been complicated by state and federal arrangements around funding, policy and delivery (Morrison et al., 2019) and research indicates that many Australian teachers feel ill-equipped to fulfil policy requirements and/or teach Indigenous students (Baynes, 2016). Reasons for this include lack of teacher confidence, knowledge and support, contested, shifting and misunderstood curriculum requirements, deficit views as well as racism (Nakata, 2011; Baynes, 2016). Moreover, schools demonstrate tokenistic efforts when incorporating Indigenous perspectives where it seems that the 'real' business of schooling takes precedence and continues to reproduce powerful messages about 'what counts' (Bishop, Vass & Thompson, 2021). Thus, in a crowded curriculum where 'cross curricular priorities' are not compulsory or assessed, they are marginalised. Importantly, the HPE learning area is not immune from these issues (see Whatman, Quennerstedt & McLaughlin, 2017).

Concomitantly, critique of initial teacher education (ITE) problematises the preparation of teachers to meet the needs of students from diverse cultural, religious and linguistic backgrounds (see Santoro, 2013; Vass, 2017; Warren, 2018). Concerns exists around deterministic notions of culture and a corresponding lack of awareness of how dominant cultures shape identities, pedagogical practices, curriculum design and classroom relationships (Moodie & Patrick, 2017; Bishop et al., 2021). For instance, such is the hegemony of an Anglo-Saxon sporting culture in HPE, it is rarely questioned as an invisible marker of identity and privilege in the field, including within ITE (Flintoff, Dowling & Fitzgerald, 2015; Azzarito & Simon, 2017). As a result, attributes associated with male team sports such as speed, strength and aggression are privileged. In this chapter, we engage with these concerns and investigate how principles of culturally responsive pedagogy (CRP) can be put into practice and activated in the learning area of HPE.

Culturally responsive pedagogy

In adopting socio-cultural understandings of learning, CRP is underpinned by the notion that all curriculum is culturally based (Gay, 2002). CRP calls for approaches to teaching and learning that draw on students' cultural resources to enhance their engagement and inclusion within specific educational contexts (Morrison et al., 2019). The aim being to support participation, enhance learning and promote success whilst building and maintaining cultural identities and capabilities (Warren, 2018). CRP also supports teachers to teach against racism, maintain respect for cultural differences and realise socially just educational outcomes (Santoro, 2013).

Theoretical orientations of CRP promote strengths-based approaches (González, Moll & Amanti, 2006), development of cultural resources (Ladson-Billings, 2014), dialogic approaches (Bishop, 2008) and focus on issues of power and agency (Delpit, 1995). While there has been significant theoretical work in the area of CRP with respect to working with Indigenous and culturally diverse students, ways to actually enact CRP within specific learning areas have been less forthcoming. Moreover, as Lowe and Yunkaporta (2013) warn, the presence of tangible elements of Indigenous cultures within curriculum does not necessarily achieve a deep knowledge and understanding of the histories and cultures of Indigenous peoples and their significance within Australia.

CRP is not a set of *one-size fits all* instructional techniques; however, guiding principles specific to HPE have been developed. Robinson, Borden and Robinson (2013), for instance, argue that if teachers are to teach *for* cultural diversity, recognition and respect, they need to develop understandings about young people's day-to-day cultural landscapes. Young and Sternod (2011) along with Flory and McCaughtry (2011) similarly advocate for recognising the cultural resources of young people and their families when designing learning experiences and pedagogical practices. This involves respecting young people and their families, holding and communicating high expectations for all and utilising child-centred and culturally mediated approaches.

In response to this, we turn to Bishop et al. (2021), who draw on Martin's (2008) 'relatedness theory' to put forward notions of working with 'relationally responsive processes'. Specifically, these processes invite teachers and students to embrace the notion that *everything* interacts in a dynamic system and proper relationships with the world are conducted through respect, responsibility, generosity and obligation. Relational protocols then determine what is known, who we are and what is to be done. These layers of relatedness are best understood through the framework of *Ways of Knowing, Ways of Being* and *Ways of Doing* (Martin & Mirraboopa, 2003).

Ways of knowing comprise knowledge of social, ecological, economic, political and historical contexts and their interrelationships. The various types of knowledge inform respectful and rightful *ways of being* – based on the premise that humans are part of a larger world where a network of relations operates between country, self and others. *Ways of doing* are informed by both *ways of knowing* and *ways of being*. They are largely seen in action, creation of artefacts and the expression of individual and group identities (Martin & Mirraboopa, 2003).

In this chapter, we provide three examples from our work in ITE that exemplify attempts to move past tokenistic efforts at placing 'cultural content' into the HPE curriculum towards relational processes of knowing, being and doing. The aim of these being to co-create and shape meanings around Indigenous perspectives and cultures for all students. We also attempt to give concrete meaning to principles of CRP and move beyond theorising towards seriously considering implications for pedagogy. Our examples are taken from pedagogical practices designed to develop the confidence and capacities of pre-service teachers to engage with and enact CRP in HPE. These practices were integral to a final year HPE course within a Bachelor of Education (primary/middle)[4] degree programme at an Australian University. Course workshops provided opportunities for theoretical concepts to be integrated with practical experiences. In addition, pre-service teachers participated in a lab-school[5] programme where they applied their understandings of CRP to planning, teaching and reflecting on practice.

Data and analysis

Photo-essays incorporating photographs, written explanations and discussion of relevant literature, together with unit outlines and reflections constitute the data discussed in this chapter. Each item was treated as separate datum and read through an interpretive lens. The initial reading focused on orientations towards CRP. A second reading followed Bishop and colleague's (2021) lead in adapting Martin's (2008) 'relatedness theory'. *Ways of knowing* provided us with a framing to analyse emergent knowledge, storylines and understandings of culture and teaching HPE. *Ways of being* provided a lens for engaging with (re)framings of rightful, respectful practices and relationships. In analysing *ways of doing*, we considered the lived interrelationship of processes and practices associated with ways of knowing and being evident in our data sources. In the following sections of the chapter, we discuss our data and relevant literature through a constellation of three themes: *knowing and being in relation to culture, supporting ways of doing CRP in HPE* and *experiencing CRP in the field*.

It is important to acknowledge that our subjectivities as white Anglo-Saxon academics are informed by the discursive and cultural resources of our life-worlds. As with the pre-service teachers we work with, our engagement with CRP has caused us to reflect deeply on the 'whiteness' of narratives, knowledge and relationships that underpin our practices. Working with the data presented in this chapter is part of this ongoing process.

Knowing and being in relation to culture

Culture is a dynamic and continuously changing construct, which is embodied and enacted in schooling practices of teaching, learning and identity work (Ladson-Billings, 2014; Vass, 2017). Accordingly, there are implications for ITE in terms of preparing pre-service teachers who can recognise, value and work constructively with the heterogeneous cultural resources students bring to their schooling (Morrison et al., 2019).

These understandings informed the structure, curriculum content and practices enacted in the pre-service teachers' final year HPE course. Specifically, reading materials addressed themes such as Indigenous perspectives, cultural and racial identities, as well as CRP for HPE. Concomitantly, reading circles were structured to support pre-service teachers in safely engaging in discussions to clarify meanings, consider implications for their practices, as well as identify knowledge gaps around culture and CRP. An outcome of these focused reading discussions were questions, such as those that follow, which pre-service teachers asked in relation to issues they expected to encounter in teaching HPE:

> How do we as teachers create HPE classes that are inclusive of diverse ethnicities and cultures? (Dani)
> How do we engage Aboriginal and Torres Strait Islander students in HPE in ways that are meaningful and authentic? (Chris)

However, in accord with findings by Santoro (2013) and Vass (2017), reading circles and guided discussions also revealed taken-for-granted assumptions that culture is held by 'others' rather than by the pre-service teachers themselves. In response, we introduced discussion topics designed to prompt dialogue about spaces, familial and community structures and associations. The aim being to explore factors that informed pre-service teachers' belief systems and, hence, how they might understand themselves in relation to culture.

These discussions influenced our selection of questions to guide the construction of individual photo-essays or collages. Guiding questions addressed role models, personal strengths, familial and community connections as well as what culture meant to them and what others should know about their culture. Pre-service teachers shared their collages with peers and provided both oral and written elaborations about how they had represented themselves in relation to culture. As exemplified in following excerpts, elaborations provided insights into tacit ways of knowing around encultured identities:

> Knowing your roots and where you came from is one of the most important aspects of culture ... the relationships that I've developed ... through family and people that I've met define who I am ... Culture is important because it is ... your personal identity ... your personal environment ... as well as the things you do. (Josh)
>
> One's culture is formulated by ... values, passions and aspects of life that are important. ... my photo essay displays my culture. I am a twenty-one-year-old Greek orthodox woman who is family oriented ... with the outdoors and nature part of my culture. (Vashti)

These excerpts suggest that discourses of family, community, sport, outdoors and life-worlds were important cultural aspects of Josh and Vashti's identities, including as HPE teachers. Importantly, as with students in schools, points of commonality are not homogenous but are permeated by both unique and diverse ways of knowing and being.

A further requirement of the photo-essay was that pre-service teachers draw on course readings and relevant literature to discuss CRP in HPE and identify implications for teaching. Some pre-service teachers integrated ways of knowing specific to CRP with potential ways of being HPE teachers. As exemplified below, they personalised links between CRP and reframed pedagogical practices:

> I recommend understanding students' backgrounds, developing positive relationships with students and their families to gain ... knowledge and understanding of students and culture. This will support individualising learning in ways that are suitable in their culture. (Addison)
>
> In considering my future HPE teaching and CRP ... I will remain a learner ... develop my understanding of the diversity and issues within

striving for social justice … I will place building positive relationships with my students and their families, knowing my students and how they learn at the forefront of my teaching. (Shannon)

Within the context of Australia, a level of discomfort exists around discussions of race, sport and culture that extends to HPE (Wrench & Garrett, 2020). It is perhaps unsurprising that some drew on discourses of the individual child in qualifying enactment of CRP in HPE. Mitch, for example, in the following excerpt, prioritises 'knowing your students' rather than engaging with ways of knowing specifically informed by ethnicity, culture or Indigeneity. In doing so, he tempers his engagement with the literature and suggests there is a correct form of CRP for HPE:

> CRP, when used correctly, supports HPE for all students. However, … we have to look beyond the race and ethnicity of culture which, I feel at times the literature focuses on heavily. I think that if we look at the culture of the individual on a personal basis … then the implementation of CRPs will be far more effective. … We must teach and focus on the individual whilst respecting their group identity … I recommend that educators focus on the implementation of CRP in HPE, but in specific focus to the individualised cultural needs of their students. (Mitch)

According to Bishop and colleagues (2021, p. 198), *ways of knowing* informed by 'colonial-majoritarian-stories' work to reinforce taken-for-granted 'truths' about Indigenous students whilst negating alternative possibilities. Mitch's focus on the individual child exemplifies how societal structures and institutional practises that contribute to the underachievement and alienation of Indigenous students from schooling can be rendered invisible or discounted (Moodie & Patrick, 2017).

In sum, reading circles, discussions and photo-essays were used pedagogically to initiate ways of knowing and being in relation to culture and identity as well as exploring orientations towards CRP. However, as the excerpt from Mitch indicates, this is not necessarily straightforward. Knowledge and awareness are insufficient on their own. We turn next to curriculum alternatives and pedagogical practices designed to develop confidence and capacities in ways of being and doing in relation to CRP.

Supporting ways of doing culturally responsive pedagogy in health and physical education

Within Western nations, such as Australia, games and sports provide a dominant cultural framing for HPE curricula. Consequently, ways of knowing, being and doing are largely informed by discourses and power relations associated with sporting cultures, which tend to privilege an Anglo-Saxon middle-class male student norm (Dowling & Flintoff, 2018; Wrench & Garrett, 2020). This can lead to the marginalisation of attributes associated with aesthetic activities along with movement forms valued in Indigenous and ethnic minority cultures. Concerns, hence, arise for those students who cannot locate their culturally informed physicality, motor competencies and movement forms in traditional games-based HPE. Importantly, as argued by Rahman (2013), all students have a right to feel culturally connected, valued and supported in all aspects of their schooling.

Aboriginal and Torres Strait Islander games sourced from the Yulunga[6] resource (Edwards, 2008) were integral to our attempts to address concerns about the dominant games-based model of HPE. In positioning culturally informed games as creditable HPE curriculum content, our aim was to foreground aspects of a movement culture 'that the dominant system has sought to marginalize for so long' (Bishop, 2008, p. 457). Traditionally, in Aboriginal communities, games and play had been used to prepare Indigenous children for pastimes and daily life, including economic, political, social and cultural aspects (Salter, 1967; Edwards, 2008).

We were cognisant that simply playing the games would not necessarily build capacities to enact culturally aware and respectful pedagogies. As reported by Dinan-Thompson, Meldrum & Sellwood (2014), when pre-service teachers are not convinced about CRP they problematise and question the utility of the Yulunga games resource. This is exemplified by Jordan, who asked, 'Can we actually teach students cultural inclusion and the importance of cultural identity through traditional Indigenous Games?'

Game play was, therefore, accompanied by questions designed to support reflection about social and cultural contributions of games. On one level, questions addressed connections to 'country'[7], skills, strategies as well as similarities to games from pre-service teachers' own and other's movement cultures. On another level, questions – such as those that follow – were designed to provoke deeper levels of critical reflection and discussion:

> Why would we include Aboriginal and Torres Strait Islander games in HPE?
> Why might it be important to foster cooperation rather than competition in playing these games?
> How do the questions you ask influence the development of forms of knowledge and understanding?

Following the recommendation of Dinan-Thompson and colleagues (2014), engagement with Indigenous ways of knowing and being in relation to games was facilitated through non-competitive and/or cooperative game play. This conditioning of game play also facilitated the incorporation of strategies suggested by an Indigenous colleague, Professor Lester-Irabinna Rigney and Aboriginal support staff in local schools. These strategies included the use of Kaurna[8] expressions such as padniadlu *(let's go)*, ngaityondi *(it's mine)* and paltondo *(shoot, throw)* in game play. We also explored the use of Aboriginal symbols to record games.

Collectively, these practices represent culturally mediated reorientations of ped-agogies, which counter normative forms of communication in HPE.

This assemblage of pedagogical practices entailed a shift in power relations that impacted on ways of doing and being in HPE classes. By means of gradual release of responsibility, pre-service teachers were provided with opportunities to use the Yulunga resource in negotiating, planning and peer teaching lessons featuring cooperative play and facilitative questioning. The aim was to build pedagogical confidence as well as capacities to teach for cultural connections and awareness. Pre-service teachers were positioned as active participants in learning 'about', 'in' and 'through' Indigenous games. These culturally mediated cur-ricular and pedagogical choices represent a departure from traditional teacher-directed approaches towards ways of knowing, doing and being in HPE.

Experiencing culturally responsive pedagogy in the field: Culture, health and physical activity

Villegas and Lucas (2002) remind us of the importance of purposeful ITE field experiences in the preparation of culturally responsive teachers and a five les-son HPE lab-school programme provided a means of addressing this within our context. The lab-school programme was enacted in primary schools located in the northern region of Adelaide, which is framed by intergenerational socio-economic disadvantage (Wrench, Hammond, McCallum & Price, 2013). Schools in this region are noted for student diversity, including significant numbers of Indigenous students. Pre-service teachers worked in pairs to plan, teach and reflect upon an 'Indigenous Games' or 'Games from Around the World' unit. Each pair taught half-classes of students aged 10–13. They were also required to incorporate cooperative play and use questions to develop cultural awareness.

Despite these guidelines, some interpreted 'Games from Around the World' in more mainstream ways and set about planning for European handball or soc-cer units. These choices highlight the dominance of mainstream sports/games within their ways of knowing in relation to HPE curriculum and pedagogy. In response, we introduced questions to guide pre-service teachers' reflections towards who might be privileged by teaching a mainstream sports/games unit. As a consequence, some pre-service teachers redesigned units to focus on the development of fundamental movement skills (FMS) through Indigenous games. In the following excerpt from their lab-school unit plan, Ali and Stevie demon-strate expanded ways of knowing around utilising Indigenous games as means for developing FMS:

> This unit focuses on FMS of catching and throwing techniques ... Throughout the unit Indigenous catching and throwing games will be incorporated to show ... the similarities and differences between com-mon sports and traditional Indigenous games ... They will recognise why

Indigenous people played these games, where they played the games and the similarities these games have to other sports. (Ali and Stevie)

They also suggest it is important to help students make cultural connections between mainstream sports and Indigenous games. More generally, pre-service teachers variously incorporated aspects of their university-based learning in designing, teaching and reflecting upon units. For example, in the following unit priorities, Aaron and Sally signify a commitment to ensuring rightful and respectful ways of being in their unit priorities, along with developing knowledge about the cultural components of games:

We MUST

- Establish and maintain high expectations of students in order to create a safe and respectful place for everyone
- Teach about the cultural aspects of the games
- Teach how the games are played and allow for students to practise these games
- Explore symbols to represent the game and how students can create their own
- Teach rules and how to umpire and manage their own games
- Develop cooperation, fair play and teamwork (Aaron and Sally)

Aaron and Sally also indicate that the structure of the learning environment as well as communication of high expectations about student relationships and participation are important. Moreover, their priorities exemplify principles of CRP outlined by Young and Sternod (2011) in relation to respect, recognition and teaching for and about culture. This extends to developing life-world skills and capacities such as being responsible and enacting fair play.

In the following example, it is the cultural landscape of Aboriginal ways of knowing, specifically Kaurna people's history, dreaming stories, cultural conventions and connections to 'country' that are identified as unit priorities:

We MUST

- Ensure all students have a clear understanding of appropriate behaviours and Kaurna history prior to visiting the Kaurna sacred area (Warriparinga Wetlands)
- Make sure that students have an understanding of the dreamtime and the Indigenous belief system prior to the bushwalk
- Make sure Aboriginal students in the class are engaged as they may already be aware of the information we teach
- Make sure we are aware of the prior knowledge of Aboriginal students, draw on this knowledge in class and add to it (Tino and Jamie)

Drawing on discourses of respect and recognition, Tino and Jamie construct Aboriginal students as knowledgeable. By signalling that Aboriginal ways of knowing, being and doing are valuable resources, they demonstrate a potential to communicate this to all students in the class no matter their cultural or ethnic background.

A requirement of the lab-school programme was that pre-service teachers reflected upon their planning and teaching in relation to CRP. Some, as is evident in Adrian and Cam's reflection below, noted student resistance founded in previous experiences with the cultural landscapes of mainstream sports/games:

> Students seemed most engaged during the Ulu Maika activity. However, when playing Veicaqe Moli (soccer-inspired activity), some students looked disinterested and were disengaged with the activity. I believe this is because soccer only accommodates those students who enjoy this type of ball sport. (Adrian and Cam)

Adrian and Cam consider the impact of students' past experiences in soccer, which they believe contributed to student disengagement. In doing so, they begin to problematise ways of being experienced by some students in mainstream sports/games such as soccer. Other reflections provided an indication of pre-service teachers' learning in relation to culture and Indigenous games. Jarrod and Matt, as evidenced in the following excerpt, provide an insight into how learning 'about' culture can occur 'through' and 'in' Indigenous games:

> From lab-school with the 5/6s we have been able to build on our knowledge and understanding of Indigenous culture by teaching and playing numerous games with the students. (Jarrod and Matt)

Sally and Emma, in the excerpt below, reflected on the merits of specific pedagogical practices such as using Aboriginal symbols as a form of recording and communication about learning:

> … the symbols worked … We scaffolded the task which meant by the final week students were able to draw their own symbols for a game they played. For many, this was a highlight of lab-school. (Sally and Emma)

Collectively, these reflections illuminated the various ways pre-service teachers considered the interrelatedness of their own and students' ways of knowing, being and doing in relation to culture. Specifically, the lab-school programme provided opportunities to apply learning about culture, Indigenous games and being respectful and inclusive within practice. Plans and reflections also revealed new possibilities for engaging in culturally responsive ways. This is evident in statements about recognising and valuing differences, broadened cultural understandings and strategies such as integration across learning areas.

Conclusion

The focus of this chapter was on the development of pedagogical practices associated with CRP, which were enacted in a final year HPE course within a Bachelor of Education degree programme. Whilst the discussion around CRP focused specifically on the Australian context, we believe that connections can be made to support pre-service teachers' preparation for working with students from diverse cultural backgrounds within other Euro-centric schooling systems. Specifically, the chapter advocates for the preparation of pre-service teachers who can teach HPE in ways that include all students, no matter their cultural, linguistic and/or religious backgrounds. As such, our focus on CRP in HPE is *embedding* culturally informed games and ways of knowing rather than treating these as add-ons.

Three sets of interrelated strategies in relation to CRP in HPE were explored. The first focused on building ways of knowing in relation to culture. The second cluster of strategies focused on building ways of knowing to produce respectful ways of being through playing and teaching Indigenous games. Conditions of cooperative play and facilitative questions were utilised to bring ways of knowing and being together with the doing practices of planning and teaching. Opportunities for further development and refinement of these interrelated practices were provided through the third strategy of a lab-school programme.

This chapter has established that whilst ways of knowing and being are interrelated, it is 'how' practices or ways of doing are enacted that give form to the adoption of CRP in HPE. In this respect, the lab-school programme provided evidence of intentionality, enactment and reflection. Specifically, this was in relation to non-traditional HPE curricula and pedagogies in the form of Indigenous games, conditions of cooperative play, using language and symbols as well as facilitative questions to build cultural awareness, connections and engagement.

Pre-service teachers did not engage with and adopt these practices in a universal manner. The strategies do, however, have potential for reshaping HPE curriculum and pedagogical practices in ITE. From these experiences, we contend that if pre-service teachers are to develop deep and generative pedagogical practices that are responsive to the diverse cultural, linguistic and embodied practices of students in schools, we too, as teacher educators, need to confront our assumptions about valued knowledge and practices.

Reflection points

- In what ways might HPE curricula and pedagogies reinforce rather than counter ways of knowing, being and doing that marginalise Indigenous and ethnic minority students?
- How can HPE curricula and pedagogies value and connect to the cultural and linguistic life-worlds of Indigenous and ethnic minority students, their families and communities?

- In what ways can pedagogical practices support and respect student input, negotiation and decision-making?

Notes

1 We use the terms Aboriginal, Torres Strait Islander and Indigenous interchangeably in this paper, whilst recognising the colonial legacy that these carry.
2 *Closing the Gap* is a National Agreement developed in partnership between Australian Governments and Aboriginal and Torres Strait Islander peak organisations that sets out targets and Priority Reforms to improve life outcomes experienced by Indigenous Australians.
3 Promoting reconciliation prioritises the need for the teaching workforce to reflect on their role in working towards reconciliation and improving the educational experiences of Aboriginal and Torres Strait Islander students.
4 Primary/middle refers to children in the 10–15-year-old age range.
5 Lab-school represents an application of theory to a practical setting through the provision of opportunities to work with groups of young adolescents in the area of HPE.
6 The Yulunga games resource is a collation of Aboriginal and Torres Strait Islander games from all parts of Australia.
7 Country encapsulates an interdependent relationship between individuals and their ancestral lands and seas that is sustained by cultural knowledge, histories and language.
8 The *Kaurna* people are the original inhabitants of Adelaide and the Adelaide Plains, South Australia. Kaurna language is, hence, the original language of the lands where the university that the pre-service teachers attended is located.

References

Australian Institute for Teaching and School Leadership. (2020). *Australian professional standards for teachers.* Melbourne, Australia: Australian Institute for Teaching and School Leadership.

Azzarito, L. and Simon, M. (2017). Interrogating whiteness in physical education teacher education. In K. A. Richards and K. L. Gaudreault (Eds.), *Teacher socialization in physical education.* New York, NY: Routledge, pp. 176–193.

Baynes, R. (2016). Teachers' attitudes to including indigenous knowledges in the Australian science curriculum. *The Australian Journal of Indigenous Education*, 45(1), 80–90.

Bishop, M., Vass, G. and Thompson, K. (2021). Decolonising schooling practices through relationality and reciprocity: Embedding local Aboriginal perspectives in the classroom. *Pedagogy, Culture & Society*, 29(2), 193–211.

Bishop, R. (2008). Te Kotahitanga: Kaupapa Maori in mainstream classrooms. In N. K. Denzin, Y. S. Lincoln and L. T. Smith (Eds.), *Handbook of critical and Indigenous methodologies.* Thousand Oaks, CA: Sage Publications, pp. 439–458.

Delpit, L. (1995). *Other people's children: Cultural conflict in the classroom.* New York, NY: W. W. Norton & Co.

Dinan-Thompson, M., Meldrum, K. and Sellwood, J. (2014). "… it is not just a game": Connecting with culture through traditional indigenous games. *American Journal of Educational Research*, 2(11), 1015–1002.

Dowling, F. and Flintoff, A. (2018). A whitewashed curriculum? The construction of race in contemporary PE curriculum policy. *Sport, Education and Society*, 23(1), 1–13.

Edwards, K. (2008). *Yulunga: Traditional Indigenous games.* Canberra: Australian Sports Commission.

Flintoff, A., Dowling, F. and Fitzgerald. H. (2015). Working through whiteness, race and (anti) racism in physical education teacher education. *Physical Education and Sport Pedagogy,* 20(5), 559–570.

Flory, S. B. and McCaughtry, N. (2011). Culturally relevant physical education in urban schools. *Research Quarterly for Exercise and Sport,* 82(1), 49–60.

Gay, G. (2002). Preparing for culturally responsive teaching. *Journal of Teacher Education,* 53(2), 106–116.

González, N., Moll, L. C. and Amanti, C. (2006). *Funds of knowledge: Theorizing practices in households, communities, and classrooms.* Mahwah NJ: Lawrence Erlbaum.

Ladson-Billings, G. (2014). Culturally relevant pedagogy 2.0: a.k.a. the remix. *Harvard Educational Review,* 84 (1), 74–84.

Lowe, K. and Yunkaporta, T. (2013). The inclusion of Aboriginal and Torres Strait Islander content in the Australian National Curriculum: A cultural, cognitive and socio-political evaluation. *Curriculum Perspectives,* 33(1), 1–14.

Martin, K. (2008). *Please knock before you enter: Aboriginal regulation of outsiders and the implications for researchers.* Brisbane: Post Pressed.

Martin, K. and Mirraboopa, B. (2003). Ways of knowing, being and doing: A theoretical framework and methods for indigenous and indigenist re-search. *Journal of Australian Studies,* 27(76), 203–214.

Moodie, N. and Patrick, R. (2017). Settler grammars and the Australian professional standards for teachers. *Asia-Pacific Journal of Teacher Education,* 45(5), 439–454.

Morrison, A., Rigney, L-I., Hattam, R. and Diplock, A. (2019). *Toward and Australian culturally responsive pedagogy: A narrative review of the literature.* Adelaide: University of South Australia.

Nakata, M. (2011). Pathways for indigenous education in the Australian curriculum framework. *The Australian Journal of Indigenous Education,* 40, 1–8.

Rahman, K. (2013). Belonging and learning to belong in school: The implications for the hidden curriculum for indigenous students. *Discourse: Studies in the Cultural Politics of Education,* 34(5), 660–672.

Robinson, D. B., Borden, L. L. and Robinson, I. M. (2013). Charting a course for culturally responsive physical education. *Alberta Journal of Educational Research,* 58(4), 526–546.

Salter, M. A. (1967). *Games and pastimes of the Australian aboriginal.* Edmonton: Master of Arts, The University of Alberta.

Santoro, N. (2013). The making of teachers for the twenty-first century: Australian professional standards and the preparation of culturally responsive teachers. In Z. Xudong and Z. Kenneth (Eds.), *Preparing teachers for the 21st century, new frontiers of educational research.* Berlin: Springer-Verlag, pp. 309–321.

Vass, G. (2017). Preparing for culturally responsive schooling: Initial teacher educators into the fray. *Journal of Teacher Education,* 68(5), 451–462.

Villegas, A. and Lucas, T. (2002). Preparing culturally responsive teachers: Rethinking the curriculum. *Journal of Teacher Education,* 53(1), 20–32.

Warren, C. A. (2018). Empathy, teacher dispositions and preparation for culturally responsive pedagogy. *Journal of Teacher Education,* 69(2), 169–183.

Whatman, S., Quennerstedt, M. and McLaughlin, J. (2017). Indigenous knowledges as a way to disrupt norms in physical education teacher education. *Asia-Pacific Journal of Health, Sport and Physical Education,* 8(2), 115–131.

Wrench, A. and Garrett, R. (2020). Navigating culturally responsive peda-gogy through an indigenous games unit. *Sport, Education and Society.* DOI: 10.1080/13573322.2020.1764520: 1–13.

Wrench, A., Hammond, C., McCallum, F. and Price, D. (2013). Inspire to aspire: Raising aspirational outcomes through a student well-being curricular focus. *International Journal of Inclusive Education,* 17(9), 932–947.

Young, S. and Sternod, B. M. (2011). Practicing culturally responsive pedagogy in phys-ical education. *Journal of Modern Educational Review,* 1(1), 1–9.

14

PROPOSALS FOR ENGAGING STUDENTS IN OUTSOURCED HEALTH AND PHYSICAL EDUCATION

Leigh Sperka, Julie Stirrup and Oliver Hooper

Introduction

Research on the outsourcing of education – and in particular, health and physical education (H/PE)[1] – has witnessed a marked growth in recent years. Outsourcing within education can be defined as 'a practice that involves establishing and maintaining some form of strategic and bilateral relationship with an external entity with the intention for that entity to either extend, substitute, or replace internal capabilities' (Sperka, 2020, p. 275). Importantly, the practice 'is neither intrinsically good nor bad' rather it is 'the way it is applied [that] has fundamental impact on how it affects organisations and people' (Bravard & Morgan, 2006, p. xii). Given this, it is crucial to consider how the practice of outsourcing is, and should be, applied within H/PE. As such, within this chapter, we offer research-informed proposals for 'best practice' in outsourcing within H/PE, including examining who should identify what is outsourced, how roles and responsibilities should be distributed in outsourcing arrangements and how the practice should be monitored and evaluated. Within each of these proposals, we pay particular attention to students, as they are the primary stakeholders in (outsourced) educational experiences. We argue that listening and responding to student voice in outsourced H/PE might lead to more engaging and educative experiences. However, before offering these proposals, we first position outsourcing as a practice that challenges public/private binaries and then explore what it looks like in H/PE in Australia and England.

Public/private binaries in education

There has been much debate about, and problematisation of, the public/private binary. According to Weintraub (1997), 'the distinction between "public" and "private" has been a central and characteristic preoccupation of Western thought since classical antiquity …' (p. 1). Focusing on this binary within education, Pring (1987) claimed over 30 years ago that 'what is certain is that the old, simple and clear distinctions between public and private no longer hold' (p. 290). More recently, Ball (2007) called the binary 'simple', arguing it is of 'limited analytical value' (p. 102) and calling instead for researchers to 'explore the blurring's and elisions between them [public/private]' (p. 15). Since then, several researchers have responded to this call to action, seeking to represent the complexity of schooling provision beyond the public/private binary (see Mockler, Hogan, Lingard, Rahimi & Thompson, 2020). While there are a number of practices that exemplify how there is a 'continuum' (Ball, 2007) or 'sliding scale' (Mockler et al., 2020) between public and private (e.g. privatisation and commercialisation), we focus specifically on outsourcing. The practice of outsourcing, as noted above, involves working with an external entity and, within the context of education, this has led to the 'inside and outside of the … teaching profession [becoming] increasingly indistinct' (Sperka, 2020, p. 279).

Outsourcing within health and physical education

The outsourcing of H/PE is not new, with studies about the practice published as early as the 1950s (e.g. Veitch, 1954). What is new, however, is its pervasiveness. While it was 'unusual' in the 1980s and 1990s to outsource H/PE work, a recent scoping review of the practice revealed it is now happening more extensively within H/PE in many countries globally (Sperka & Enright, 2018). However, that is not to say that outsourced H/PE 'looks' the same in these different countries. Context plays a particularly important role in determining whether and how outsourcing takes place in H/PE, as illustrated by the following examples from Australia and England.

Australia

The Australian timeline on the outsourcing of H/PE provided by Sperka (2020) reveals that the practice has a long history, albeit in different forms. Currently, the outsourcing of H/PE in Australia involves either generalist primary teachers or specialist H/PE secondary teachers purchasing products or services to be delivered in the subject. These products and services can be created by government agencies, sporting associations, private companies and not-for-profit organisations (Sperka & Enright, 2019a) and are delivered by either the teachers or external entity employees. Several changes have amplified the 'fertile conditions' (Griggs, 2012, p. 261) for the outsourcing of H/PE in Australia. Firstly, the introduction of the Australian Curriculum: Health and Physical Education standardised, to a greater extent than previously, the curriculum taught in each Australian state and territory. For external entities involved in education in Australia, this means they no longer need to tailor their products and services for every individual curriculum context across the country and can now create one 'ready-made' product instead, thus increasing profitability. Secondly, new Australian Government initiatives, such as Sporting Schools (Hogan & Stylianou, 2018; Sperka, Enright & McCuaig, 2018), are also supporting and funding the opening up of H/PE to sporting associations. Therefore, in the present Australian H/PE context, there is much potential for outsourcing practices to expand further.

England

There was a shift in England, in 2002, from specialist to generalist training for teachers through 'Qualifying to Teach' (DfES, 2002), which meant that primary school teachers did not need subject specialisms in addition to their initial teacher training. This reduction in subject specialisms was further impacted by national strategies from government such as Physical Education, School Sport and Club Links (PESSCL) and Physical Education and School Sport for Young People (PESSYP) both of which changed the nature, structure and workforce of physical education (PE) and school sport. The purpose of these strategies was to transform the delivery of PE and school sport, by raising standards and increasing the amount of time students (aged 5–16 years) spent participating in high quality PE and school sport. These strategies saw the introduction of school sports coordinators and primary link teachers whose roles were to reinforce links between primary feeder schools and their respective secondary schools. Specifically, they focused on developing school-club links and promoting high quality PE which arguably initiated the practice of outsourcing within England, albeit to qualified PE teachers (usually working within neighbouring secondary schools) in the first instance. Following the end of the PESSCL and PESSYP strategies – and their associated funding – the resultant deskilling of primary teachers became evident and, unsurprisingly, what Kirk (2010, p. 128) terms, the 'emerging community of degree qualified sports coaches' were used to fill this 'gap', delivering not only extracurricular PE but now also curriculum PE (Griggs, 2010). From 2012 onwards, outsourcing has continued to gain popularity due to the increased focus, from government and beyond, on issues of health, well-being and physical activity. In line with this, schools have increasingly been turned to as vehicles through which to address public health outcomes (see Chapter 6, this volume). This has resulted in increased government funding to support PE and school sport provision, particularly within primary schools via the PE and Sport Premium (PESP) funding (see Lindsey, Metcalfe, Gemar, Alderman & Armstrong, 2021 and Chapter 1, this volume).

Putting outsourcing to work

It is clear from this brief overview of these two differing contexts that the outsourcing of H/PE is 'here to stay'. Within both Australia and England, the increasing prevalence – and pervasiveness – of outsourcing has changed who delivers H/PE as well as the purpose/position of the subject within an increasingly privatised neoliberal education system. In the following sections, we pose questions about who should identify what is outsourced, how roles and responsibilities should be distributed in outsourcing arrangements and how the practice should be monitored and evaluated, offering research-informed proposals for 'best practice' in response to each.

Who should be identifying the (outsourced) learning experiences?

One way to interrogate who is currently determining what gets outsourced in H/PE is to use the concepts of supply (i.e. what products and services are available) and demand (i.e. what products and services are wanted and/or needed). While Williams and Macdonald (2015) explain that these concepts are 'generated through a process of joint elaboration' (p. 67), only external entities and school staff appear to routinely be part of this process. With regard to external entities, many of them construct their products and services by identifying 'problems' that need to be 'solved', such as physical inactivity and/or obesity (e.g. Powell, 2014, 2018 and Chapter 8, this volume). Although these products and services are targeted at students, there is little research on whether these entities work with students to identify 'problems' that are relevant to them. A study by Welch, Alfrey and Harris (2021) – in which they examined a food and nutrition resource called 'Phenomenom!', co-designed with both teachers and students – represents a notable exception in this regard, though it did not focus specifically on outsourcing within H/PE. Meanwhile, turning to school staff, the justifications they offer for outsourcing H/PE include that it enables access to perceived 'expertise' (Sperka & Enright, 2018) and provides more variety and diversity within the H/PE curriculum (Williams, Hay & Macdonald, 2011; Williams & Macdonald, 2015). While it could be argued that both of these justifications have students' 'best interests' at heart – that is, ensuring they get 'the best knowledge possible' (Williams & Macdonald, 2015, p. 60) and increasing choice within H/PE – it appears that teachers are speaking *for* students rather than speaking *with* them about these educational decisions. As such, if students are not actively involved in outsourcing decisions, their agency is not being recognised.

We therefore propose that students and teachers engage in dialogic communication (Robinson & Taylor, 2007) about (outsourced) learning experiences in H/PE. This might look similar to the processes of curriculum negotiation already taking place in the subject (e.g. Enright & O'Sullivan, 2010). Students could identify a H/PE-related topic that is relevant to them and which they would like to learn more about. Teachers, by critically reading and interpreting the curriculum, can determine the key content that would need to be covered on that topic. Subsequently, through a collaborative process, students and teachers can plan the unit, including the objectives, the learning activities and the assessment. During this planning stage, teachers can determine whether the school has internal capabilities to cover that particular topic. If the school does not have the required knowledge or skills, and/or if the students indicate that they would benefit from hearing from someone outside of the school, it is at that point that they would turn to external entities. Engaging students meaningfully from the beginning would recognise their knowledge and expertise, something which has been 'notably absent' from outsourcing practices within H/PE to date (Enright, Kirk & Macdonald, 2020, p. 220). Further, it would position them as key stakeholders in the strategic and bilateral relationship between external entities and schools (Sperka, 2020), helping to ensure that their experiences are shaped by their own needs and interests.

How should the roles and responsibilities in outsourcing arrangements be distributed?

Existing literature on the outsourcing of H/PE reflects the idea that 'every out-sourcing arrangement is … unique' (Sperka, 2020, p. 274). Within some studies, researchers found that teachers were completely relinquishing control of H/PE to external entities (Ní Chróinín & O'Brien, 2019), whereas in others, teachers were found to be co-teaching with external entities (Sperka & Enright, 2019b). Regardless of what form the outsourcing arrangement takes, there will inevitably be an impact on teachers' roles.

Researchers have already begun to propose how a teacher's role might change as a result of the outsourcing of H/PE. More specifically, it has been suggested that they should become knowledge-brokers and boundary span-ners (e.g. Sperka et al., 2018; Sperka & Enright, 2019b). Macdonald (2015) introduced the idea of teacher-as-knowledge-broker in purchasing/accessing products and services. This involves teachers making 'ongoing judgments about the cost/benefit of [external entities'] products, resources and services with respect to their programme's goals' (p. 34). Building on this, Sperka and colleagues (2018) suggested that teachers need to be supported to develop their critical analysis skills when knowledge-brokering so that they can effec-tively evaluate how external entities construct their products and services in relation to curriculum, pedagogy and assessment. Allied to this, is the notion of teachers becoming boundary spanners. Boundary spanning as an idea was introduced by Webb (1991) and Williams (2002, 2012) and it has since been translated to the H/PE field through research on outsourcing (e.g. Petrie, Penney & Fellows, 2015; Hogan & Stylianou, 2018; Sperka et al., 2018; Sperka & Enright, 2019b). According to Sperka and Enright (2019b, p. 580), a teacher's role as a boundary spanner includes:

> being a reticulist (i.e. bridging the interests of [external entities], the school, and the students – see Sperka et al., 2018) as well as an interpreter/communicator (i.e. integrating perspectives from all stakeholders in the

[external entities'] unit to achieve shared understanding about roles and responsibilities).

To date, what these roles 'look like' in practice has not been fully articulated. We believe that being a knowledge-broker and boundary spanner should involve teachers engaging with a potential external entity at an early stage to discuss the division of labour in relation to curriculum, pedagogy and assessment in H/PE (Williams et al., 2011; Williams & Macdonald, 2015). This would be a relatively significant departure from common practice, where 'detailed conversations about teaching, learning and assessment in physical education [are] absent from interactions between the teachers and the external providers ...' (Ní Chróinín & O'Brien, 2019, p. 334).

With regard to curriculum, in addition to negotiating this with students, we propose that teachers should determine their capacity to modify any products or services that an external entity will provide. Presently, there is limited space for teachers to adjust products and services within H/PE. This is, at least partially, a result of product 'integrity' (Kirk, 2020) and 'fidelity' (McCuaig & Hay, 2014) being valued by external entities. When products and services are 'locked down' (Kirk, 2020) or take a 'one-size-fits-all' approach, they can fail 'to meet the wide-ranging educational, physical, emotional, language, spiritual, social, behavioural needs of the children' (Powell, 2015, p. 84). It is therefore crucial that teachers are able to make relevant contextual modifications to ensure any products and services provided in H/PE are responsive to students' learning needs and interests.

Pedagogically, we propose that teachers should always be actively involved in outsourced H/PE lessons. This proposal aligns with emerging outsourcing guidelines (see Tatton, 2018) and scholarly calls for external entities to collaborate with teachers rather than replace them (e.g. Webster, 2001; Lavin, Swindlehurst & Foster, 2008; Sperka & Enright, 2019b; Randall, 2020). While external entity employees bring their sport- or health-specific knowledge, experience and/or skills to outsourced lessons (Blair & Capel, 2011; Powell, 2015; Sperka & Enright, 2019b; Randall, 2020), teachers bring their knowledge, experience and/or skills of curriculum, pedagogy, assessment and, perhaps most importantly, the students. More specifically, teachers should be making curricular links within outsourced H/PE lessons and ensuring that learning experiences are logically sequenced and appropriate for all students. Conversations between the teachers and external entity employees about the needs of specific children and the management of behaviour should continue to happen (Ní Chróinín & O'Brien, 2019). Overall, this approach would have several benefits. It would give students access to the 'vibrancy of new ways of teaching and learning' that are articulated in commercial products and services (Macdonald, 2015, p. 28), while ensuring that the H/PE curriculum is not narrowed (e.g. Powell, 2015) and that the educative intent of the subject is retained (e.g. Quennerstedt, 2019). Further, it may help to address previously raised concerns about the pedagogical capacity of external providers (e.g. Blair & Capel, 2011; Powell, 2015; Smith, 2015). Finally, if teachers remain actively involved in H/PE lessons, they can mediate any of the potentially problematic notions articulated/practised by external entity employees, such as those associated with performative pedagogy (see Stirrup, 2020).

As for assessment, it is a comparatively under-researched area in the outsourcing of H/PE. Within the few studies that do explore this (see Gordon, Cowan, McKenzie & Dyson, 2013; Dyson, Gordon, Cowan & McKenzie, 2016; Sperka & Enright, 2019b), there is limited detail about what might be considered 'best practice'. Sperka and Enright (2019b) highlight how the inclusion of external entities 'adds complexity to assessment practices in H/PE and may compromise instructional alignment and student learning' (p. 577). As noted above, we propose that the construction of assessment in outsourced H/PE should be a collaborative process between students and teachers. Therefore, before the commencement of any services, teachers and external entity employees should liaise about the negotiated assessment, including what knowledge and skills are to be assessed and how, what evidence is required and who should be responsible for collecting that evidence. With teachers and external entity employees working together, we hope that this will begin to address previous issues around assessment in outsourced H/PE.

How should we monitor and evaluate the outcomes of outsourced learning experiences?

This aspect of outsourced H/PE is an area that has been identified as needing further inquiry. Within some studies, participants reported that external entities' products and services were rarely evaluated (e.g. Gordon et al., 2013 and Dyson et al., 2016), whereas in others it was suggested that teachers were 'discerning about aspects of [outsourced H/PE] delivery as evidenced by the fact that not all external providers were equally valued' (Ní Chróinín & O'Brien, 2019, p. 332). As part of the latter study, teachers judged external providers based on their ability to set tasks that were appropriate for students' stage of learning and their enthusiasm while delivering their service. Sperka (2020) has called for investigations into exactly 'how schools make the decision to continue outsourcing … [including the] processes employed by schools to evaluate the quality of external entities or determine whether the division of labour for curriculum, pedagogy, and assessment is appropriate and effective' (p. 277).

We propose that, in addition to teachers and external entity employees discussing the division of labour in relation to curriculum, pedagogy and assessment in H/PE at an early stage, they should also determine the duration of engagement and explicitly outline the objectives and expectations of the outsourced learning experiences. During any extended periods of outsourced H/PE, there should be repeated 'check-ins' to see whether those objectives and expectations are being worked towards and/or achieved. This should include working with students to see whether their needs and interests are being met as well as whether they are making progress in their learning. At the end of the outsourcing arrangement, there should be a debrief between teachers and the external entity employees about the provided service and a discussion about whether the division of labour was appropriate. By having such discussions, we would hope that a strategic relationship between the school and the external entity could be established and maintained (Sperka, 2020).

Conclusion

The 'best practice' proposals that we offer in this chapter are *research-informed*. Whilst we have endeavoured to utilise as much of the existing literature on the outsourcing of H/PE as possible, there are a few noteworthy points about the process that are important to discuss. Firstly, many of the studies that we drew on focused on the PE aspect of H/PE. A scoping review on the outsourcing of H/PE, conducted by Sperka and Enright (2018), found that of the 31 studies, 24 were about PE and/or sport, four were about H/PE and three were about health education. Since then, more studies have continued to be published in the PE space (e.g. Parnell, Cope, Bailey & Widdop, 2017; Sperka & Enright, 2019b; Bowles & O'Sullivan, 2020; Mangione, Parker, O'Sullivan & Quayle, 2020; Stirrup, 2020) than in the H/PE and health education spaces (e.g. Kirk, 2020; McCuaig, Woolcock, Stylianou, Ng & Ha, 2020; Rossi & Kirk, 2020). While this could be the result of differing conceptualisations of H/PE globally, it nevertheless highlights that outsourcing within health education might need more scholarly attention. Secondly, the research we utilised rarely sought the perspectives of all stakeholders in outsourced H/PE (i.e. students, teachers and external entity employees) with regard to what might make for the most effective implementation of the practice. We therefore suggest that *practice-based* proposals should be generated separate to our research-informed ones. This would involve observing outsourcing practices in H/PE across numerous school contexts as well as engaging directly with students, teachers and external entity employees to seek their perspectives. Such practice-based proposals could be compared with the research-informed proposals we have offered to identify commonalities, differences and to amend/refine these as necessary. Overall, if outsourcing is indeed 'here to stay' in H/PE, it is crucial that we carefully consider how we employ the practice to ensure students have positive learning experiences within the subject. We hope that our research-informed proposals might act as a starting point for this.

Reflection points

- What (if any) outsourcing takes place within your context and what does this 'look like'?
- What are the potential limitations of outsourcing within H/PE?
- What value might there be in outsourcing?
- How might it be ensured that students' experiences of outsourced H/PE are educative?

Note

1 We refer to H/PE within this chapter in recognition of the contextual differences between Australia and England. The subject is conceptualised as health and physical education within Australia, while in England it is physical education.

References

Ball, S. J. (2007). *Education plc. Understanding private sector participation in public sector.* London: Routledge.

Blair, R., and Capel, S. (2011). Primary physical education, coaches and continuing professional development. *Sport, Education and Society,* 16(4): 485–505.

Bowles, R., and O'Sullivan, M. (2020). Opportunity knocks: The intersection between schools, their teachers and external providers of physical education and school sport. *Discourse: Studies in the Cultural Politics of Education,* 41(2), 251–267.

Bravard, J. L., and Morgan, R. (2006). *Smarter outsourcing: An executive guide to understanding, planning and exploiting successful outsourcing relationships.* Harlow, UK: FT/Prentice Hall.

DfES. (2002). *Qualifying to Teach: Professional Standards for Qualified Teacher Status and Requirements for Initial Teacher Training.* London: TTA.

Dyson, B., Gordon, B., Cowan, J., and McKenzie, A. (2016). External providers and their impact on primary physical education in Aotearoa/New Zealand. *Asia-Pacific Journal of Health, Sport and Physical Education,* 7(1), 3–19.

Enright, E., and O'Sullivan, M. (2010). 'Can I do it in my pyjamas?' Negotiating a physical education curriculum with teenage girls. *European Physical Education Review,* 16(3), 203–222.

Enright, E., Kirk, D., and Macdonald, D. (2020). Expertise, neoliberal governmentality and the outsourcing of health and physical education. *Discourse: Studies in the Cultural Politics of Education,* 41(2), 206–222.

Gordon, B., Cowan, J., McKenzie, A., and Dyson, B. (2013). Primary school physical education in Aotearoa/New Zealand: The voices of teachers. *New Zealand Physical Educator,* 46(2), 9–12.

Griggs, G. (2010). For sale – Primary physical education. £20 per hour or nearest offer. Education, 38, 3–13.

Griggs, G. (2012). Standing on the touchline of chaos: Explaining the development of the use of sports coaches in UK primary schools with the aid of complexity theory. *Education 3–13,* 40(3), 259–269.

Hogan, A., and Stylianou, M. (2018). School-based sports development and the role of NSOs as 'boundary spanners': Benefits, disbenefits and unintended consequences of the sporting schools policy initiative. *Sport, Education and Society,* 23(4), 367–380.

Kirk, D. (2010). Physical education futures. Oxon: Routledge.

Kirk, D. (2020). Turning outsourcing inside-out? The case of the mindfulness in schools project. *Discourse: Studies in the Cultural Politics of Education,* 41(2), 238–250.

Lavin, J., Swindlehurst, G., and Foster, V. (2008). The use of coaches, adults supporting learning and teaching assistants in the teaching of physical education in the primary school. *Physical Education Matters,* 9–11.

Lindsey, I., Metcalfe, S., Gemar, A., Alderman, J., and Armstrong, J. (2021). Simplistic policy, skewed consequences: Taking stock of English physical education, school sport and physical activity policy since 2013. *European Physical Education Review,* 27(2), 278–296.

Macdonald, D. (2015). Teacher-as-knowledge-broker in a futures-oriented health and physical education. *Sport, Education and Society, 20*(1), 27–41.

Mangione, J., Parker, M., O'Sullivan, M., and Quayle, M. (2020). Mapping the landscape of physical education external provision in Irish primary schools. *Irish Educational Studies, 39*(4), 475–494.

McCuaig, L., and Hay, P. J. (2014). Towards an understanding of fidelity within the context of school-based health education. *Critical Public Health, 24*(2), 143–158.

McCuaig, L., Woolcock, L., Stylianou, M., Ng, J. Y. Y., and Ha, A. S. (2020). Prophets, pastors and profiteering: Exploring external providers' enactment of pastoral power in school wellbeing programs. *Discourse: Studies in the Cultural Politics of Education, 41*(2), 223–237.

Mockler, N., Hogan, A., Lingard, B., Rahimi, M., and Thompson, G. (2020). Explaining publicness: A typology for understanding the provision of schooling in contemporary times. In A. Hogan & G. Thompson (Eds.), *Privatisation and commercialisation in public education: How the nature of public schooling is changing* (pp.198–211). London: Routledge.

Ní Chróinín, D., and O'Brien, N. (2019). Primary school teachers' experiences of external providers in Ireland: Learning lessons from physical education. *Irish Educational Studies, 38*(3), 327–341.

Parnell, D., Cope, E., Bailey, R., & Widdop, P. (2017). Sport policy and English primary physical education: The role of professional football clubs in outsourcing. *Sport in Society, 20*(2), 292–302.

Petrie, K., Penney, D., and Fellows, S. (2015). HPE in Aotearoa New Zealand: The reconfiguration of policy and pedagogic relations and privatisation of curriculum and pedagogy. *Sport, Education and Society, 20*(1), 42.

Powell, D. (2014). Childhood obesity, corporate philanthropy and the creeping privatisation of health education. *Critical Public Health, 24*(2), 226–238.

Powell, D. (2015). Assembling the privatisation of physical education and the 'inexpert' teacher. *Sport, Education and Society, 20*(1), 73–88.

Powell, D. (2018). Governing the (un)healthy child-consumer in the age of the childhood obesity crisis. *Sport, Education and Society, 23*(4), 297–310.

Pring, R. (1987). Privatization in education. *Journal of Education Policy, 2*(4), 289–299.

Quennerstedt, M. (2019). Physical education and the art of teaching: Transformative learning and teaching in physical education and sports pedagogy. *Sport, Education and Society, 24*(6), 611–623.

Randall, V. (2020). Becoming a primary physical educator. *Education 3–13, 48*(2), 133–146.

Robinson, C., and Taylor, C. (2007). Theorizing student voice: Values and perspectives. *Improving Schools, 10*(1), 5–17.

Rossi, T., and Kirk, D. (2020). The pedagogisation of health knowledge and outsourcing of curriculum development: The case of the Stephanie Alexander Kitchen Garden initiative. *Discourse: Studies in the Cultural Politics of Education, 41*(2), 281–298.

Smith, A. (2015). Primary school physical education and sports coaches: Evidence from a study of school sport partnerships in north-west England. *Sport, Education and Society, 20*(7), 872–888.

Sperka, L. (2020). (Re)defining outsourcing in education. *Discourse: Studies in the Cultural Politics of Education, 41*(2), 268–280.

Sperka, L., and Enright, E. (2018). The outsourcing of health and physical education: A scoping review. *European Physical Education Review, 24*(3), 349–371.

Sperka, L., and Enright, E. (2019a). Network ethnography applied: Understanding the evolving health and physical education knowledge landscape. *Sport, Education and Society, 24*(2), 168–181.

Sperka, L., and Enright, E. (2019b). And if you can't hear us?: Students as customers of neo-HPE. *Sport, Education and Society, 24*(6), 570–583.

Sperka, L., Enright, E., and McCuaig, L. (2018). Brokering and bridging knowledge in health and physical education: A critical discourse analysis of one external provider's curriculum. *Physical Education and Sport Pedagogy, 23*(3), 328–343.

Stirrup, J. (2020). Performance pedagogy at play: Pupils perspectives on primary PE. *Sport, Education and Society, 25*(1), 14–26.

Tatton, D. (2018). *Best practice guidance for post primary schools in the use of programmes and/or external facilitators in promoting wellbeing consistent with the Department of education and skills' wellbeing policy statement and framework for practice (Circular No. 0043/2018).* Ireland: Department of Education and Skills.

Veitch, M. (1954). The organisation of winter sport in an Australian junior technical school. *Physical Education Journal, 2*(1), 16–19.

Webb, A. (1991). Coordination: A problem in public sector management. *Policy & Politics, 19*(4), 229–242.

Webster, P. J. (2001). *Teachers' perceptions of physical education within the K-6 personal development, health and physical education (PDHPE) key learning area (KLA): Executive summary.*

Weintraub, J. (1997). The theory and politics of the public/private distinction. In J. Weintraub & K. Kumar (Eds.), *Public private in thought practice: Perspectives on a grand dichotomy* (pp. 1–42). Chicago, IL: University of Chicago Press.

Welch, R., Alfrey, L., and Harris, A. (2021). Creativity in Australian health and physical education curriculum and pedagogy. *Sport, Education and Society,* 1–15. 26(5), 471–485.

Williams, B. J., and Macdonald, D. (2015). Explaining outsourcing in health, sport and physical education. *Sport, Education and Society, 20*(1), 57–72.

Williams, B. J., Hay, P. J., and Macdonald, D. (2011). The outsourcing of health, sport and physical educational work: A state of play. *Physical Education and Sport Pedagogy, 16*(4), 399–415.

Williams, P. (2002). The competent boundary spanner. *Public Administration, 80*(1), 103–124.

Williams, P. (2012). *Collaboration in public policy and practice: Perspectives on boundary spanners.* Bristol, UK: Policy Press.

INDEX

Printed in Great Britain
by Amazon

24332554R00137